PERCEPTION AND PERFORMANCE UNDER WATER

PERCEPTION
AND PERFORMANCE
UNDER WATER

JOHN ADOLFSON

THOMAS BERGHAGE

A WILEY-INTERSCIENCE PUBLICATION

JOHN WILEY & SONS, New York · London · Sydney · Toronto

The opinions and assertions contained
herein are those of the authors and are
not to be construed as official or reflecting
the views of the Navy Department.

Library of Congress Cataloging in Publication Data
Adolfson, John.
  Perception and performance under water.

  (Wiley series in human factors)
  Bibliography: p.
  "A Wiley-interscience publication."
  1. Underwater physiology. I. Berghage, Thomas,
joint author. II. Title. [DNLM: 1. Adaptation,
Physiological. 2. Diving. 3. Perception. 4. Submarine medicine.   WD650 A239p 1974]

RC1015.A32   627.7'2   73-23009
ISBN 0-471-00900-8

Printed in the United States of America

10 9 8 7 6 5 4 3 2 1

To
MAY and DIANE
with love

"All our knowledge originates in our sensibilities"

Leonardo da Vinci (1452–1519)

FOREWORD

For centuries man has been involved in underwater activities ranging from those performed by the military divers of Alexander the Great and ancient Oriental pearl divers to today's herculean feats of salvage.

With continued advances in undersea exploration and technology, the tasks required of divers are becoming more sophisticated and demanding, both physically and psychologically. If we are to fully utilize man's unique capabilities in accomplishing these new tasks, it is imperative that the nature of his assets and limitations be clearly identified.

This book is the first attempt to compile in one source the major studies relating to human performance in the underwater environment. Not only do the authors review relevant fundamental laboratory investigations, but they also include studies performed under difficult field conditions. The text also includes descriptions of methodology and data-gathering techniques, thus providing a much needed source for those who plan to study the performance of "wet" man.

Although advances in modern technology continue at an accelerating pace, the sensory capabilities of individuals and the judgments emanating from these capabilities will always play a critical role in man's future. The authors of this book, by summarizing the principal work done to date in this pioneering field, have achieved a major step toward increasing our knowledge about man and his role under the seas.

The knowledge thus gained will contribute to our ability to operate in, to understand, and to develop the water resources of this planet.

JAMES W. MILLER
*Deputy Director of Manned
Undersea Science and Technology
National Oceanographic and Atmospheric
Administration*

SERIES PREFACE

Technology is effective to the extent that men can operate and maintain the machines they design. Equipment design which consciously takes advantage of human capabilities and constrains itself within human limitations amplifies and increases system output. If it does not, system performance is reduced and the purpose for which the equipment was designed is endangered. This consideration is even more significant today than in the past because the highly complex systems that we develop are pushing human functions more and more to their limits of efficient performance.

How can one ensure that machine and machine operations are actually designed for human use? Behavioral data, principles, and recommendations—in short, the Human Factors discipline—must be translated into meaningful design practices. Concepts like ease of operation or error-free performance must be interpretable in hardware and system terms.

Human Factors is one of the newer engineering disciplines. Perhaps because of this, engineering and human-factors specialists lack a common orientation with which their respective disciplines can communicate. The goal of the Wiley Human Factors Series is to help in the communication process by describing what behavioral principles mean for system design and by suggesting the behavioral research that must be performed to solve design problems. The premise on which the series is based and on which each book is written is that Human Factors has utility only to the degree that it supports engineering development; hence the Series emphasizes the *practical application* to design of human-factors concepts.

Because of the many talents on which Human Factors depends for its implementation (design and systems engineering, industrial and experimental psychology, anthropology, physiology, and operations research, to name only a few), the Series is directed to as wide an audience as possible. Each book is intended to illustrate the usefulness of Human

Factors to some significant aspect of system development, such as human factors in design or testing or simulation. Although cookbook answers are not provided, it is hoped that this pragmatic approach will enable the many specialists concerned with problems of equipment design to solve these problems more efficiently.

DAVID MEISTER
Series Editor

PREFACE

During the last 100 years man has grown increasingly interested in exploration and exploitation of the ocean depths. Although manned submersibles or robots may be of great value in this task, at least at very great depths, man himself will be the most valuable and least expensive instrument for undersea work. Today man can reach and work on the continental shelf, which lies close to the coast and at a depth down to 300 m (984 ft).

Most of the psychological research in the field of diving has been done during the last 25 to 30 years. So far no attempt has been made to put this information together in a concise form.

This book has been designed as a survey of the literature on man's sensory-perceptual and performance capability in dry and wet hyperbaric environments. It is intended to summarize our present knowledge in this area, and also to bring to the reader's attention the areas in need of future investigation. With the foreseen exploration and exploitation of the ocean and the seabed, this need for basic information will be strongly increased.

The organization of the chapters that follow has been governed for the most part by the amount of material available. Those sensory modalities that have received detailed attention are presented as single chapters. The sensory modalities that have stimulated little or no research are grouped together in a single chapter. If one were to organize the senses according to their importance in the atmospheric environment, one might come up with a very similar type of classification. In other words, those sense modalities that seem important to the functioning of man in the surface atmospheric environment are the ones that receive the most attention in the undersea environment.

While dealing with the chapters that follow, the reader should keep in mind the relative contribution of the various sensory systems as addressed here. In many cases a great deal of research effort has been expended on sensory systems that assume secondary importance for the immersed man.

During the period 1970–1971 Dr. Adolfson worked as a foreign guest scientist (research psychologist) at the Behavioral Sciences Department, U.S. Naval Medical Research Institute, National Naval Medical Center, Bethesda, Maryland. This made it possible for him to become acquainted with Lieutenant Berghage at the U.S. Experimental Diving Unit, Washington, D.C. Through this association the idea of combining the results of psychological research reported by different authors in various journals from all over the world was developed. The need for this was obvious, and the U.S. Naval Medical Research Institute as well as the U.S. Navy Experimental Diving Unit supported the idea. That support made this book possible. We are profoundly grateful to the commanding officers of both these institutions.

We are especially indebted to Professor Arthur J. Bachrach, head of the Behavioral Sciences Department of the U.S. Naval Medical Research Institute, and Commanders J. K. Summitt, and W. H. Spaur, Senior Medical Officers at the U.S. Navy Experimental Diving Unit, who by their interest and knowledge gave us continual intellectual stimulation.

The chapters have been read in various versions and parts by several knowledgeable persons, and to them we are greatly indebted. Thus at an early stage the vision chapter was reviewed by Dr. Jo-Ann Kinney, New London, Connecticut, the audition chapter by Dr. Gilbert Tolhurst, Office of Naval Research, Washington, D.C., and the orientation chapter by Lieutenant Commander Robert S. Kennedy, Naval Medical Research Institute, Bethesda, Maryland. In formulation, Lt. Cdr. Robert Kennedy provided invaluable assistance by arguing with us, and sometimes even agreeing, and thereby lessened the obscurity that the readers felt now and then.

During all the time that the collection of literature was in progress we received ample support from Mrs. Thelma Robinson, Head of the Technical Reference Library, Naval Medical Research Institute. Without her help it would have been impossible to find many of the articles cited. We would like to acknowledge our indebtedness for her extremely valuable support.

Dr. James W. Miller of the National Oceanographic and Atmospheric Administration has followed and supported our work from the very beginning. His interest at various stages encouraged us to continue, and without his extremely valuable advice and constructive criticism it would have been impossible to complete this book. We are profoundly grateful to Dr. Miller.

A special note of appreciation is due to Keith Tidman and his associates at Potomac Research, Inc. Without Keith's technical writing, editing, and graphic arts support, this book would never have been completed.

Last but not least, grateful appreciation is extended to the following organizations for permission to reproduce material: Doubleday & Company, Inc.; American *Journal of Optometry;* Pergamon Press; Johns Hopkins Press; American Association for the Advancement of Science; Aerospace Medical Society; *Journal of the Acoustical Society of America;* Cambridge University Press; Association of Military Surgeons of the United States; Houghton Mifflin Company; McGraw-Hill Book Company; Compass Publications, Inc.; Science; and the Marine Technology Society.

It is our hope that this book will act as a guide for interested students, and for the numerous investigators and writers who have studied different details in the general pattern of divers' behavior.

JOHN A. ADOLFSON
THOMAS E. BERGHAGE

Stockholm, Sweden
Washington, D. C.
September 1973

CONTENTS

PERCEPTION AND PERFORMANCE UNDER WATER

I

INTRODUCTION

The undersea environment — Optical properties of seawater — Acoustic properties in hyperbaric environments and seawater — Thermal environment under water — The hyperbaric environment — Hyperbaric physiology — Decompression — Oxygen toxicity — Inert gas toxicity — Gas density and viscosity — Hydrostatic pressure effects — Underwater technological research and development — Diver work systems — Man as a system component — Summary

The physical properties of seawater greatly change stimulus energy inputs to the organisms. The undersea environment—water—is about 60 times more viscous, more than 800 times as dense, and has a thermal conductivity 25 times higher than that of air on land. The changes in stimulus energy caused by the transmitting gas and seawater medium are discussed.

Of special interest for the psychologist are the alterations in man's sensory-perceptual ability underwater. Because of the changes in stimulus energy and perceived sensory signals, the undersea explorer has to modify the emphasis he has previously placed on various sensory modalities.

Hyperbaric physiology is very briefly summarized in the chapter, along with underwater technological research and development. It is necessary to know at least something about various underwater systems. Because the diver is often the most important component within the system, it is essential to understand his behavioral reactions and his affected performance. This is also the reason why the principal types of diver work systems are shown schematically.

THE UNDERSEA ENVIRONMENT

The undersea environment is dangerous, and as greater depths are reached the hazards increase at an exponential rate (Berghage,

1

1966). To minimize the hazards involved, it is essential that man be an effective sensor of the environmental conditions to which he is exposed.

As an individual enters the undersea world, the sensory information he receives is greatly altered. The physicochemical qualities of the environment act on both the signal (stimulus energy) and the receiver (man's sensory-perceptual system). As Albano (1970) has put it: "The moment the diver goes underwater he is in an environment that is about 60 times more viscous, more than 800 times as dense, and having a thermal conductivity 25 times higher than that to which he is accustomed." Figure 1-1 shows the three elements of human performance along with stress factors associated with the hyperbaric environment.

Alterations in Stimulus Energy

The changes in stimulus energy caused by the transmitting gas and seawater medium are summarized by Albano (1970) in Table 1-1.

The Optical Properties of Seawater

In the introduction to his book, *Optical Properties of the Sea,* Jerome Williams (1970) has written:

"Of the five senses utilized in forming impressions of our outside environment, certainly sight is the most important. We can detect the presence of objects in the hydrosphere by means of sonic energy, but until we see the objects we really are not quite sure what they are. We can feel objects, smell them, taste them, but again, unless we see them, most of us have difficulty relating them to every day experience.

Sound, of course, is present, but the hearing apparatus that we have is not quite sophisticated enough to draw pictures of the outside world from echoes of the ambient sound. However, echoes of ambient light are of such a nature that image formation and interpretation devices, such as our own eye-brain system, are readily available. Thus, we find that the most common method of detection and identification of objects as we proceed on our normal course of events is our vision apparatus, and it is only natural to extend its use into the hydrosphere."

The use of the underwater breathing apparatuses by marine re-

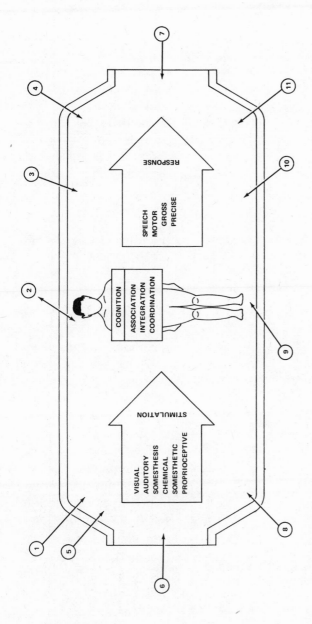

1. TEMPERATURE & HUMIDITY
2. PARTIAL PRESSURE OF OXYGEN
3. DENSITY OF BREATHING MEDIA
4. WET OR DRY EFFECTS
5. LIGHT & NOISE EFFECTS
6. RATE OF COMPRESSION
7. TIME UNDER PRESSURE
8. CARBON DIOXIDE EFFECTS
9. PRESSURE EFFECTS
10. EFFECTS OF INERT GAS
11. EQUIPMENT LIMITATIONS

FACTORS AFFECTING MAN'S PERFORMANCE IN A
HYPERBARIC ENVIRONMENT

Figure 1-1. Factors affecting man's performance in a hyperbaric environment. (Berghage, 1969.)

3

Table 1-1 Physical Characteristics of the Matter at a Temperature of 15°C (288 ± 0.03°K)^a (Albano, 1970)

Characteristics	Air	Helium	Distilled Water	Sea Water
Viscosity (poise = dynes × sec/cm²)	1.7932×10^{-4}	2.5×10^{-4}	114×10^{-4}	138×10^{-4}
Density (g/cc)	1.225×10^{-3}	0.175×10^{-3}	999.13×10^{-3}	1026×10^{-3}
Pressure (mm Hg); where t_m = average temperature; depth (m)	Antilog $2.88\text{--}18{,}400 \left(1 + \dfrac{t_m}{273}\right)$ (alt. in m)		$73.49 \times$ depth	$75.47 \times$ depth
Compressibility coefficient (ml/ml atm); where H = pressure (atm)	$(H-1)/H$	$(H-1)/H$	$4.7 \times 10^{-5}(H-1)$	$4.7 \times 10^{-5}(H-1)$
Mass thermal capacity, or specific heat at constant pressure (C_p) (kcal/g °C)	0.241×10^{-3}	1.21×10^{-3}	0.99976	0.9998
Ratio of specific heats (C_p/c_v)	1.41	1.66	1.00	1.00
Coefficient of thermal conductivity: (kcal/cm × hr × °C/m²)	2.3	19.3	53.8	53.0
Sound velocity (cm/sec)	340×10^2	$\approx\!970 \times 10^2$	1437×10^2	1460×10^2
Acoustic resistance (g/cm × sec)	41.7	≈15	143,574	149,796
Sound absorption coefficient (sec²/cm); where f = Hertz frequency	$40 \times 10^{-13} \times f^2$		$25 \times 10^{-17} \times f^2$	$25 \times 10^{-17} \times f^2$
Index of light refraction, for λ = 589 Å	1.00029		1.3336	1.3417
Light velocity (cm/sec)	299.746×10^8		244.774×10^8	223.445×10^3
Light absorption coefficient			$7 \times 10^{43}/\lambda^4$	$7 \times 10^{43}/\lambda^4$

search, salvage, and construction personnel has forced man to deal with the problem of how far and how clearly he can see while immersed. Detection of objects under water can be accomplished using several different sense modalities, but their identification can be made only visually or tactically. For the visual sense to be at all functional in the underwater environment, the level of photic energy must exceed the excitation threshold of the visual system. The amount of radiant energy available in the water depends upon several factors which are discussed below.

The Extinction of Incoming Radiation

Parallel radiation entering a layer of seawater is gradually weakened by three factors: (1) absorption by the pure seawater, (2) scattering by the pure seawater, and (3) scattering, diffraction, and reflection by suspended particles in the water (impurity of the seawater) (Defant, 1961).

The transformation of radiant energy to a different form of energy by the intervention of matter is called absorption. Once the light, whether it be sunlight or artificially produced light, is within the hydrosphere, absorption means the conversion of light into heat energy (Williams, 1970). Scattering is the spreading of rays, and diffraction is defined as the separation of light into component parts, thus producing interference phenomena such as lines, bands, or spot patterns. Reflection is the turning back of a ray of light from a surface upon which it impinges without penetrating. In seawater the last two factors do not change the form of energy, but divert part of the radiation from its original direction. A beam of visual radiation passing through a distance in water is reduced in intensity by an amount proportional to the intensity and to the distance traveled through the water (Defant 1961).

Absorption

The absorption coefficient κ takes account of the effects of both scattering and absorption and applies to solar radiation and diffuse sky radiation taken together.

Detailed measurements have been made of the absorption coefficient of water over the whole spectral region. From about 480 nm toward the red end of the spectrum and beyond, the absorption

coefficient increases strongly and continuously. The absorption depends slightly upon the temperature and the salinity of the water
but, according to Defant, the absorption in pure seawater is about
the same as in pure fresh water. The spectrum of the sunlight at
different depths has been calculated (Defant, 1961), and the reduction in intensity after it passes through very thin layers of water is
quite considerable. For a layer 1 cm thick, wavelengths greater than
1500 nm are completely eliminated, and the spectrum extends only
to 900 nm. For layers 100 m (328 ft) thick, the remaining energy
falls to less than 1.5%. Spectral absorption curves for various depths
of clear ocean water are illustrated in Figure 1-2.

Scattering

The water of the sea, however, is not optically pure, and always contains large amounts of suspended organic and inorganic material.
The intensity of the light passing through the water is further reduced by the scattering of energy by these particles, as well as by
ordinary absorption. When radiation passes through water, it undergoes a progressive alteration both qualitatively and quantitatively.
The long and shortwave sections of the spectrum are filtered out
almost at once, so that the light soon adopts a bluish-green or blue
color. This is known as the Tyndall effect. Tyndall light is generally
blue or blue-green in color because the scattering affects the shorter
wavelengths to a greater extent than the long wavelengths. With
greater optical impurity, the effect of the scattering is less color-
selective. The light is more greenish or, with strong turbidity, even
yellowish-green (Pettersson, 1935).

Luria and Kinney (1970) have confirmed that as water becomes
more turbid the transmission of various wavelengths is greatly
altered and reduced (Figure 1-3). In very polluted water there is a
greater transmission loss at the bluish-green end of the spectrum
than at the red end.

Refraction and Reflection of Radiation

The parallel radiation incident on the surface of water is partly
reflected and partly enters the water. The angle of reflection is the
same as the angle of incidence, but the ratio of the intensities of the
incident and the reflected beam are dependent upon the angle of
incidence of the original radiation itself. Radiation entering the re-

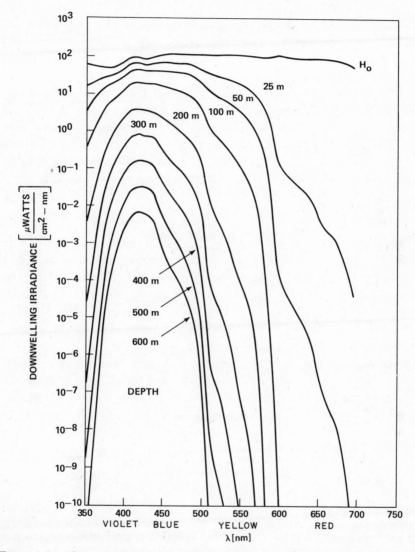

Figure 1-2. The spectral absorption characteristics of clear water. (Smith & Tyler, 1967.)

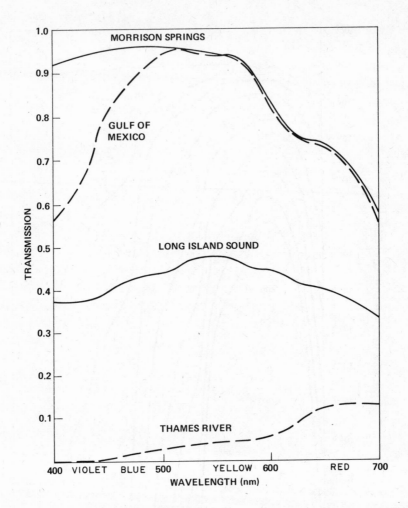

Figure 1-3. Transmission of various wavelengths through a distance of 1 m of various bodies of water. (The water varies from exceptionally clear in Morrison Springs, Florida, to very turbid in the Thames River at New London, Connecticut. The peak transmission shifts toward the long wavelengths as turbidity increases. (Luria & Kinney 1970.)

flecting medium undergoes a change in direction on passing through the surface, and the angle of this reflected beam is given by the equation:

$$\frac{\sin i}{\sin r} = n$$

where i = angle of incidence
r = angle of refraction
n = refractive index.

For light passing from air to pure water, the refractive index is almost exactly 1.333338 or $n = 4/3$. That is, in water that is optically denser, the beam is refracted toward the perpendicular. The refractive index for a ray passing from the water into the air is $1/n$ or $n = 0.75$. If the angle of incidence of radiation passing from the water into the air increases, the angle i will increase faster than the angle r until finally the value of i reaches 90°; the outgoing ray then passes along the surface of the water. The critical angle for total reflection occurs when $r = 48.5°$ (Defant, 1961). If r increases still further, radiation cannot enter the air but is reflected entirely within the water.

With an increasing angle of incidence, the reflected energy increases slowly until $i = 60°$, but thereafter increases very rapidly. The larger the angle of incidence, the more energy is reflected; at 70°, more than 13%; at 80°, more than 35% (Defant, 1961).

In addition to direct sunlight, which may be regarded as unilateral parallel radiation, there is also a general diffuse radiation for which conditions relative to the sea surface are rather different. The diffuse radiation on the surface of the sea includes:

1. Diffuse sky light (light that is essentially shortwave radiation and is present only in the daytime).

2. Long-wave radiation from the atmosphere which is present both day and night.

The refractive index is slightly different for different parts of the spectrum, and its values vary between 5 and 10% (Defant, 1961). For a more detailed discussion, the reader is directed to Williams (1970).

The Acoustic Properties in Hyperbaric Environments and Seawater

There are many ocean parameters that alter the properties of an acoustic signal, the two of greatest importance being the density of the medium and the coefficient of absorption. Berghage (1969) has discussed the sound transmission problems associated with *dry* hyperbaric environments. Essentially, sound transmission appears to be affected by two interrelated factors, namely, gas density and gas molecular weight. The lighter the gas the greater the velocity of transmission, and the greater the density the greater the velocity of transmission. According to Gerstman (1967), the relationship between gas density and sound velocity is described by the formula:

$$V = \left(\frac{\gamma p}{\rho}\right)^{1/2}$$

where p = pressure
ρ = density
γ = the ratio between specific heat at a constant pressure and specific heat at a constant volume, namely

$$\gamma = \frac{C_P}{C_V}$$

In a *wet* hyperbaric environment, the speed of sound through water c is given by the formula:

$$c^2 = \frac{1}{\rho Ka}$$

where Ka = adiabatic compressibility
ρ = density.

"The speed of sound is 1471.46 m/sec for sea water of salinity 35% at atmospheric pressure at 5°C. It increases by about 1.0 m/sec per 1% increase in salinity, by 3.5 m/sec per °C increase in temperature and by 0.16 m/sec per atmosphere increase in pressure" (Schulkin & Pryce, 1965).

The absorption of sound in ocean water increases with the acoustic frequency and is dependent upon salinity, temperature, and pressure. Schulkin and Pryce have calculated the absorption to be approximately 0.01 dB/km at 10^3 Hz and 1 dB/km at 10^4 Hz.

The Thermal Environment under Water

The thermal environment confronting man under water is considerably different than that to which he is accustomed. The temperature of water at deep ocean depths is relatively constant; it changes very little from locale to locale and from season to season. Temperature variations under water are much smaller than those in the atmosphere.

Scientists have arbitrarily assigned the value 1.00 as a measure of the thermal capacity of water. The ability of other materials to soak up heat is compared to this figure and is called specific heat. The specific heat of nearly all the gases, metals, and solids tested so far has proved to be less than that of water. This means that water is slow to show an increase or decrease in temperature.

For a man immersed in water, the important temperature consideration is the thermal conductivity of the water. The thermal conductivity of water is much higher (53.0 kcal/hr m^2 °C) than that of air (2.3 kcal/hr m^2 °C). Body temperature control thus becomes a very critical problem for the undersea explorer.

Alterations in Man's Sensory-Perceptual System under Water

When man enters the undersea environment he experiences some rather significant changes in his sensory perceptual capabilities. Equipment configurations limit his visual field, his primary auditory receptive mechanism shifts from air to bone conduction, and his surface skin temperature drops to the point where it often reduces his tactile sensitivity. There are also significant changes in man's ability to interpret sensory signals once he receives them. Environmental and psychological factors produce changes which interfere with man's cognitive interpretive processes.

Because of the changes in stimulus energy and perceived sensory signals, an undersea explorer has to modify the emphasis he has previously established for his various sensory modalities. If we evaluate man's sensory modalities by means of a discrete attribute analysis, we can comprehend the shift in emphasis that must accompany a sojourn in the depths of the ocean.

In Table 1-2 we have listed as row headings what Sherrington would have termed exteroceptors and teleceptors: those sensory modalities from which man receives information concerning the near and distant environment. As column headings in Table 1-2, we have listed four attributes that seem important for a sensory system

Table 1-2   The Influence of the Subsurface Environment on Sensory
Capability

	Detection Range	Discrimination Precision	Localization Precision	Directionally	Change from dry to wet environment
Vision					
Dry	Good	Outstanding	Outstanding	Good	Large
Wet	Fair to none	Good to none	Outstanding to none	Poor	
Audition					
Dry	Outstanding	Outstanding	Good	Outstanding	Moderate
Wet	Outstanding	Good	Fair	Outstanding	
Somesthetic					
Dry	Poor	Fair	Good	Poor	Small
Wet	Poor	Fair	Fair	Poor	
Chemical					
Dry	Poor	Poor	Poor	Good	Small
Wet	Poor to none	Poor to none	Poor to none	Good	

and for which a comparison can be made between wet and dry
environments. Each sensory group has been evaluated on each
attribute using a four-point rating scale.

In the final column on the right, we have subjectively scaled the
change that takes place when moving from a dry to a wet environment. As can be seen, vision seems to suffer the greatest from immersion. Even under ideal conditions vision is limited to 30 to 60 m
(100–200 ft), but most commonly it is closer to 6 m (20 ft) or less.
The information available via the visual system is very dependent
upon local conditions.

Hearing suffers moderately from immersion, but it is not nearly
as dependent as vision on local water conditions. Regardless of
water conditions, the auditory information received by man remains
essentially the same. The ability of man to sense vibratory pressure
changes appears to hold great promise for man's future in the sea.
From an evolutionary point of view, it is interesting to note that the
most successful predator of the sea, the shark, uses a midline vibratory detector to locate its prey, and the porpoise uses echo soundings

to identify underwater objects.

The somesthetic senses appear to be altered very little by the undersea environment. Providing the individual's cognitive processes are functional and the stimulus is close at hand, it appears that somesthetic senses may be very useful and should be utilized in future system design.

The chemical senses of olfaction and taste are useless as exteroceptors in a wet hyperbaric environment. They still retain some utility in a dry ambient pressure habitat, but their contribution is minimal.

THE HYPERBARIC ENVIRONMENT

Man's dependence on a respirable gaseous milieu is one of the major restrictions hindering him in his explorations of the earth's hydrosphere. In the hyperbaric environment the ambient atmospheric pressure is raised above the normal atmospheric pressure of 1 atm absolute (ATA). In diving, the ambient pressure increases by 1 ATA for each 10 m (33 ft) of seawater depth; for example, a depth of 10 m = 2 ATA, a depth of 50 m = 6 ATA, and so forth. The gas mixture the diver breathes (i.e., air or different mixtures of oxygen and some inert gas, usually nitrogen or helium) must be raised to the same hydrostatic pressure as the ambient pressure in order to make it possible for the diver to breathe. The combination of gases to be used at various depths must be selected with great care in order to maintain the physiological integrity of the diver. It has been shown by several investigators that the increased partial pressures of the breathing medium constituents can alter man's sensory and mental processing capabilities. Any individual planning research on sensory systems should be aware of the physical and physiological laws governing the behavior of biological systems in high pressure environments. A good review of these principles can be found in the *U.S. Navy Diving Manual* (1970).

Hyperbaric Physiology

To satisfy the combined goals of prolonged habitation and accomplishment of meaningful work by man at ocean depths, studies are being performed to seek a better understanding of the physiological and psychological problems related to exposing man to this ambient environment. Following is a brief review of the underwater physiological research being performed, and the technology associated with supporting an unshielded man. The psychological aspects of diving research are focused toward the measurement and understanding of diver performance impairment within the diving system.

Also reviewed here are current physiological research efforts directed toward such problem areas as decompression, oxygen toxicity, inert gas toxicity, gas density and viscosity, temperature, and hydrostatic force effects. Technological advances in research and development are reviewed, which are closely integrated with psychological and physiological research. These efforts are concerned with individual life-support elements and operation-like elements. We also discuss the development of advanced diving concepts and the most important diving system options. The reviews of physiological and technological research and development efforts are based on an excellent synopsis by Bien and McDonough (1970).

Decompression

Man cannot go under water without experiencing an increase in environmental pressure; consequently, he cannot return to the surface without undergoing decompression. Exposure to high hydrostatic pressures during a dive causes components of the breathing gas to be absorbed and accumulated by the blood and tissues of the body in increasing quantities. The route taken by the gases (lungs → blood → tissue) is a simple and direct adjustment to the increased alveolar partial pressures. When the decreased pressure of the ascent occurs, the process reverses and the gases are carried by the blood from the tissues back to the lungs (Miles, 1965).

The rate of return to the surface is absolutely limited by the rate at which excess dissolved gases in the tissues can be eliminated. The rate of gas uptake or elimination is directly related to the type of inert gas and gas partial-pressure gradient at the tissue–blood and lung–blood interfaces. Reliable decompression tables indicating safe ascent rates for extended depth-time dives are being developed through improved methods of computation and experimentation. It is estimated by diving physiologists that, regardless of the inert

gas used in a breathing mixture, the rate of ascent following a saturation exposure will never be increased much beyond the 1.8 m/hr
(or 10 min/ft) now achieved. This means that normal unaided decompression following a saturation dive to 150 m (492 ft) will continue to require about 3½ days. Present U. S. Navy decompression
procedures require 5 days of decompression from a dive of this
depth. Inert gas elimination by unaided decompression will remain
the primary factor limiting diving efficiency, that is, useful diving
time per unit of total time invested. See Table 1-3 for the U.S. Navy
standard air decompression schedules.

Table 1-3   Adapted from U.S. Navy Standard Air Decompression Table

Depth (ft) (m)	Bottom Time (min)	Time to First Stop (m)	50 15	40 12	30 9	20 6	10 3	Total Ascent Time	Repet. Group
	200						0	0.7	*
	210	0.5					2	2.5	N
40	230	0.5					7	7.5	N
12	250	0.5					11	11.5	O
	270	0.5					15	15.5	O
	300	0.5					19	19.5	Z
	100						0	0.8	*
	110	0.7					3	3.7	L
	120	0.7					5	5.7	M
	140	0.7					10	10.7	M
50	160	0.7					21	21.7	N
15	180	0.7					29	29.7	O
	200	0.7					35	35.7	O
	220	0.7					40	40.7	Z
	240	0.7					47	47.7	Z
	60						0	1.0	*
	70	0.8					2	2.8	K
	80	0.8					7	7.8	L
60	100	0.8					14	14.8	M
18	120	0.8					26	26.8	N
	140	0.8					39	39.8	O
	160	0.8					48	48.8	Z
	180	0.8					56	56.8	Z
	200	0.6				1	69	70.6	Z

Depth (ft) (m)	Bottom Time (min)	Time to First Stop	Decompression Stops						Total Ascent Time	Repet. Group
			(ft) 50 (m) 15	40 12	30 9	20 6	10 3			
	50							0	1.2	*
	60	1.0						8	9.0	K
	70	1.0						14	15.0	L
	80	1.0						18	19.0	M
	90	1.0						23	24.0	N
70	100	1.0						33	34.0	N
21	110	0.8					2	41	43.8	O
	120	0.8					4	47	51.8	O
	130	0.8					6	52	58.8	O
	140	0.8					8	56	64.8	Z
	150	0.8					9	61	70.8	Z
	160	0.8					13	72	85.8	Z
	170	0.8					19	79	98.8	Z
	40							0	1.3	*
	50	1.2						10	11.2	K
	60	1.2						17	18.2	L
	70	1.2						23	24.2	M
	80	1.0					2	31	34.0	N
80	90	1.0					7	39	47.0	N
24	100	1.0					11	46	58.0	O
	110	1.0					13	53	67.0	O
	120	1.0					17	56	74.0	Z
	130	1.0					19	63	83.0	Z
	140	1.0					26	69	96.0	Z
	150	1.0					32	77	11.00	Z
	30							0	1.5	*
	40	1.3						7	8.3	J
	50	1.3						18	19.3	L
	60	1.3						25	26.3	M
90	70	1.2					7	30	38.2	N
27	80	1.2					13	40	54.2	N
	90	1.2					18	48	67.2	O
	100	1.2					21	54	76.2	Z
	110	1.2					24	61	86.2	Z
	120	1.2					32	68	101.2	Z
	130	1.0				5	36	74	116.0	Z

Depth (ft) (m)	Bottom Time (min)	Time to First (ft) Stop (m)	Decompression Stops					Total Ascent Time	Repet. Group
			50 15	40 12	30 9	20 6	10 3		
	25						0	1.7	*
	30	1.5					3	4.5	I
	40	1.5					15	16.5	K
	50	1.3				2	24	27.3	L
	60	1.3				9	28	38.3	N
100	70	1.3				17	39	57.3	O
30	80	1.3				23	48	72.3	O
	90	1.2			3	23	57	84.2	Z
	100	1.2			7	23	66	97.2	Z
	110	1.2			10	34	72	117.2	Z
	120	1.2			12	41	78	132.2	Z
	20						0	1.8	*
	25	1.7					3	4.7	H
	30	1.7					7	8.7	J
	40	1.5				2	21	24.5	L
110	50	1.5				8	26	35.5	M
34	60	1.5				18	36	55.5	N
	70	1.3			1	23	48	73.3	O
	80	1.3			7	23	57	88.3	Z
	90	1.3			12	30	64	107.3	Z
	100	1.3			15	37	72	125.3	Z
	15						0	2.0	*
	20	1.8					2	3.8	H
	25	1.8					6	7.8	I
	30	1.8					14	15.8	J
120	40	1.7				5	25	31.7	L
37	50	1.7				15	31	47.7	N
	60	1.5			2	22	45	70.5	O
	70	1.5			9	23	55	88.5	O
	80	1.5			15	27	63	106.5	Z
	90	1.5			19	37	74	131.5	Z
	100	1.5			23	45	80	149.5	Z

Depth (ft) (m)	Bottom Time (min)	Time to First Stop	(ft) 50 (m) 15	40 12	30 9	20 6	10 3	Total Ascent Time	Repet. Group
					Decompression Stops				
	10						0	2.2	*
	15	2.0					1	3.0	F
	20	2.0					4	6.0	H
	25	2.0					10	12.0	J
130	30	1.8				3	18	22.8	M
40	40	1.8				10	25	36.8	N
	50	1.7			3	21	37	62.7	O
	60	1.7			9	23	52	85.7	Z
	70	1.7			16	24	61	102.7	Z
	80	1.5		3	19	35	72	130.5	Z
	90	1.5		8	19	45	80	153.5	Z
	10						0	2.3	*
	15	2.2					2	4.2	G
	20	2.2					6	8.2	I
	25	2.0				2	14	18.0	J
140	30	2.0				5	21	28.0	K
43	40	1.8			2	16	26	45.8	N
	50	1.8			6	24	44	75.8	O
	60	1.8			16	23	56	96.8	Z
	70	1.7		4	19	32	68	124.7	Z
	80	1.7		10	23	41	79	154.7	Z
	5						0	2.5	C
	10	2.3					1	3.3	E
	15	2.3					3	5.3	G
	20	2.2				2	7	11.2	H
150	25	2.2				4	17	23.2	K
46	30	2.2				8	24	34.2	L
	40	2.0			5	19	33	59.0	N
	50	2.0			12	23	51	88.0	O
	60	1.8		3	19	26	62	111.8	Z
	70	1.8		11	19	39	75	145.8	Z
	80	1.7	1	17	19	50	84	172.7	Z

| Depth (ft) (m) | Bottom Time (min) | Time to First Stop | Decompression Stops (ft) (m) | | | | | Total Ascent Time | Repet. Group |
			50 15	40 12	30 9	20 6	10 3		
160 49	5						0	2.7	D
	10	2.5					1	3.5	F
	15	2.3				1	4	7.3	H
	20	2.3				3	11	16.3	J
	25	2.3				7	20	29.3	K
	30	2.2			2	11	25	40.2	M
	40	2.2			7	23	39	71.2	N
	50	2.0		2	16	23	55	98.0	Z
	60	2.0		9	19	33	69	132.0	Z
	70	1.8	1	17	22	44	80	165.8	Z
170 52	5						0	2.8	D
	10	2.7					2	4.7	F
	15	2.5				2	5	9.5	H
	20	2.5				4	15	21.5	J
	25	2.3			2	7	23	34.3	L
	30	2.3			4	13	26	15.3	M
	40	2.2		1	10	23	45	81.2	O
	50	2.2		5	18	23	61	109.2	Z
	60	2.0	2	15	22	37	74	152.0	Z
	70	2.0	8	17	19	51	36	183.0	Z
180 55	5						0	3.0	D
	10	2.8					3	5.8	F
	15	2.7				3	8	11.7	I
	20	2.5			1	5	17	25.5	K
	25	2.5			3	10	24	39.5	L
	30	2.5			6	17	27	52.5	N
	40	2.3		3	14	23	50	92.3	O
	50	2.2	2	9	19	30	65	127.2	Z
	60	2.2	5	16	19	44	81	167.2	Z
190 58	5						0	3.2	D
	10	2.8				1	3	6.8	G
	15	2.8				4	7	13.8	I
	20	2.7			2	6	20	30.7	K
	25	2.7			5	11	25	43.7	M
	30	2.5		1	8	19	32	62.5	N
	40	2.5		8	14	23	55	102.5	O
	50	2.3	4	13	22	33	72	146.3	Z
	60	2.3	10	17	19	50	85	182.3	Z

Several techniques are being examined which may provide practical aids to accelerate decompression or to improve the safety of decompression. These aids include:

1. The use of high oxygen tension.
2. The use of methods for extending oxygen tolerance.
3. The use of multiple gas mixtures.
4. The alteration of inert gases in the breathing mixture.
5. The combining of alternation of inert gases with fluctuation of oxygen tension.
6. The use of drugs to accelerate blood flow.

A very advanced technique which is still in the development stage is fluid breathing. This technique is an attempt to circumvent the whole problem of decompression by eliminating the need for inert gas.

High Oxygen Tension.   The use of high oxygen tension was probably the first decompression aid discovered, and will probably continue to be the most useful technique to speed up decompression (Murray, 1943; Clarke, Humm & Nims 1944; Bateman, 1951). The technique calls for the use of a high concentration of oxygen in the breathing mixture. The physiological principles utilized by this technique involve minimizing the inert gas diffusion gradient (partial-pressure difference at the lung–blood and tissue–blood interfaces) during descent and maximizing the diffusion gradient during ascent. The extent that the high oxygen tension technique can be used to aid decompression is limited by the lack of an adequate definition of human oxygen tolerance (Workman, 1964).

Interrupted Exposure to High Oxygen Tension.   The use of interrupted exposure to high oxygen tension is an attempt to circumvent oxygen tolerance limits. It has been found that animals exposed intermittently to high oxygen tensions can better tolerate high oxygen tension exposure (Meijne and Straub, 1966; Nashimoto, 1967). Lambertsen (1955) found that by giving guinea pigs short, intermittent exposures to low oxygen tensions he could extend the onset time of oxygen toxicity by a factor of 3. Field experiments carried out during World War II indicate that a 10-min interruption of oxygen breathing is close to the minimum that will produce a practical extension of oxygen tolerance (Lambertsen, 1955).

Multiple Inert Gas.   The use of multiple inert gases in breathing mixtures to aid decompression has been considered for several decades. The fundamental assumption is that each gas in a gas mixture, or dissolved in body fluids, behaves as though it were the only gas present. The principle is that individual inert gas partial pressure is decreased proportionately with the increased number of inert gases used. Thus the diffusion gradient for each gas is reduced (Webster, 1955). Keller and Buhlmann (1965) state that changes in the inert gas in the breathing mixture permit a considerable shortening of decompression time; in addition, Keller (1967) tested a theory purporting that the use of inert gases alternately during decompression would enable a shortening of decompression times as well as make it safer. He decreased the decompression time for seven subjects who spent 2 hr at a depth of 120 ft (37 m) to 15 min by switching the inert breathing gas from helium to argon. The normal decompression time for an air dive to this depth is about 90 min, and for a helium dive about 60 min.

Schreiner (1968, 1969) calculated the specific time constants for transport of inert gases to the main tissues of the organism and deducted from them the periods and levels of decompression. He also worked out a mathematical model of inert gas transport and found that neon appeared to exhibt a decompression advantage over helium and that both these gases had an advantage over nitrogen.

Nevertheless, severe decompression sickness does occur after exposure to multiple-gas mixtures. An explanation for this effect, given by Bien and McDonough (1970), is that once a cavity or a small bubble is formed its growth depends upon the sum of the partial pressures of all the gases in the tissue.

Alteration in Inert Gases and Fluctuation of High Oxygen Tension.   A logical extension of the multiple-gas breathing mixture technique and the high oxygen tension technique to accelerate decompression is the combined use of both techniques. This combination of the two methods continues to occupy the research efforts of diving physiologists. As an example of the advantage of this advanced decompression technique, Buhlmann (1969) demonstrated a fivefold reduction in decompression time for a 330-ft (11 ATA), 60-min dive. The breathing gas during the dive consisted of 15% oxygen and 85% helium, and during the decompression Buhlmann changed the inert gas from helium to nitrogen with different oxygen partial pressures. At pressures less than 2.5 ATA, he used 100% oxygen. The total decompression time was 105 min. Normally, a dive of this depth and duration, using standard U.S. Navy procedures, requires over 450 min of decompression.

Drugs for Accelerating Blood Flow. According to Bien and McDonough, the use of drugs has been suggested as a means of accelerating blood circulation in tissues during ascent to enhance the elimination of inert gases. The reverse effects, that is, slowing up blood circulation during descent, minimize inert gas take-up. However, no data seem to be available to assess its possible contribution to the decompression problem.

Philp (1964) studied the protective effects in decompression sickness of heparin, partially depolymerized hyaluronate (PDHA, a substance reported to have antilipemic properties) and bishydroxy-coumarin (an anticoagulant) by a standardized compression-decompression technique in rats. Bishydroxycoumarin did not afford any significant degree of protection, while heparin significantly reduced the incidence of decompression sickness in the rats. PDHA produced the most marked reduction in both incidence and severity.

Bennett and Brook (1969) administered carbachol, Prostigmin, adrenalin hyoscine, Doriden, phenacetin, adrenalin, aspirin, Methedrine, Megimide, leptazol alcohol γ-aminobutyric acid and thiethyperazine to rats prior to compression with air at 60 ft/min to 400 ft (13 ATA) for 1 hr. Fifty rats were exposed to each of the 13 drugs and also to compression without drugs, involving a total of 700 rats. This was followed by decompression at 45 ft/min. (14 m/min). The animals were observed for 30 min after decompression, and the number of rats that died or developed spinal bends were counted. Carbachol, Doriden, phenacetin, adrenalin, and leptazol caused significant increases in deaths and spinal bends. Megimide and hyoscine showed a definite tendency to potentiate decompression sickness, although the results were not statistically significant. The remaining drugs had no effect.

Oxygen Toxicity

Pressure has a significant effect on a diver's oxygen tolerance. Too much oxygen (hyperoxia) is almost as dangerous as too little oxygen (hypoxia). Short-term exposure to high oxygen tension can affect the central nervous system, causing localized muscular twitching and convulsions, while long-term exposure to high oxygen tension impairs the process of gas exchange in the alveoli of the lungs (Bert, 1878; Smith, 1899; Bean, 1963; Wood, 1969).

Experience to date indicates that the partial pressure of oxygen should be kept between about 150 and 300 mm Hg during the at-depth phase of a long saturation dive. Bien and McDonough mention 400 mm Hg as the upper limit, but 300 mm Hg seems to be the more common *general* upper level. The oxygen in the air we breath at sea level is 160 mm Hg (21% of 760). If oxygen is kept at 21% of the mixture, however, its partial pressure increases with depth, rising to 1120 mm Hg at 7 ATA. As a result, the proportion of oxygen in the breathing mixture must be reduced as depth increases to maintain a partial pressure range of 150 to 300 mm Hg. Therefore the band of tolerable oxygen percentage narrows rapidly with increased depth. The need for increasing accuracy in systems that analyze and control the breathing gas mixture for long-term saturation dives is clearly indicated.

Inert Gas Toxicity

Although such gases as nitrogen and helium are biochemically inert in the atmospheric pressure environment, they are not so under increased pressure. Nitrogen, which is physiologically inert at sea level, has an anesthetic effect under pressure. At depths greater than 30 m (100 ft), an average and less experienced diver may suffer from nitrogen narcosis (Figure 1-4). The effects (e.g., impairment in judgment and psychomotor ability) can render all divers completely unable to cope with emergencies if the depth is great enough.

Helium has been found to be much less narcotic and is currently used instead of nitrogen in almost all deep-sea dives to more than 40 m (130 ft). Some experiments are also being conducted to determine the narcotic effect of hydrogen, since there are indications that hydrogen has even less of a narcotic effect than helium (Zetterstrom, 1948). There is ongoing experimentation on the use of oxygen–hydrogen and oxygen–hydrogen–helium mixtures for depths

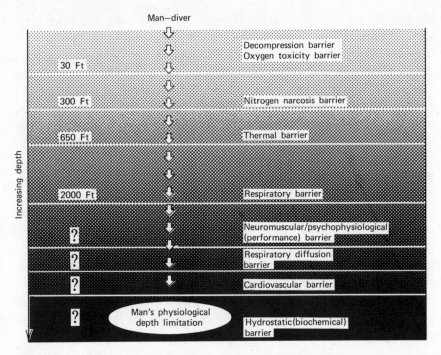

Figure 1-4. Physiological barriers to man's ultimate depth limits.

greater than 305 m (1000 ft). Furthermore, experimental dives with oxygen–helium mixtures to depths of 450 to 609 m (1500 to 2000 ft) have recently been performed in Great Britain, the United States, and France. The physiological inert gas toxicity is described by Bennett (1966) and Bennett and Elliot (1969).

Gas Density and Viscosity

Elevation of pressure on any gas mixture, including that for breathing, increases its density and viscosity, resulting in increased resistance to movement of gas through the small respiratory passages. This resistance not only interferes directly with pulmonary ventilation, but also increases the work of breathing itself. The use of helium in the breathing gas mixture reduces inert gas narcosis effects, and circumvents some of the breathing resistance problems. Since nitrogen is about seven times more dense than helium at 1 ATA, the density of nitrogen at about 60 m (196 ft) of seawater is as great as that of helium at 300 m (984 ft). The principal method for reducing respiratory resistance at very great depths is the use of less dense and less viscous gases such as helium or hydrogen. A technological solution to the respiratory resistance problem might be the development of a respiratory pump. Such a pump would provide the necessary assistance in moving air in and out of the lungs (Bien & McDonough, 1970).

Thermal Balance

The human body can maintain its thermal equilibrium only within very narrow limits. Both high and low temperatures represent human physiological limitations. In water above normal body temperature, fever develops even when one is in a restful state, and exercise accelerates its onset. In water below normal body temperature, an unprotected man loses heat about 21 times faster than he would in normal air at the same ambient temperature. Metabolic heat produced by exercise extends man's tolerance to cold water, and the combination of insulation and work provides useful periods of time in water at temperatures as low as 10 to 15°C. In water significant improvement in the degree of human temperature tolerance cannot be expected from the use of drugs or physiological adaptation, despite the fact that cold acclimatization in the air is a well-known experience among outdoor workers in arctic.

Human temperature tolerance in water must be achieved by the use of insulating and external heating methods properly integrated with an understanding of physiological heat exchange. Such technical heating methods must also include preheating of the gas mixture to be breathed, because a significant amount of body heat is lost through the lungs when cold gas is breathed at high pressures. The temperature of gas inspired is normally equal to the temperature of the ambient water, and Hoke, Jackson, Alexander, and Flynn (1971) found that, at depths beyond 600 ft (183 m) and at water temperatures of 40°F (4.2°C) or less, divers suffered a progressive negative thermal balance. They also found that the rate of heat loss increased as respiratory volume per minute increased at higher work rates. These investigators concluded that, when respiratory heat loss exceeds about 350 W, a diver will soon be in danger.

Hydrostatic Pressure Effects

If the problems of decompression, oxygen toxicity, inert gas toxicity, gas density and viscosity, and temperature can be circumvented through physiological research and technological improvements, the final barrier to man's attempt to go deeper into the sea might be the direct effects of hydrostatic pressure (Fenn, 1969). Although the effects of pressure on human cellular structure and the resultant functional impairments are essentially unknown, experiments have been conducted with animals and animal tissues indicating the existence of direct pressure effects. A major difficulty in studies of this type is the inability to isolate causes of observed effects. Fenn states that most of these effects, however, are measurable only at pressures far higher than those divers are ever likely to encounter.

According to the excellent summary of physiological effects of hydrostatic pressures given by Fenn (1969), these effects include:

1. Failure of gel formation (Marsland, 1938).
2. Failure of cell division (Marsland, 1939).
3. Failure of ameboid movement (Brown & Marsland, 1936).
4. Inhibition of biological luminiscence (Dubois & Regnard, 1884; Johnson, 1957).
5. Inhibition of the growth of bacteria (Fenn, 1967).

Most of these effects appear to be related to volume changes in cells. It is important for diving physiologists to know that bacterial growth is inhibited by pressures as low as 300 m (984 ft) of seawater. This effect suggests the possibility that hydrostatic pressure has some influence at the depths where man still hopes to live for long periods. Divers working at depths exceeding 180 m (590 ft) have also shown susceptibility to dislocated joints. Although the number of incidents cannot support firm conclusions, there appear to be some bone-muscle effects resulting from high hydrostatic pressures, which must be investigated.

UNDERWATER TECHNOLOGICAL RESEARCH
AND DEVELOPMENT

Research and development efforts in diving technology can be separated into two categories. The first is associated with the life-support aspects of technology, that is, the hardware of systems needed to maintain the physiological environment deemed essential to sustain life under the ambient ocean pressure. The second is associated with the functional support of man, that is, the hardware or systems (diver tools, communication equipment, etc.) that aid man in accomplishing undersea tasks. The following discussion deals only with life-support technology.

Individual Life-Support Elements

It was indicated in our brief discussion of the physiological problems of diving that increasing diving depths places more stringent requirements on the makeup of breathing gas mixtures and the monitoring of gas concentrations. The physiological effects of oxygen, inert gases, and contaminants are generally proportional to partial pressure rather than to percentage concentration. Since partial pressure is the product of concentration and total pressure, the allowable concentration of any substance decreases as diving depth increases. For example, at 30 m (98 ft) the range of oxygen percentage is about 5 to 10%, and of carbon dioxide percentage 0 to 0.2%. At 300 m (984 ft) the oxygen percentage is about 0.5 to 1%, and the carbon dioxide percentage is 0 to 0.02%. Because of these effects reliable devices for sensing, monitoring, and controlling the gas environment at high pressure must be developed. Moreover, methods of detecting and eliminating contaminants, such as carbon monoxide, must be developed. Unless atmospheric gases can be reliably controlled, full exploitation of the diving capabilities of man will not be possible.

Current breathing devices are limited in depth-time capability, because of the need to exhaust portions of the breathing gas during each breath. Open or semiclosed underwater breathing devices do not fully exploit the full amount of gas a free-swimming man can carry. However, a totally closed-circuit oxygen rebreather is limited in depth because of the problems of oxygen toxicity.

In an *open-circuit* standard underwater breathing apparatus (scuba), the expired gases are discharged into the water during exhalation. Normal compressed air is the breathing gas medium, although it is possible to use mixed gases for deep dives. Open-circuit systems are inherently wasteful of gases, since about three-fourths of the oxygen in each breath drawn from the gas cylinder is discharged into the water. The principal component of the open-circuit scuba is the demand regulator which releases compressed gas to the diver on inspiring. A pressure regulator maintains the breathing system at ambient depth pressure; the regulator opens to create a slight negative pressure at the start of inspiration and remains open until the end of the process.

In a *semiclosed-circuit* mixed-gas breathing device, the gas mixture can be oxygen–nitrogen or oxygen–helium, depending upon the diving depths required. A volume of gas mixture flows from storage cylinders through a regulator into an inhalation breathing bag. Exhaled gas is then forced into a exhalation bag where a small portion is exhausted into the water. The remaining gas is channeled through a canister designed to remove carbon dioxide and back into the inhalation bag. As oxygen is used up in the breathing volume (inhalation bag), a "critical" level is reached. The constant metered flow of fresh gas keeps the oxygen in the bag from going below this critical level. This form of recirculating breathing apparatus allows maximum utilization of available oxygen, thereby increasing diving duration. But the need to exhaust inert gases, nonetheless, still limits the useful dive duration.

In *closed-circuit* oxygen scuba, pure oxygen is used as the breathing medium rather than mixed gases. The device can be used only to depths of less than 10 m (33 ft) because of the oxygen toxicity problem. The primary purpose of such a device is to maximize covertness. No waste gas needs to be exhausted into the sea, thereby eliminating tell-tale bubbles.

Recently, a new closed-circuit device has been developed in which mixed gases are used. This apparatus has been of very great value to scientists investigating marine animal life at shallow depths, because the equipment is silent and there are no bubbles to frighten the animals (Adolfson & Miller, 1971).

The *mixed-gas, closed-circuit* scuba has an advantage over the closed-circuit oxygen apparatus in that its depth of operation is not restricted to 10 m (33 ft). It has been used on experimental dives down to depths of 488 m (1600 ft). Operational divers have been hesitant to adopt this new equipment because of its reliance on electronic gas sensing, high cost, and maintenance requirements.

Operation Life-Support Elements

In addition to underwater breathing apparatus, life-support elements are required for the overall diving operation. From the viewpoint of technological research and development, the most critical part of the operational life-support equipment is the precision monitoring, and control of breathing gas composition. This includes the required breathing gas supply for the diver at a particular working depth and for the stages of decompression within the decompression chamber during ascent. As mentioned earlier, the need for precision control over gas composition increases greatly as diving depth increases. Furthermore, since the diver's sensitivity to contaminants also increases greatly with increased diving depth, extreme care must be exercised in formulating the breathing gas supply. The major technological development in operational life-support systems is on-site gas mixing. Previously, diving operations required the use of a premixed gas supply, which greatly limited operational flexibility. The achievement of an on-site gas mixing capability resulted from the availability of reliable and portable gas-analysis sensors allowing the composition of breathing gas to be controlled within required tolerances.

Advanced Diving Concepts

There have been two new theoretical developments aimed at sending man to deeper ocean depths for longer periods of time. These developments are (1) the use of artificial gills for gas exchange, and (2) techniques of fluid breathing. Experimental evidence indicating that the mammalian lung can function as gills was presented in 1962 by Kylstra, Tissing, and van der Maen. They found that adult white mice stayed alive for up to 18 hr while breathing a balanced, buffered salt solution at 20°C, which was in equilibrium with oxygen at a tension of 8 ATA. Under these conditions the submerged mammals continued to make respiratory movements and were apparently capable of extracting adequate amounts of dissolved oxygen from the aqueous environment. Furthermore, the animals were not killed by hydrostatic pressures of up to 160 ATA, which is equivalent to an ocean depth of about 1600 m (about 1 mile).

The potential practical importance of fluid breathing is clear. The problem of decompression sickness would be circumvented since inert diluent gas would no longer be present. No inert gas could dissolve in the blood and tissues of a diver with fluid-filled lungs (Kylstra, 1965, 1965a). Consequently, he would be free to ascend to the surface at any time and as rapidly as desired without fear of bubble formation. The problem of inert gas narcosis would also be avoided. Hence, if the fluid-breathing concept proves to be physiologically feasible, the depth that man could reach as a diver would be limited only by the effects of hydrostatic pressure on cellular structure. However, the use of the fluid-breathing technique by humans is still in the future, because the physiological effects of fluids on the lung tissues are still not known. According to Kylstra (1967), gas exchange in liquid-filled lungs is diffusion-limited, and at least 60 times more work is required to propel equal amounts of water instead of air through the lung passages. Kylstra notes that these factors seriously restrict carbon dioxide elimination in water-breathing mammals. He found that, in mechanically ventilated water-breathing dogs, carbon dioxide elimination was always deficient.

The use of fluid-breathing techniques by man will become a reality only through extensive research into the effects of fluids on lung tissue and through the solution of the problem of carbon dioxide elimination. For further studies of the developing research in this field, the interested reader is directed to Kylstra, Paganelli, and Lanphier (1966), Kylstra, Paganelli, and Rahn (1967), Golland and Clark (1967), Kylstra, Nantz, Crowe, Wagner, and Saltzman (1967), and Kylstra (1968, 1968a).

Fish obtain oxygen for their metabolic demands by diffusion from the seawater in which they swim; elimination of carbon dioxide is accomplished in the same way. Diffusion takes place in the gills of the fish where water and blood are in intimate contact, separated mainly by a series of cell membranes. The same physical factors that operate to supply oxygen and eliminate carbon dioxide in fish gills, that is membranes with appropriate permeability properties, can be used in the design of artificial gills (Paganelli, Bateman & Rahn, 1967).

An artificial gill, enabling a submerged man to obtain oxygen by diffusion from water, would have obvious advantages. Work on such gills has been carried out in several laboratories; Bodell's construction, described in 1965, seems to have been the first (Bodell 1965). The problem of obtaining oxygen by diffusion from water is essentially one of developing a proper membrane which would permit passage of oxygen molecules while restraining water molecules.

There are membranes in existence that satisfy the diffusion requirements (Bodell, 1967).

The ultimate system that would allow man to roam the ocean freely for long periods of time might evolve from the combined use of the fluid-breathing technique with the extraction of oxygen from seawater by artificial gills. The development of such a system is very far in the future and will materialize only through extensive effort.

Diver Work Systems

Many configurational variations are possible in integrating components in an undersea work system. The selection of a particular variation is governed by the specific work site environment and by task requirements. All programs concerned with developing undersea work systems are directed toward enhancing man's ability to accomplish useful work down to the depth of the continental shelf (about 200 m or 650 ft) and determining man's ultimate depth-time limits in the undersea environment (Workman, 1966).

Direct Surface-Supported Systems

The growing interest in and concern with the exploration of the oceans, and in particular, the exploitation of the ocean's resources, have resulted in the evolution of several systems for accomplishing undersea tasks. The most familiar form of these systems is the tethered or free-swimming man operating from a surface-support platform. The three specific forms of direct surface-supported systems are:

1. The hard-hat diver.
2. The free-swimming diver.
3. The tethered or hooka swimmer (Figure 1-5).

A hard-hat diver, tethered to a breathing gas supply on a surface ship, was the earliest form of the system. The average diving depth for a compressed air dive is 45 to 60 m (148 to 197 ft), the limit being established by individual susceptibility to compressed air narcosis. Working dives to 100 to 200 m (328 to 656 ft) can be accomplished with the use of a helium–oxygen gas supply. The time limit is established primarily by the physical endurance of the individual diver. A basic functional limit of the tethered hard-hat diver is his mobility and maneuverability.

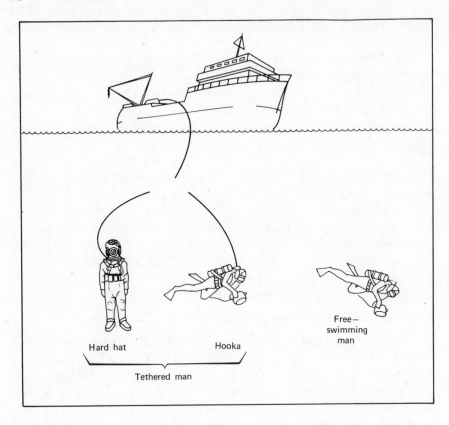

Figure 1-5. Direct surface-supported systems. (Bien & McDonough, 1970.)

A free-swimming diver overcomes the mobility and maneuverability constraints of a hard-hat diver, but a compromise is made on diving duration. Time constraints are established by the limited life-support stores a diver can carry and his dependency upon the particular breathing system employed. Standard open-cycle air scubas have a limited depth-time function, and closed-cycle oxygen rebreathers are limited by oxygen toxicity to use above 10 m (33 ft). However, semiclosed mixed-gas scubas allow greater depth-time capability than either of the two systems mentioned above. Meanwhile, advanced closed-cycle mixed-gas systems capable of several hours at 200 m (197 ft) are being developed (some have already been introduced) and will overcome many of the present free-swimmer limitations.

The tethered swimmer (hooka) is a compromise solution to the mobility constraints of the hard-hat diver and the time constraints of the free swimmer. The tethered swimmer is supplied by surface-breathing gas stores of compressed air or mixed gases.

All three forms of the direct surface-supported systems described above involve the use of decompression. That is, the diver is required to remain in the water at predetermined depth stages and durations during ascent. Decompression chambers are usually on hand for emergency purposes.

Augmented Surface-Supported Systems

Figure 1-6 illustrates the first category of augmented surface-supported systems which uses a personnel transfer capsule (PTC) together with a deck decompression chamber (DDC). The PTC serves the diving team as a transfer elevator to and from its underwater work site, while maintaining a required pressurized breathing environment of compressed air or mixed gas. Primarily, the capsule carries divers to the work site or to the spot from which diver excursions will be made. The capsule maintains the diver in an air or mixed-gas atmosphere having a gas pressure equal to the seawater pressure at the diver's destination depth. Upon reaching depth the diver may leave the capsule through a lower lock. The diver may operate out of the PTC on a tether which supplies breathing gas for long work periods, or he may use self-contained equipment as an untethered swimmer.

The PTC is also functional as a diving bell with the atmospheric air equivalent to the surface pressure environment (1 ATA). In this case the capsule is used for the observation and inspection of work or the work site. If inspection establishes that divers are needed, the PTC can then be pressurized to ambient pressure and divers deployed for in-water work.

The DDC provides a pressurized environment aboard the surface support ship compatible with the ambient pressure conditions of the work site. An entrance lock provides a pressure connection between the DDC and the PTC, allowing transfer of divers while maintaining their pressurized environmental conditions. In addition to its

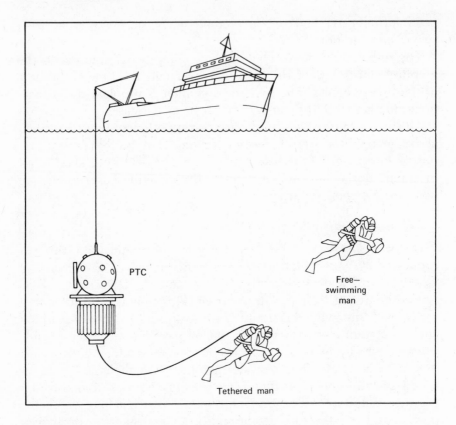

Figure 1-6. Augmented surface-supported systems—personnel transfer capsule. (Bien & McDonough, 1970.)

decompression function, the DDC may also function as a habitat for multiple-dive operations. That is, the diver can make many trips between the surface and the work site without the need for decompression after each dive. While in the DDC he is maintained at the ambient pressure of the work site. Only one decompression cycle is needed following the completion of a multiple-dive operation. The term "bounce dive" or "subsaturation dive" has been applied to the technique of decompression after each dive, while the term "saturation dive" is used to refer to the technique of a single decompression cycle after a long-term multiple-dive operation.

The second category of augmented surface-supported systems is

illustrated in Figure 1-7. These systems use a personnel transfer
vehicle (PTV) together with a DDC. The PTV is used in the same
manner as the PTC described in the preceding system. The PTV has
the advantage over the PTC system in that it has horizontal movement. If so desired divers can remain in the PTV and be decom-
pressed there during recovery. The additional use of the PTV as a
decompression facility has evolved a system referred to as the mobil
habitat (Figure 1-8).

A summary of man-in-the-sea system options, defined by Bien
and MacDonough (1970) as those underwater systems in which man
is exposed to the ambient pressure in the ocean environment, is given
in Table 1-4.

Man is the focal point in all these underwater work systems. The

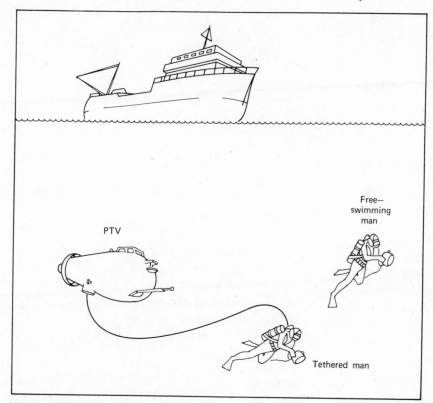

Figure 1-7. Augmented surface-supported system—personnel transfer vehicle.
(Bien & McDonough, 1970.)

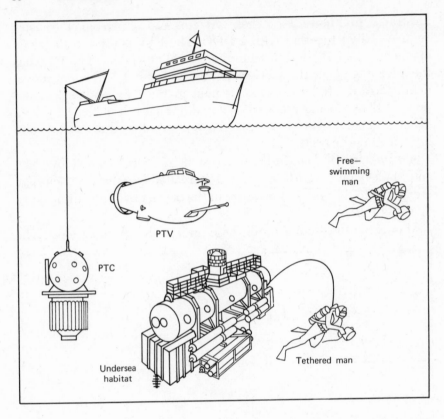

Figure 1-8.   Augmented surface-supported system—habitat. (Bien & McDonough, 1970.)

development of the abundant resources within the sea that can be used for man's benefit requires that he be able to live and work productively for extended periods of time beneath its surface. It seems important, therefore, to correlate and adapt the advanced technological development to the physiological changes in the organism and the psychological behavioral alterations and variations caused by the hostile and unusual environment.

The Optimum System Design

In the actual design of undersea systems there is some debate as to the optimum system configuration. Should the man in the system be

Table 1-4   Man-in-the-Sea Systems Options (Bien & McDonough, 1971)

Principal Man-in-the-Sea Systems Components

Man-in-the-Sea Systems Options	Surface-Support Ship	Subsurface-Support Ship (Submarine)	Subsurface-Support Habitat	Decompression Chamber	Personnel Transport Capsule (PTC)	Personnel Transport Vehicle (PTV)	Free-Swimming—Personnel Support	Tethered—Personnel Support	Notes
Direct surface-supported system (Figure 1-5)				①			②	②	1. Emergency use only
Augmented surface-supported system— PTC (Figure 1-6)				③					2. Either free-swimming or tethered
Augmented surface-supported system— PTV (Figure 1-7)									3. On surface-support ship
Augmented surface supported system— habitat (Figure 1-8)					④	④			4. Either PTC or PTV
Direct subsurface-supported system				⑤					5. On submarine
Augmented subsurface-supported system—PTV									
Augmented subsurface-supported system—habitat						⑥			6. Optional personnel transport

kept at normal atmospheric pressure and isolated from the hostile undersea environment, or should he be exposed to ambient pressure and allowed free interaction with the environment? Efforts are presently underway to quantify the performances of both system configurations (Pesch, Hill & Klepser, 1970). Trade-off studies dealing with this problem present two questions:

1. Can both system configurations accomplish the job safely?
2. Which one is least expensive?

In an attempt to answer the first question, Pesch, Hill, and Klepser conducted a study to compare divers' performances with those of operators in a submersible using manipulators. Both the divers and the submersible operators performed the same operational tasks which varied widely in their complexity. The tasks ranged from a simple sample collection effort to a complex drilling and connect/disconnect maneuver. Measures of time and accuracy were obtained on discrete components of each task. Based on overall performance, the divers were four times faster than the manipulators. There was, however, a great deal of variation among the various tasks. The performance time for the divers ranged from 31 times faster than the manipulators for close tolerance tasks such as connect/disconnect maneuvers, to 1.3 times faster for tapping holes.

As a result of their discrete-element analysis of the various tasks, Pesch et al. (1970) concluded that: "A manipulator could actually use a tool almost as fast as a diver and usually more accurately. The problems for a manipulator were in the preuse elements, such as alignment and travel."

Pesch (personal communication) observed that a major shortcoming of the submersible manipulator was its lack of feedback. A diver is kinesthetically aware of where his limbs are and can identify tactually the objects upon which he is to work. An isolated operator in a submersible, however, is completely dependent upon *visual* feedback, and unless he can see his manipulator and the job piece he is essentially ineffective. Pesch et al. observed that: "In the case of the diver system, the diver is environment-dependent with respect to depth, temperature, current and hostile organic life; however, he is capable of utilizing his natural abilities of motor control and sensory feedback, indirectly modified by the water environment. The manipulator system, on the other hand, provides the operator with a nearly normal environment, but he undergoes, in most cases, more severe attenuation of his control and feedback processes" (Pesch, et al., 1970).

Until the manipulator control system is improved to provide some type of feedback circuit, and as long as the major ocean projects are undertaken within the pressure ranges that are physiologically feasible for the man, the ambient-pressure diver system will probably continue to flourish.

If the above assumptions regarding future undersea systems are correct, we should actively seek information about the performance of man in hyperbaric environments. To date, there have been few systematic attempts to study the effects of undersea environments on human performance. A limited number of studies have focused on the perceptual-motor and cognitive aspects of diver behavior. These studies are essential for a complete understanding of man's performance in this type of environment, however, the first step should be the study of the diver's sensory-perceptual capabilities. Studies of the functioning and output of a system are of little practical value without knowledge of the inputs to the system.

MAN AS A SYSTEM COMPONENT

Several ambitious programs have been embarked upon in the last 5 to 10 years to allow man access to the rich and wondrous world beneath the sea. Sophisticated underwater systems are being designed and constructed for a wide variety of undertakings from ocean bottom studies of the behavior and habits of marine life to the mining of rare metals.

Like most operational systems, these new undersea designs include man as a vital system component. The decision to include man is usually based upon his unique capabilities. Morgan, Cook, Chapanis, and Lund (1963) delineate eight tasks for which man is ideally equipped:

1. Tasks requiring the discrimination of signals in noise.
2. Tasks requiring pattern discrimination in a changing field.
3. Tasks in which discrimination must be made between multiple inputs.
4. Tasks in which flexibility is required in unforeseen situations.
5. Tasks requiring problem solving.
6. Tasks which use man as a monitor, with override capabilities, in automatic and semiautomatic systems.
7. Tasks in which the sensing and reporting of incidental intelli-

gence is expected in the course of a mission having other objectives.

8. Tasks in which alternate modes of operation are likely to be required.

Of these eight unique functions man can perform, five are directly related to his sensory-perceptual capabilities. The remaining three are associated with man as a decision maker, and are consequently indirectly related to sensory-perceptual inputs. Because of this great emphasis on man as a sensor, it seems reasonable to conclude that the first step in designing an underwater system should be the evaluation of man's sensory-perceptual processes.

CLASSIFICATION OF MAN'S SENSORY SUBSYSTEMS

In distinguishing between the sensing and perceiving of energy forms, physiologists and psychologists usually point out that sensation involves the awareness of sensory activations, while perception involves the use of the data provided by the senses.

According to Bartley (1970), there are four criteria for determining the existence and number of sense modalities. "They are (a) a unique class of sensation (awareness), (b) a unique sense organ, (c) a specific form and range of energy, and (d) a separate path from sense organ to brain." Up to now, 10 separate sense modalities have been identified, but not all of them meet all the above criteria.

The sensory subsystems have been classified in many different ways. Each one of the various classification schemes has certain merits, and each is used in part in discussions of man's sensory capabilities. The two most widely used schemes are Sherrington's classification and the clinical classification as discussed below.

Sherrington's classification (Sherrington, 1906) is based on the source of the stimulus and the location of the receptor. The *proprioceptors*, found in muscles, tendons and joints, and in the labyrinth, give information concerning the movements and position of the body in space. The *exteroceptors*, the sense organs of the skin, give information on changes in the immediate external environment. The *interoceptors* transmit impulses from the visceral organs. The *teleceptors*, or distance receptors, are the sense organs of the eyes, ears and nose and give information concerning changes in the more remote environment.

The clinical classification of the senses is strongly influenced by morphological considerations. Ruch (1955) offers the following list which shows how the modalities of sensation are grouped by clinicians:

A. Special senses served by the cranial nerves:(1) vision, (2) audition, (3) taste, (4) olfaction, and (5) vestibular.

B. Superficial or cutaneous sensations served by the cutaneous branches of spinal and certain cranial nerves: (1) touch-pressure, (2) warmth, (3) cold, and (4) pain.

C. Deep sensations served by muscular branches of spinal nerves and certain cranial nerves: (1) muscle, tendon and joint sensibility, or position sense, (2) deep pain, and (3) deep pressure.

D. Visceral sensations served by fibers conducted with the autonomic nervous system: (1) organic sensation (e.g., hunger and nausea), and (2) visceral pain.

Bartley (1970) points out that there are a number of receptors in the body that have been isolated, and functions attributed to them, but for which no specific sense modality has been named. He suggests that the following enumerated group of sensory receptors be considered as a homeostatic perceptual system. "(a) *carotid sinus receptors* in the cardiovascular system, (b) *sensory endings* in the walls of venae cavae and pulmonary veins, (c) sensory cells in the supraoptic and paraventricular nuclei, (d) thermosensitive neurons in the hypothalamus, and (e) certain receptors in the tracheobronchial tree which respond to pulmonary inflation and deflation." Bartley's homeostatic receptors generally fail to meet the first criterion he set down for determining the existence of a sense modality. Man is usually unaware of their functioning. Although the effects of the hyperbaric environment on all these sensory receptors are important, only those that meet all Bartley's criteria are included in this book.

Gibson (1966) identified the following five modes of attention: listening, touching, smelling, tasting, and looking, which are found in Table 1-5. For Gibson, these modes of attention, along with their associated forms of physical energy, mechanical, thermal, chemical, and photic (light sensing) determine the perceptual systems.

Although the classification schemes described above are useful in organizing one's thinking about the various sensory subsystems, they are very rarely used in total. Writers in the sensory field seem to be more eclectic in their organizational approach, and we are no exception. We have chosen to organize our chapters in a manner that lends itself to none of the above standard classifications.

SUMMARY

The undersea environment is dangerous, and as greater depths are reached the hazards increase at an exponential rate. As an individual enters the undersea world, the sensory information he receives is greatly altered. The physiochemical qualities of the environment act on both the signal and the receiver. The changes in stimulus energy caused by the transmitting gas and the seawater also affect a diver's behavior and his performance. For man detection of objects underwater can be accomplished using several different sense modalities, but their identification can only be made visually or sometimes tactically. For the visual sense to be at all functional in the underwater environment, the level of photic energy must exceed the excitation threshold of the visual system. Parallel radiation entering a layer of seawater is gradually weakened by three factors: absorption, scattering and refraction, and reflection.

Sound transmission essentially appears to be affected by two interrelated factors, namely, gas density and gas molecular weight. The lighter the gas the greater the velocity of transmission, and the greater the density the greater the velocity of transmission.

The temperature of water at deep ocean depths is relatively constant insofar as it changes very little from locale to locale and from season to season. For a man immersed in water, the important temperature consideration is the thermal conductivity of the water, which is about 25 times higher than that of air.

Man's sensory-perceptual ability underwater is greatly altered. Even under ideal conditions, vision is limited to 30 to 50 m, (98 to 164 ft) but most commonly it is less than 5 to 10 m (16 to 33 ft). Hearing suffers moderately from immersion, while the somesthetic senses appear to be altered very little by the undersea environment. The chemical senses of olfaction and taste are useless as exteroceptors in the water and their contribution in the dry ambient pressure habitat is minimal.

Table 1-5 The Perceptual Systems (Gibson, 1966)

Name	Mode of Attention.	Receptive Units	Anatomy of the Organ	Activity of the Organ	Stimuli Available	External Information Obtained
The basic orienting system	General orientation	Mechano-receptors	Vestibular organs	Body equilibrium	Forces of gravity and accelera-tion	Direction of gravity, being pushed
The audi-tory system	Listening	Mechano-receptors	Cochlear organs with middle ear and auricle	Orienting to sounds	Vibration in the air	Nature and location of vibratory events
The haptic system	Touching	Mechano-receptors and possibly thermo-receptors	Skin (including attach-ments and openings) Joints (including liga-ments) Muscles (including tendons)	Exploration of many kinds	Deformations of tissues Configuration of joints Stretching of muscle fibers	Contact with the earth Mechanical encounters Object shapes Material states, solidity or viscosity
The taste-smell system	Smelling	Chemorecep-tors	Nasal cavity (nose)	Sniffing	Composition of the medium	Nature of volatile sources
	Tasting	Chemo- and mechano-receptors	Oral cavity (mouth)	Savoring	Composition of ingested objects	Nutritive and bio-chemical values
The visual system	Looking	Photoreceptors	Ocular mechanism (eyes, with intrinsic and extrinsic eye muscles, as related to the vestibular organs, the head, and the whole body)	Accommoda-tion, Pupillary ad-justment, Fixation, convergence Exploration	The variables of structure in ambient light	Everything that can be specified by the vari-ables of optical struc-ture (information about objects, ani-mals, motions, events, and places)

A brief review is given in the chapter on hyperbaric physiology. Thus, decompression, oxygen toxicity, inert gas toxicity, gas density, and viscosity and hydrostatic pressure effects are generally discussed from a physiological point of view. This is also the case with underwater technological research and development. The importance of developing reliable devices for sensing, monitoring, and controlling the gas environment at high pressures is pointed out. Unless atmospheric gases can be reliably controlled, full exploitation of the diving capabilities of man will not be possible.

Current underwater breathing devices are described in point of principle, and the techniques of fluid breathing and the use of artificial gills for gas exchange are discussed. It is predicted that the future ultimate system that would allow man to roam the ocean freely for long periods of time might evolve from the combined use of the fluid-breathing technique with the extraction of oxygen from seawater by artificial gills.

Finally, man as a system component is discussed against the background of the principal types of diver work systems. Man is the center of these systems. It might be concluded that although manned submersibles or robots may be of very great value, at least at very great depths, man himself will continue to be the most valuable and cheapest instrument for undersea work.

II

VISION

Introduction — Vision in the dry hyperbaric environment — Vision in the wet hyperbaric environment — Visual acuity — The diver's field of view — Range of visibility under water — Distance perception and size under water — Dark adaptation in the undersea environment — Color discrimination under water — Perceptual learning in the undersea environment — Blind or blindfolded divers — Environmental stress and visual perception — Summary

Vision is man's primary source of information concerning his environment. In dry hyperbaric environments, such as, manned underwater laboratories and habitats, there are no essential changes in human visual functioning, provided that a low-density nonnarcotic breathing mixture is used. Under water, vision is quite restricted because of the physical properties of seawater. Thus visual acuity measured under water without face masks is exceedingly poor. Face masks or contact lenses are used to restore normal refraction to the eye by reestablishing the air–corneal interface, but these devices reduce the diver's field of view.

It is a common observation that underwater objects appear to be both larger and closer than they really are. Distance perception and perception of size are discussed in the chapter. It is suggested that polarized light could be of some advantage in perceiving distant objects under water.

Color discrimination under water is very much dependent upon the clarity of the water. A list of colors for best and poorest visibility is found in the chapter.

It seems that there is excellent agreement between the amount of prior underwater experience and the amount of compensation for visual distortion. Adaptation and habituation to the undersea environment are discussed. The stress factors associated with the underwater world as they relate to visual perception are also mentioned.

INTRODUCTION

Vision is man's primary source of information concerning his environment. The stimulus is radiant energy which originates at a primary source, namely, the sun or a light bulb. The energy sometimes comes directly to the eye, but more commonly it reaches the eye after reflection from sundry objects. Fortunately, the energy travels in straight lines, permitting it to form a retinal image resembling the surface from which it is reflected.

Much vision in ordinary day-by-day living is vision at close range. An individual must be able to perceive small objects and visually separate adjacent objects and borders. The same kind of visual ability is required for regarding distant objects and separations between them (Bartley, 1969). Through the utilization of vision man not only obtains knowledge concerning the size, shape, color, and location of objects, but he is also able to determine his orientation and position within the environment. A major advantage of vision over the other senses is its ability to obtain precise information on distant objects very quickly, a factor that can be of life-saving importance for a diver in the sea.

VISION IN A DRY HYPERBARIC ENVIRONMENT

The most complete assessment of human vision in a dry hyperbaric environment was made by Kelley, Burch, Bradley, and Campbell (1968) at the U.S. Navy Experimental Diving Unit, Washington, D.C. Fifteen different tests of visual functioning were performed on fourteen navy divers in a hyperbaric helium–oxygen environment during chamber saturation dives to 26, 19, 15, and 11 ATA. Measurements were obtained before the dive, during the dive, during the decompression phase, and again at the completion of the dive.

"The visual tests employed are listed in Table 2-1. Visual acuity in each eye was determined with an Armed Forces Clinical Test Chart at 20 feet at normal chamber illumination. Near vision was determined at 14 inches with an American Optical reading card. Maximum accommodation was measured by finding the near point at which the smallest print on the reading card was seen to blur.

Peripheral visual fields were measured in each eye with a Schweiger hand perimeter, using a one mm white test object in twelve meridians. The figures for peripheral fields are the total of the twelve measures in each eye. Central field defects were looked for, utilizing an Amsler Grid. Color vision determinations were made with H-R-R Pseudoisochromatic Plates.

Ocular motility was observed in the primary, secondary, and tertiary positions of gaze. A red glass was used in an attempt to elicit diplopia in these positions. A Maddox Wing was utilized in determining horizontal, vertical, and cyclophorias. Subjective fusion ranges were measured with base in and base out prisms while the subject fixed on a hand light. A Worth 4-dot test was used to detect gross suppression. Steriopsis was quantitated with the Titmus Stereotest" (p. 828). Finally, dark adaptation was determined with the MRL night vision test.

No statistically significant changes were found between the measurements obtained on the surface and those taken at the various depths. Kelley et al. did report an extremely negligible 2% reduction in field of view at increased pressure, and a slight change in accommodation. In the accommodation test the range of distance at which objects became blurred changed from surface readings of 15–9 cm (5.75–3.50 in.), to 9.5–9 cm (3.75–3.50 in.) at depth. According to these investigators, there are no essential changes in human visual functioning at ambient pressures to 26 ATA, provided a low-density nonnarcotic breathing mixture is used (Table 2-1).

There is evidence, however, that hyperbaric *air* might cause changes in human vision. Among the psychosensorial phenomena noted by Adolfson (1967) during a series of chamber dives to 13 ATA with air as the breathing medium, micropsia as well as changes in figure-background contrast were reported by one subject during two different dives. The diver experienced a change in the relation between foreground and background in two different experimental situations, specifically a form contraction with intensified contrasts. The objects inside the chamber seemed to be diminished in size, their outlines became "sharp as a razor," and all details stood out

Table 2-1   Physiological Factors in Visual Function Studies (Kelley, Burch, Bradley & Campbell, 1968)

Test	Surface Control (range)	Depth (range)
Distance vision	20/15 to 20/20 + 2	20/15 + 5 to 20/20
Near vision	0.5 to 1.0 D	0.5 to 1.0 D
Accommodation	3.5 to 13 in.	3 to 11 in.
Peripheral fields	725 to 855°	740 to 840°
Central fields	Normal	Normal
Color vision	Normal	Normal
Ductions	Normal	Normal
Ductions with red glass	No diplopia	No diplopia
Maddox wing	Horizontal 1 to 2 scale units	Horizontal 0 to 4 scale units
	Vertical 1 to 2 scale units	Vertical 0 to 2 scale units
	Cyclo-0 to 1 scale unit	Cyclo-0 to 1 scale unit
Prism fusion	Convergent 8 to 18 diopters	Convergent 8 to 18 diopters
	Divergent 14 to 40 diopters	Divergent 18 to 40 diopters
Worth four-dot	Fusion	Fusion
Titmus Sterotest	40 sec at 16 in.	40 sec at 16 in.
Optokinetic nystagmus	Normal	Normal
Dark adaptation	39 to 55 correct	25 to 54 correct
Subjective visual symptoms	None	None

much more clearly than earlier. The subject, who had pronounced myopia, noted no difference in visual acuity when he removed his glasses. The phenomenon disappeared as soon as the ambient pressure was lowered. On a later occasion this subject described the same sensation as a gradual transition from diminution of objects and increased sharpness in normal sight when the pressure was lowered from 13 to 10 ATA. Controlled quantitative studies should be undertaken to verify experimentally these observed phenomena.

In an initial study on this topic Biersner (1972) attempted to simulate the narcosis associated with the hyperbaric air environment by using nitrous oxide on the surface. He estimated that 30% nitrous oxide would be equivalent to the anesthetic properties of air at a depth of 210 ft (64 m) of seawater (Cherkin, 1968). Biersner used several measures of visual function. Visual acuity at 20 ft (6 m) was estimated using a standard Snellen Chart, whereas near-visual acuity was measured with an American Optical reading card held 14 in. (5.36 cm) from the eyes. Extraocular muscle function was tested by observing the eyes in three places, with and without a red glass cover. Subjects were asked to describe any diplopia. Phorias were estimated using the Maddox Wing. Proximal accommodation was determined with both eyes simultaneously, measuring the distance at which the smallest characters on the vision card became indistinguishable. Intraocular pressure was tested with a Schiotz Tonometer, while stereopsis was evaluated using standard Titmus rings. Each subject was examined for spontaneous nystagmus. Asymmetrical optokinetic nystagmus was tested using a standard optokinetic drum. It should be noted that corrective lenses were not used during these tests.

Results of the visual tests are shown in Table 2-2. The data indicate that vision is not significantly impaired while subjects breath 30% nitrous oxide. The differences that do exist are small, inconsistent, and within normal limits. Biersner reports that "all subjects were able to read the smallest characters on the near-vision card while breathing nitrous oxide. Results using the nine Titmus stereopsis patterns were normal, as were tests of interocular pressure and accommodation. Spontaneous nystagmus was not detected, while tests of optokinetic nystagmus found normal, symmetrical movements under both test conditions. Tests of extraocular muscle function showed conjugate reflexes to be normal. Subjective diplopia was not reported. Evidence of slight insignificant exophoria was found in 10 subjects using the Maddox Wing; vertical phorias, however, were not detected. Some subjects also showed slight, insignificant impairment in distance vision" (Biersner, 1972). This study does not put to rest the subjective observations of Adolfson because the question of the effects of pressure still exists. A well-controlled quantitative study is still needed that examines this phenomena in the hyperbaric environment.

With respect to future long saturation dives in undersea habitats, one other factor that may affect man's vision in the dry undersea system should be mentioned here. Schwartz and Sandberg (1954)

Table 2-2   Results of Visual Tests (Biersner, 1972)

Test	Air	Nitrous Oxide
Visual acuity		
Near	0.5D line	0.5D line
Distant	20/15–20/40	20/15–20/40
Titmus stereopsis	All correct	All correct
Intraocular pressure (scale units)	4.75–7.00	3.50–7.00
	Normal	Normal
Optokinetic nystagmus	Normal	Normal
Versions	Normal	Normal
Accommodation (in.)	4.0–10.5	3.5–11.0
Maddox wing (scale units)		
Horizontal	0–2	0–6
Vertical	0	0

reported: "With increased time in the submarine service there is a decrease in visual acuity for distant and near objects, accompanied by a tendency toward esophoria." These investigators hypothesized that this loss of visual efficiency may be related to the confining nature of the submarine environment. If this hypothesis is true, similar observations may be made during long saturation dives.

It has been theorized that small submarine compartments necessitate almost constant accommodation for near distances. This in turn is accompanied by binocular convergence (Alpern, 1962). Extended confinement is presumed to result eventually in a loss of ability to relax accommodation. Consequently, there is an increase in myopia and loss of visual acuity, and the two eyes begin to assume some degree of convergence in the resting position. The last-mentioned is called esophoria (Luria, Newmark & Beatty, 1970).

The submarine findings are consistent with numerous animal studies which have shown that monkeys placed in a confining visual environment suffer progressive visual impairment, notably an increase in myopia and a resulting loss of distance vision (Young, 1967). Since some animal studies indicate that the vision of adult monkeys begins to show some deterioration as soon as the visual restrictions are imposed (Young, 1965), the question arises whether or not there are any measurable changes in the visual processes of submariners during only one submarine patrol.

Luria, Newmark, and Beatty (1970) made two separate studies to answer this question. In one, the Snellen acuity and subjective refraction of 100 officers and men were measured at the start and near the completion of a 40-day patrol. In the second, checkboard acuity, phoria, and depth perception were measured in 49 men at the start of and throughout the course of a 10-week patrol.

These investigators found that there was a statistically significant decrease in the mean score of lateral phoria at nearer distances, but were unable to demonstrate any deteriorating elements in the other parameters. They found no real changes in visual acuity, and no changes in the refractive power of the eyes occurred. In addition, depth perception did not manifest any significant alteration during the patrol. However, although there were no radical decrements in acuity, stereoacuity, or refractive error, there were systematic and statistically consequential changes in near lateral phorias. These amounted to nearly one prism diopter in the direction of esophoria and away from the appreciable degree of esophoria large-scale studies have shown to be the norm for near vision in a young population (Weitzman, Kinney & Ryan, 1966).

There exist at the present time very few studies on the effects of various hyperbaric gases on visual acuity, depth perception, dark adaptation, visual fields, visual thresholds, and color perception. Experiments have been conducted in air contaminated by different percentages of carbon dioxide at normal atmospheric pressure and evidence has been compiled on visual impairment associated with extended carbon dioxide inhalation. Observations by Alpern & Hendley (1952) on the effects of respiratory acidosis (induced by breathing a mixture of 7% carbon dioxide and 93% oxygen) on critical flicker fusion (CFF) suggest that an increase in carbon dioxide tension causes a decrease in CFF. Wald, Harper, Goodmand & Krieger (1942) studied the absolute visual threshold and found noticeable deterioration of this function when the carbon dioxide content in air was raised to 5%. Schaefer and Carey (1954) demonstrated important changes in CFF frequency in the latency of alpha blocking at concentrations of 3%. However, Faucett and Newman (1953) did not find any decrements in sensory functioning as a result of prolonged exposure to 1.5% carbon dioxide. In general, reliable amounts of impairment have been found only when the percentage of carbon dioxide in the air was 3 to 5% or greater.

Weitzman, Kinney, and Luria (1969) investigated the visual effects of repeated exposure to carbon dioxide at levels commonly regarded as innocous. Exposure to carbon dioxide varied cyclically from 0.03 to 3.0%, at 1 ATA (air), every 24 hr for a period of 6 days. A battery of visual tests was administered during this period and in control periods before and after the exposure to carbon dioxide. Among the various tests night vision sensitivity and color sensitivity for green were the only ones that repeatedly detected impairment of efficiency during the period of exposure. All other visual functions remained normal.

There is insufficient information pertaining to the effects of carbon dioxide and other gases in hyperbaric environments such as underwater habitats. A real need for further research in this area exists. Although vision is usually very limited in a wet operational environment, it is still a salient element in man's performance in a dry hyperbaric environment. Dry undersea ambient pressure systems may require different types of visual displays for their operators than are currently available. Visual tests may also be good devices for detecting early adverse environmental effects such as the visual narrowing in early oxygen toxicity.

VISION IN A WET HYPERBARIC ENVIRONMENT

As previously mentioned, the underwater environment is usually not very transparent, and vision is consequently quite restricted. The penetration of natural light into the various bodies of water in the world varies greatly. In clear tropical waters useful levels of natural illumination are found at depths of between 60 to 90 m (197 to 295 ft), while in most rivers and harbors useful natural illumination is limited to depths of 3 m (10 ft) or less. Divers working in deep or turbid water prefer to use some form of artificial light, but there are restrictions associated with this type of illumination.

The use of artificial light underwater presents at least two problems to the viewer. First, there is the distance between the light source and the target object that the light must traverse; hence, due to energy attenuation, the light available at the object is greatly reduced. Second, the light unavoidably illuminates the suspended particles that cause the light to be scattered back to the observer just as occurs with the headlights of a car in a dense fog. This backscatter creates a bright foreground and reduces the object to foreground contrast (Briggs & Hatchett, 1965). This is quite in accordance with existing theories; see, for example, Frank (1950) and Defant (1961).

According to Luria and Kinney (1970): "Scattering causes a loss of energy from the line of sight between the object and the eye, blurring of the outline of the object and decreasing the natural contrast between the object and its environment. As a rough rule of thumb, we can say that the luminance contrast between an object and its background must be at least two percent in order for the object to be visible." (p. 1454)

It should be noted that luminance is defined as the amount of light emitted from a source and projected onto a surface, while brightness is a subjective quality of light as measured by the eye. Usually, underwater objects are seen because they appear to be either brighter or darker than the water background but, as the visual range between the object and the eye increases, so the apparent contrast between it and its background decreases. When the apparent contrast reaches a value too low for the eye to detect, the object becomes invisible.

As mentioned earlier, the absorption coefficient increases strongly from about 400 μm toward the red end of the spectrum and beyond, and there is greater transmission at the bluish-green end of the spectrum than at the red end. In turbid waters, however, just the opposite occurs, and the greatest transmission is found in the red-yellow region of the spectrum. This is of importance for the visual performance of sea animals living in turbid waters. It has been shown by Munz (1958, 1958a, 1964), as well as by others, that fish living in the yellow-stained waters found close inshore tend to have visual pigments more sensitive to long wavelength light than do those living in the blue water of the open sea. Thus there is general support for the view that fish possess visual pigments with maximum absorption at a wavelength (λ_{max}) coincidental with the wavelength of maximum transmission of the water. In terms of visual range and by means of a specially designed diver-operated instrument (Figures 2-1 and 2-2), Lythgoe (1968) investigated the advantages in using various visual filters in one type of coastal Mediterranean water. He adopted Stiles' data for the human eye (Wyszecki & Stiles, 1967), because this absorption curve is similar to that found in some coastal water fish (Denton, 1956).

Briefly, Lythgoe found by employing the method shown in Figures 2-1 and 2-2 that in shallow water the spectral radiance of a grey object differs from that of the water background. He concluded:

"The visual pigments present in the eye will, therefore, affect the perceived contrast between an object and its water background, and hence, the range at which the object can be seen underwater. The data obtained show that in Mediterranean waters those visual pigments with λ_{max} corresponding to the wavelength of maximum light transmission through the water are best suited for detecting large very dark or very bright objects. But 'offset' visual pigments are more suitable for detecting small grey objects in shallow water." (p. 1005)

Some trials have been performed to apply Lythgoe's theories to the diver by using filtered face masks. However, according to Kinney (personal communication), filters placed in front of the eye do not change the absorption spectrum of the photopigments; they simply reduce the intensity of light entering the eye. If the target and the water background have the same spectral energy distribution, filters do nothing but reduce each proportionally, merely resulting in less light by which to see. However, if the target differs from its background, then filters can be selected that enhance the contrast between them. Other filters can reduce the contrast between them. A filter mask can improve contrast, render it worse, or have no effect, depending upon what object one is looking at.

Most of the studies completed to date that are related to man's visual performance in water have been made with free-swimming divers in less than 18 m (59 ft) of water. These studies provide a good base from which to work, and probably account for most of the variables that act to reduce visual functioning. However, greater depths have some additional influence, and we can expect further decrease in visual efficacy because of decreased natural light, psychological stress, and inert gas narcosis.

Visual Acuity Defined

A Dutch ophthalmologist, Hermann Snellen, introduced the now

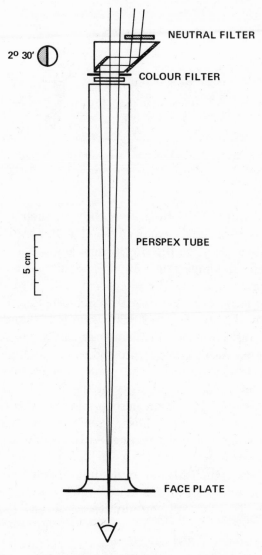

Figure 2-1.   Device used to measure visual pigments and visual range under water. (Lythgoe, 1968.)

famous ophthalmological test chart that measures the degree of visual acuity of an individual through the use of various sized letters. This test is adequate for determining the presence of optical defects that may be corrected by glasses, but its usefulness beyond that point is greatly limited. An improved chart is one employing Landolt

Figure 2-2.   The sighting range used to measure the spectral contrast between a target and its water background. The diver is holding the device shown in Figure 2-1. (Lythgoe, 1968.)

rings as a substitute for letters. It is through such a chart that one may record the so-called visual angle. It is the angle subtended at the eye by the gap within the ring. Visual angle is an inverted measure: the bigger the angle, the worse the acuity. Hence it is conventional to express acuity as the reciprocal of the visual angle, measured in minutes of arc (Woodworth & Schlosberg, 1960). Expressed as the reciprocal of the angle, 20/20 vision is 1.00 and 20/40 is 0.50.

Numerous tasks are used in the assessment of visual acuity. Each gives a different result when expressed in visual angle terms. Minimum visible acuity refers to the perceptual capacity to detect a point, a task in which the intensity of the stimulus is the main determinant of acuity. Minimum perceptible acuity is the capacity to discriminate small objects or lines against a plain background, and minimum separable acuity (also called resolution acuity) refers to the capacity to discriminate between details (lines, points) when they are close together. Minimum distinguishable acuity, sometimes called vernier acuity, or "form sense," refers to the capacity to distinguish irregularities or discontinuities.

Visual Acuity under Water

When the cornea of the vertebrate eye interfaces with water rather than air, it loses a great deal of its refractive power because the index of refraction of the cornea is nearly the same as that of water. Barnard (1961) reported: "The replacement of air by water at the corneal surface produces a gross hypermetropia due to the loss of about two-thirds of the refracting power of the eye." It is well known that the lens of the eye accounts for only a small fraction of the refractive power of the eye. Sixty percent or more of the refraction of light rays is accomplished at the cornea–air interface. When the eye is immersed in water, this interface is lost, and with it most of the refractive power of the eye.

Luria and Kinney (1969) found that visual acuity measured under water without face masks was exceedingly poor. Under the most ideal conditions it was reduced to the level found for night vision, that is, the target had to be 10 times as large as the target in the air to be seen. Further losses result from decreasing light level and reduced target contrast. The acuity of all individuals was much more nearly equal under water than it was in air. Hence emmetropes (persons having normal vision) suffered the greatest loss in water; they required targets more than 20 times as large as those they could see in air. Myops (near-sighted persons) suffered the least loss; they required an increase in target size by a factor of only 7. There was no correlation between acuity in air and that under water. These investigators also pointed out that water clarity must always be considered. Water turbidity sets the limit beyond which no target can be seen regardless of how large it may be.

Pinnipeds have apparently compensated for the loss of refractive power of the cornea under water by possessing a large spherical lens which provides enough accommodation to focus a reasonably well-defined image on the retina (Piggins, 1970). Schusterman and Balliet (1970, 1970a) found experimental evidence which supports the view that several pinniped forms, including the California sea lion (*Zalophus californianus*), Steller's sea lion (*Eumetropias jubuta*), and the harbor seal (*Phoca vitulina*), have good visual acuity underwater in moderate light. All animals observed were capable of consistently resolving gratings subtending visual angles from 5 to 8 minutes of arc in a variety of test situations. They also found experimental evidence indicating that in moderate light the visual acuity of the sea lion in air is essentially the same as it is under water.

Since before the seventeenth century, man has used goggles to replace the air at the corneal surface in an attempt to restore normal vision under water. More recently, various diving masks have been used. These masks and goggles restore normal refraction to the eye by reestablishing the air–cornea interface; however, they produce a refraction at their own outer surface which tends to magnify objects in the water by a factor of 1.25 to 1.33 (Barnard, 1961). With a typical face mask, the magnification is approximately 27%. Kent (1966) and Christianson (1968) have both reported that divers using face masks in clear shallow water with good illumination can see as well as, if not better than, through the masks than they can on the surface. Both of these investigators used Landolt ring targets at distances of about 5 m (16 ft) or less.

An alternative to face masks are contact lenses. As mentioned above, the human cornea and water have virtually the same index of refraction. Therefore approximately 43 diopters of corneal refractive power is lost under water, and a large absolute hyperopia results (Adler, 1950; Luria & Kinney, 1969). The power of an optical system, in diopters, is defined as the reciprocal of its focal length, where the focal length is expressed in meters. The higher the diopter value, the greater the degree of refractive power exhibited. The eyeball is a short-focal-length system, about 17 mm (0.68 in.), corresponding to a refractive power of about 60 diopters.

Duane, Emrich, and Shepler (1958) found that a planoconvex spectacle-type lens of +64.5 diopters (in air), when placed in front of the eye in water, compensated for the hyperopia, enabling the eye to focus incident light rays on the retina and thereby restoring visual acuity. However, such a lens does not protect the eye and limits the visual field to 20°. A better answer to the problem would be a double-walled contact lens (Faust & Beckman, 1966).

Barnard (1961) described an early molded underwater contact lens made of glass or plastic, which consisted of a scleral lens with a conical anterior enclosing an air chamber. At about the same time, Nagel and Monical (1954) independently developed a flat-front, air-chambered scleral lens for underwater swimming.

Earlier underwater contact lenses were asymmetric fitted lenses of glass and/or plastic which were molded from casts of the eyes of the individual wearer. The tight fit of such a lens restricted tear flow to the cornea and sclera. In 1963, Grant produced a symmetric acrylic lens molded in varying sizes according to measured corneal curvature and eye dimensions. This type of lens did not require individual molds for the eyes; it was symmetric, and therefore smaller than the actual globe size so that the flow of tear fluid behind the lens was adequate without a fenestration.

Faust and Beckman (1966) performed a study of underwater vision using a swimmer's face mask and a contact air/water lens system called SCAWLS (*swimmer's contact air-water lens system*); normal vision in air was referenced as a control. The results of this study showed that the contact lens system provided an excellent underwater visual field, whereas the standard swimmer's face mask greatly reduced the visual field. Underwater visual acuity obtained with the contact lens was comparable to, or slightly better than, the face mask, and had the added advantage of incorporating corrections for refractive errors. In operational testing the underwater contact lenses were worn up to 3 hr in seawater and gave improved underwater vision. Factors found to limit the general use of the underwater contact lens were:

1. The individual fitting required.
2. The significant conjunctival irritation that occur in seawater.
3. The halation and blurred vision that occur whenever the scleral lenses are worn for extended periods.

On the basis of this evaluation the underwater contact lenses were judged by these investigators to be of value for specialized use when a face mask would be disadvantageous. Despite these favorable results the use of underwater contact lenses has not been very widespread. Until some less expensive method of maintaining the air–cornea interface is discovered, human underwater observers will probably continue to use face masks.

The Diver's Field of View

For any particular position of the eye, head, and body, only part of the visible surroundings is in view. This part may be called the field of view. The field of view thus consists of those sources and surfaces in the visible surroundings from which light enters the pupil of the eye (Howard & Templeton, 1966).

The diver's restricted field of view is due to two factors:

1. The rubber portions of the mask that make the seal with the diver's face.
2. The refraction of light at the water–air interface tends totally to reflect light beyond some critical angle. Barnard (1961) reported that this critical angle is about 48.6°. It might be recalled that this is

the same angle mentioned in the discussion concerning the penetration of atmospheric light into the sea.

Diver visual fields have also been studied by Workman and Prickett (1957) and Weltman, Christianson, and Egstrom (1965, 1965a), who all made perimetrical measurements under water in an effort to account for the factors discussed above. Workman and Prickett reported: "Little significant differences were found in limitation of the visual field and distortion for the same mask used by different subjects in air and in water." They concluded that, if comparison between masks is the only item of interest, the measurement can safely be made on the surface.

The investigators found in their evaluation of 14 different diving masks that the human field of vision is reduced by 5 to 50° in the lateral fields, 30 to 60° upward, and 30 to 50° downward. The average values for all 14 masks are shown in Figure 2-3.

Weltman, Christianson, and Egstrom (1965) evaluated five different diver face masks, one of which was a wraparound type. Although the wraparound mask greatly extended the lateral field of vision, the curvature of the glass introduced a very uncomfortable distortion. In this same study three standard masks were tested, and the differences found are presented in Table 2-3.

The big difference in upward and downward vision in this study, as compared with the study of Workman and Prickett, is probably due to the position of the mask on the diver's face and the position of the diver during testing. The subjects of Workman and Prickett were seated relatively motionless, while the subjects of Weltman et al. were in a swimming position (Figure 2-4). The important thing to note is that the total percentage of visual field reduction is about the same.

Weltman and co-workers concluded that for the foreseeable future man will wear a face mask upon entering the sea, and that the design of this mask will have to be a compromise among such factors as peripheral vision, binocular vision, distortion, comfort, and buoyancy.

Range of Visibility under Water

From subjective responses obtained from both scuba and hard-hat divers, it appears that operational divers do not normally experience

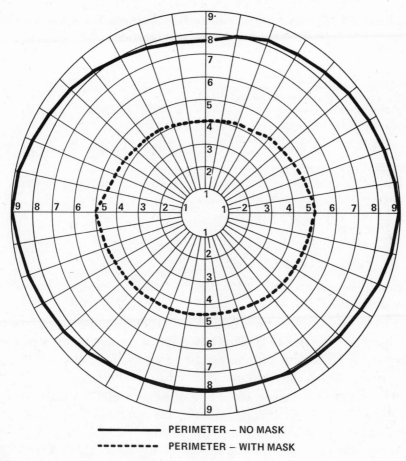

——————— PERIMETER – NO MASK

- - - - - - - - PERIMETER – WITH MASK

Figure 2-3. Average visual field of a scuba diver (Adapted from Workman & Prickett, 1957.)

an enhancement of visual acuity. That is to say, the water in which they dive is far from clear, illuminance levels are greatly reduced, their face masks are often "fogged up," and object contrast is usually close to zero.

Kent (1966) asked 100 qualified Navy divers to compare their ability to see under water and on the surface. The question asked was: "While under water, do underwater objects within about 20 feet of you appear (a) less clear than on the surface, (b) clearer than on the surface, or (c) no difference?" Of the scuba divers 50% responded "less clear," 11% "clearer," and 39% "no difference." For

Table 2-3   Average Field of View in Degrees through a Scuba Mask
(Weltman, Christianson and Egstrom, 1965)

	Upward	Lateral	Downward
Field of vision (binocular plus monocular			
Normal field of view	60–70	100	80
Average field of view through a			
Scuba mask	55	45	15
Difference	10	55	65
Binocular field of vision only			
Normal binocular field	60–70	60	80
Average binocular field of view through			
a Scuba mask	55	34	8
Difference	10	26	72

the hard-hat divers it was 61% "less clear," 7% "clearer," and 32% "no difference."

Kent's subjects had no worse than 20/30 distance visual acuity each eye, correctable to 20/20. Only three of the divers reported that they wore glasses for distance vision. Two of these claimed to see less well under water, and one claimed to see better.

The scuba divers were asked two questions related to depth perception. The first question posed was: "Do you think that your depth perception (or ability to judge the distance of objects away from you) is different underwater than on the surface?" There were 78% affirmative answers, 18% negative answers, and 4% were undecided. The second question was: "If your depth perception underwater seems different than on the surface, do you think that objects underwater appear (a) nearer to you, or (b) farther away?" There were 94% who responded "nearer," and 6% who responded "farther away."

The underwater visibility range is contingent upon so many factors that all calculations must necessarily be only approximations. For instance, if a collimated beam of monochromatic light is projected into macroscopically homogeneous water by means of an underwater projector, it is found that the residual radiant power P_r^0 reaching a distance r without being deviated by any type of scattering process is:

$$P_r^0 = P_0 e^{\alpha r}$$

where P_0 represents the total flux content of the beam as it leaves the projector. The zero superscript in P_r^0 denotes the zero scattering order, that is, nonscattered radiant power. The spectral volume attenuation coefficient α, used in the equation, is a function of the reciprocal of viewing distance and can be expressed in natural logarithm units per meter ($\ln/m$).

The attenuation of a beam of light by water results from two independent mechanisms, scattering and absorption. The attenuation

Figure 2-4. Diver-restraint device for underwater experimentation. (Weltman, Christianson & Egstrom, 1965.)

coefficient α is the sum of the absorption coefficient a and the scattering coefficient s; thus $\alpha = a + s$ (Duntley, 1963).

The attenuation coefficient of all water (pure, distilled, or natural) varies markedly with wavelength. The reciprocal of the volume attenuation coefficient, called attenuation length, is used rather than attenuation coefficient for three reasons:

1. A distance is easier to visualize and to remember than a reciprocal distance.

2. Visibility calculations and many experiments by swimmers show that any large dark object (such as a dark-suited swimming companion) is just visible at a horizontal distance of about 4 attenuation lengths when there is "sufficient" underwater daylight.

3. Many physicists like to characterize any absorbing/scattering medium (such as water) by the mean free path for a photon in the ordinary kinetic theory sense; this is the attenuation length 1α. The term "20-meter water," signifying water having an attenuation length of 20 m/ln, facilitates verbal discussions (Duntley, 1963).

The theoretical reasoning by Duntley may help us to develop a formula for predicting the probable maximum range of underwater visibility by a human observer in "clear" water. The following formula might be of some assistance:

$$R = \beta \, 1/\alpha$$

where R = visibility range
β = constant [based upon light angle and object reflectivity which usually lies between 2.5 and 6, with the most commonly used value being 3.5 (Duntley, 1963)]
$1/\alpha$ = attenuation length.

Briggs and Hatchett (1965) have tried to determine the maximum underwater visibility range for the human eye in clear seawater. Figure 2-5 represents their estimations.

Distance and Size

When man is asked to make an estimate of size or distance in his normal environment, he usually uses his past experience as a reference point with which to compare the present stimulus. Kinesthetic, auditory, and visual stimuli, along with familiarity with the object

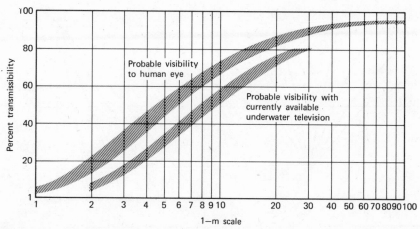

Figure 2-5. Visibility range versus transmissibility as measured with 1-m and 10-cm transmissions. (Briggs & Hatchett, 1965.)

or distance, together act as a perceptual Gestalt to allow him to make an estimation. The most obvious way to perceive distance is through vision. But we can also use our ears to locate the source of a sound, and use the movements of our limbs to estimate a distance traveled. These different types of sense perception generally agree with each other in their estimations, and we have no serious problems involving the spatial relationship of objects in the world around us. Under water, though, we may well have problems, since the visual stimuli are changed, auditory localization is poor, and a distance covered by swimming may not feel the same as a distance covered by walking. It is not surprising, then, that when man is placed in the unfamiliar undersea environment he makes great errors in size and distance estimations.

The problems of size and distance estimations and size constancy are perhaps the best researched areas in the underwater sensory-perceptual field. Various illustrations of distortions caused by light energy passing from water into air, and vice versa, are shown in Figure 2-6.

The water–air interface is only part of the problem. Additional problems involve the individual's perceptual response to the visual stimuli available, and his ability to integrate these with his other sensory inputs.

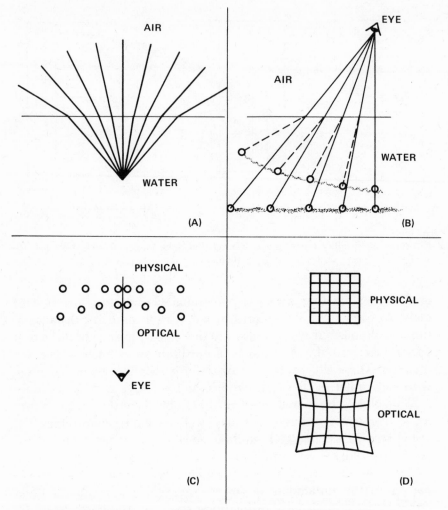

Figure 2-6. Illustrations of refraction of light at the interface between air and water. (A) Light rays emanating from a point in the water. (B) An illusion of the water becoming shallower as the bottom recedes from the viewer in air. (C and D) Distortions in the shape of regular objects due to refraction. (Kinney, Luria, Weitzman & Markowitz, 1970.)

As mentioned above, and as pointed out by Ross (1968), man normally integrates inputs from several sources to establish distance and size judgments. It is safe to say that when man enters the water all his sensory inputs are changed and his experiential background is very limited.

Because of the almost complete lack of experience with underwater kinesthetic and sound distance stimuli, man must rely first of all upon visual information for estimates of distance and size. Ross reported that, of all the visual stimuli that are altered underwater, the two most important are enlarged visual images due to the refractory index of the water–air interface, and reduced object to background contrast due to the scatter and absorption of light in water.

It is necessary here to mention briefly brightness contrast and its importance to the perception of light. The relative stability of lightness and brightness with changes in illumination is dependent upon the object's background or surroundings. If the background is obscured from view, judgments are made largely in terms of total luminance rather than reflectance. Constantcy and contrast constitute a continuum of perceptual judgments. As incident illumination of an object changes, so background luminance provides the information necessary to resolve perceptually the ambiguous retinal representation of object lightness and brightness (Day, 1969).

The same physical phenomena that affect visual targets underwater also alter every other visual cue used by humans for making size and distance estimations. The increased refractory index tends to increase binocular disparity and proximal size depth stimuli, and light scatter and absorption tend to eliminate brightness, shading, and texture stimuli. With all these factors working against man, one might think an underwater search and identification task would be impossible. Man, however, is a remarkably adaptive creature and is able to overcome most of these obstacles.

Distance Distortion

In 1970, Luria and Kinney observed that underwater estimates of distance were less than land estimates at near distances, but that beyond 12 m (40 ft) they became increasingly greater. They proposed that this was due to object/background contrast, and consequently went on to suggest a formula for figuring contrast. Their philosophy was: "If an object differs from the water background in brightness only, the contrast it presents is described by the equation

$$\text{contrast} = \frac{\begin{array}{cc}\text{object brightness} & \text{— background brightness}\\ \text{(luminance)} & \text{(luminance)}\end{array}}{\text{background brightness (luminance)}}$$

The contrast presented by an object at the eye decreases as the object recedes from the eye according to the approximation

$$C_r = C_0 e^{-\alpha K \cos \theta \, r}$$

where C_0 is the contrast at zero distance (the inherent contrast), C_r is the contrast at distance r, e is the base for natural logarithms, α is the beam attenuation coefficient and θ is the angle of sight measured from the vertical." In most experiments the path of the sight is horizontal, so that $\theta = 90°$.

Although there is considerable agreement among experienced divers that objects appear closer under water than in air, as mentioned by Kent (1966), the pertinent experiments do not substantiate this agreement. Thus, in an investigation of perception of distance under water from 4.5 to 23 m (15 to 75 ft), Ross (1965) found underestimation for all distances up to 12 m (39 ft), with estimates under water slightly less than estimates in air. At distances greater than 12 m (40 ft), the subjects tended toward overestimation (estimations greater than in air). Kent (1966) found overestimation of the actual distance for stimuli at distances farther than 1 m (3.28 ft) from the diver, and Luria, Kinney, and Weissman (1967) reported considerable overestimation for stimuli at distances of 1.5 to 3.5 m (5 to 12 ft).

It appears, then, that at some point distance estimation changes from underestimation to overestimation. Beyond this critical point the relationship between distance judgments and physical distance becomes increasingly divergent.

Investigations by Kinney and associates indicate that the crossover point between underestimation and overestimation of distance is dependent upon the clarity of the water. That is, the more turbid the water, the less the object-to-background contrast, and the further the perceived distance. Degree of overestimation and variability of estimates both increases as a function of distance and turbidity.

Figure 2-7 shows data obtained by Luria and Kinney (1970) that

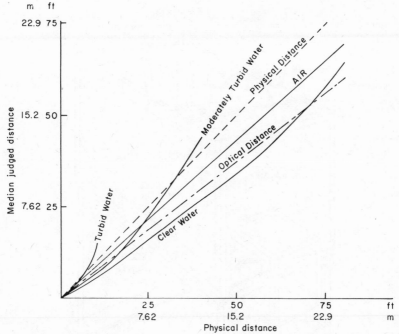

Figure 2-7.   Distance judgment made in water of different clarities and at relatively close distances. (Luria & Kinney, 1970.)

demonstrate the interaction of optical distortion with varying degrees of turbidity, and the general tendency to underestimate underwater distances. Target distances were underestimated when the target was closer than 1.2 m. Beyond that the median estimates were always too great. Moreover, the median estimates of distance were invariably greater under more turbid conditions (Ferris, 1972).

Ono, O'Reilly, and Herman (1970) performed an experiment dealing with apparent distance within arm's length and utilizing a pointing response as the indicator of perceived distance. The relevance of the close range was that working divers usually have little better than 1 to 2 m (3 to 6 ft) visibility, and the task under water generally requires responses within this range. Ono et al. designed a viewing apparatus for the experiment (Figure 2-8), which was constructed in such a manner that a subject could indicate with his hand the apparent distance of a target when he looked through the face mask into the interior of the tank. With his right hand the sub-

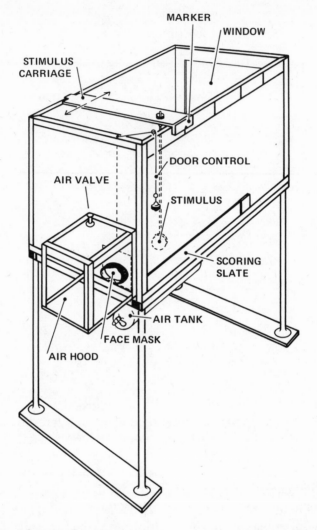

Figure 2-8. Schematic drawing of a viewing apparatus. (Ono, O'Reilly & Herman, 1970.)

ject marked the perceived location of the stimulus target on a scoring slate affixed to the side of the apparatus. The subject was unable to see his hand while indicating the perceived location.

The results, illustrated in Figure 2-9, clearly indicated that the apparent distance of an object under water within arm's reach is closer than the apparent distance of the object in air.

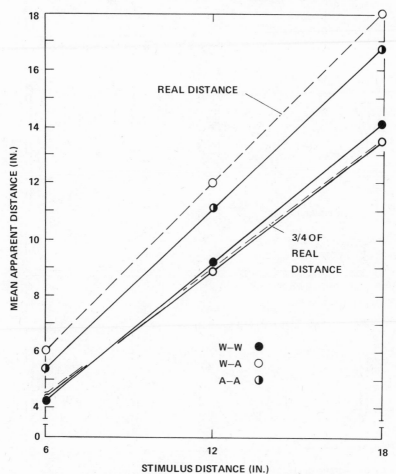

Figure 2-9. Mean apparent distances as a function of stimulus location for three experimental conditions: water-water (W-W), water-air (W-A), and Air-Air (A-A). (Ono, O'Reilly & Herman, 1970.)

The findings of Ono et al. concur with the findings of Luria and Kinney, but also point out that the convergence and accommodation requirements that accompany the viewing of an object through a face mask under water are significant variables. They also indicate that all the above variables are dependent upon the thickness of the glass plate, the distance from the glass plate to the observer, and the distance of the object from the glass plate. Refer to Figure 2-10.

In a discussion concerned with the judging of distances under

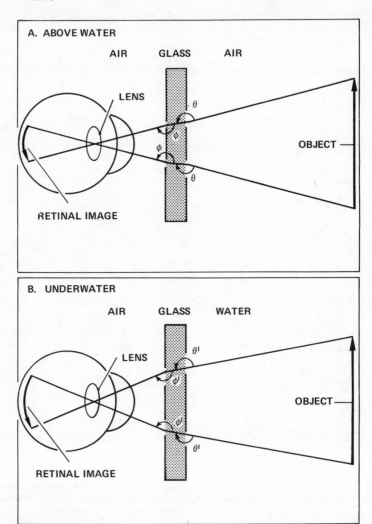

Figure 2-10.   Schematic drawings comparing visual angles and retinal images under two viewing situations. (Ono, O'Reilly & Herman, 1970.)

water, Ross (1968) points out that there are two important changes in visual stimuli under water, each having very different effects. The first effect is that objects are located optically at about three-quarters of their real distance because of the refraction of light passing from water into the air in the diver's face mask. This does not mean that objects are necessarily seen at their optical distance, however. The other effect is the reduction of brightness contrast with viewing distance due to the scattering and absorption of light by particles in the water. This affects distance judgments in two ways:

1. It reduces visual acuity, so that the fine details of many cues are lost.

2. It makes objects look further away, as though they were far off on a misty horizon.

The latter effect is called aerial perspective. It is so compelling that it may make some objects appear further away under water than they would appear to be on land (Ross, 1968).

The effect of the underwater environment on horizontal distance estimates is now fairly well understood. Objects appear near only while they are at close distances in clear water. In murky water, or at far distances in clear water, they usually appear further away. However, there are few experimental data concerning distance estimates in the vertical plane, and Ross, King, and Snowden (1970) suggested that the results may not be the same as that for the horizontal plane. These workers pointed out that occasionally the diver appears to be at the center of a uniform visual globe. This may occur in fairly shallow, turbid water when the upwelling light is equal to the downwelling light, but neither the surface nor the bottom is visible. It may also occur at greater depths in clear, deep water. Normally, however, the light intensity is greater when one is looking upward than when looking downward. Light from the surface may be visible to considerable depths when the sun catches the waves. When the sun is low in the sky, a greater portion of the direct surface light is reflected and light penetration is greatly reduced.

Objects viewed horizontally are normally seen against a fairly dark water background, while those viewed vertically upward, as may be expected, are seen against a brighter background. The seabed may present a bright or dark background, depending upon its composition. It seems therefore that the contrast of objects varies with different viewing directions. Given the same inherent contrast with their backgrounds, objects lose contrast less rapidly over vertical than over horizontal distances (Duntley, 1960). Objects therefore tend to have higher contrast when viewed vertically, which should make them look closer. Vertically viewed objects are also normally seen through empty water, while with horizontal viewing other objects are likely to be present. Empty space is inclined to make objects appear closer than filled space (Künnapas, 1967; Luria, Kinney & Weissman 1967a), so this is an additional reason why vertical distances are underestimated (Ross, King & Snowden 1970). Divers often believe that they are quite near the surface or seabed when in fact a considerable distance intervenes. This is a very dangerous type of error for a diver to make.

To determine whether or not underestimation in vertical viewing is a typical fault, Ross, King, and Snowden (1970) undertook a series of experiments in which four to six subjects made vertical size and distance estimations in clear water off Malta. The results showed that divers tend to underestimate the distance to the surface more than that to the seabed. Underestimation was most marked in clear empty water, but disappeared with practice. Objects viewed vertically downward tended to be correctly estimated in size. However, these investigators concluded that this was an underestimation in comparison with the overestimation that normally occurs with horizontal viewing.

Stereoacuity or Stereoscopic Acuity. The stimulus of binocular disparity, the slight difference in the images of an object in the two eyes, leads to stereoscopic or three-dimensional depth perception. It enables us to detect very slight differences in the relative distance of objects, but it does not tell us anything about absolute distance. The same degree of disparity could be given by two widely-separated objects at a far distance, or two close objects at a near distance. The angle of convergence of the eyes seems to act as a crude range setter for the stereoscopic mechanism, affecting the perceived separation of objects. Because objects are optically nearer under water, the binocular disparity is increased. Together with the increased convergence, this should lead to a decrease in the apparent distance of underwater objects, and an increased ability to detect differences in distance (Ross, 1968).

Ross (1967a) measured stereoacuity in open water at distances of 6, 12, and 18 m (20, 40, and 60 ft). Her results indicated that stereoacuity under water is worse than on land, which was confirmed by Luria and Kinney (1970). Ross found that under fairly typical Mediterranean diving conditions the deterioration was likely to be by a factor of 3. She concluded that in murky water, or at greater depth, the reduction is likely to be much greater due to the lower illumination and contrast. Variability between subjects was greater in water than on land. These results are the opposite of those found for visual acuity. Distance judgments for disks within 9 m (30 ft) of the submerged observer were as accurate, if not better, than estimates on land. Beyond 9 m, however, visual distance cues such as binocular vision and ground perspective, lost their effectiveness, and the observer was forced to rely on the relative size of the object. The smaller of two equidistant disks was judged further away, and distance was increasingly overestimated. Ross concluded that the combination of poor eyesight and low contrast may be particularly disabling, and may result in complete loss of stereopsis before the limits of visibility are reached.

In one experiment, Luria (1968) compared stereoscopic acuity for a target in air and under water, and in a second study it was measured in water of varying clarity. Stereoacuity was found to be degraded in water, increasingly so as the clarity of the water decreased. The function of acuity versus clarity was found to be similar to that reported for stereoacuity versus brightness contrast, suggesting that a main cause of the drop in stereoacuity with decreasing water clarity is the decrease in target contrast. In a third experiment stereoacuity was found to decrease in air when there was a loss of peripheral visual stimuli. Luria concluded that the loss of peripheral stimulation in water is a significant cause of the drop in stereoacuity under water.

According to Luria (1970), there is a loss in duction as the field of view is progressively restricted while the light level is held constant. This is similar to the loss in stereoacuity that occurs for navy divers under the same conditions, and to the loss in duction that occurs in the dark. However, introducing a few simple peripheral stimuli into the empty visual field apparently restores the level of duction, but not that of stereoacuity. Luria desired to know whether or not in an empty visual field poor duction is the basis for diminution in stereoacuity. He found it unlikely, and states that the underwater stereoacuity in navy divers is not improved by methods that improve duction.

Luria and Kinney (1970) concluded from their research that reduced visual acuity is due in part to the loss of contrast produced by increased water turbidity. However, they found that this does not explain why stereoacuity is about three times poorer in the clearest water where there appears to be no loss of contrast of target visibility. They pointed out that one aspect of the underwater scene that is distinct from conditions in air seems pertinent; this is, that there are *few* clearly visible objects. The world appears hazy; it lacks definition and it approaches what is known in psychology as a *Ganzfeld*, an unstructured, homogenous field of view. It is well known that a *Ganzfeld* distorts many visual functions, impairs target detection, and degrades other processes which are considered basically foveal, such as reading. Therefore the investigators tested the hypothesis that the loss of much of the usual peripheral stimulation as occurs in water is the cause of the drop in stereoacuity.

They found that resolution acuity was not systematically affected by reduction in the field of view. However, such a reduction had a deleterious effect on stereoacuity. Under every condition of restricted view, there was an increase in both the error and the variability of the equidistance setting as compared to performance when the field of view was unrestricted (Figure 2-11). The conclusion was that it is the typical lack of peripheral stimulation in the undersea environment that causes the decrease in stereoacuity.

Perception of Size

It is a common observation that underwater objects appear to be both larger and closer than they really are. This distortion is clearly seen when one stands with head erect and looks at a partially submerged object with the face mask half out of the water. The face mask worn by a diver produces distortions similar in some respects to those obtained with a lens system. The mask introduces an air–water interface through which objects are viewed. As light rays pass through this interface, they are refracted so that the retinal projection of a submerged object is enlarged by about four-thirds and an image is formed at about three-fourths of the object's physical distance. The precise effect varies with the distance of the eye behind the face plate, and with the angular eccentricity of the object (Ross, Franklin, Weltman & Lennie, 1970).

The main effect of this optical transformation is to distort the normal relation between object size, image size, and image distance.

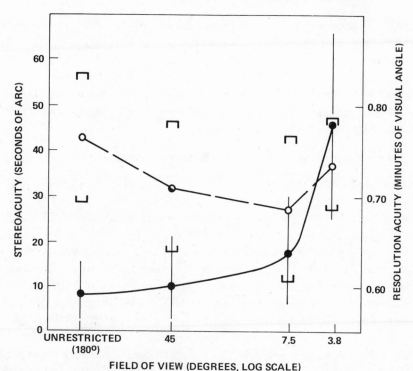

Figure 2-11. Resolution acuity (dashed line) and stereoacuity (solid line) with various fields of view. (Luria & Kinney, 1970.)

Size constancy normally operates in air, so that objects appear the correct size if they are seen at their correct distance, and judgments of object size remain relatively constant. Ross et al. have pointed out that, if size constancy remains unchanged under water, objects should appear the correct size if one sees them at their optical distance (about three-fourths physical distance), and increasingly enlarged if one sees them at further distances. A novice diver therefore perceives the size or the distance (or both) incorrectly. In practice most divers perceive objects under water as enlarged, and overestimate the optical distance (Luria, Kinney & Weissman, 1967; Ross, 1967). Ross found that size estimates are a linear function of the physical size over the range tested.

Generally speaking, the perception of size can be predicted accurately from the magnification of the optical image (Luria & Kinney,

1970). Kinney et al., for example, asked subjects to judge under water the size of disks in relation to the size of certain coins. All subjects made selections that were much too small relative to the actual size of the coins, thus overestimating the size of the disks in the water. The size of the magnified retinal image of the selection did, however, correspond to the actual coin sizes (Kinney, Luria, Weitzman & Markowitz, 1970).

Relationship between Size and Distance Estimations

Size and distance estimations are linked by what is known as the size-distance invariance hypothesis, or size constancy. In size constancy we deal with the ability of the observer to perceive metric size "true size" regardless of target distance.

Perception of object size follows one set of laws in an unstructured field and a different set of laws in a structured field. This means that, when the stimulus in question is the only object in the visual field, the field contributes nothing to object identification. The only thing that is structured is the small region that constitutes the object itself. If a target comprising a rectangular blank card is the only visual differentiation provided in a dark room, it may be perceived as almost any size. Since it is only the retinal image and the contribution of the perceiver himself that determine the perceptual end result, object size becomes dependent upon the distance at which the object is projected in perception. Size and distance are reciprocal for any fixed retinal image. The observer sees the object as a certain size and at a certain distance. The two are related to each other, as would be expected from the trigonometry involved in target size, target distance, and the retinal image produced. The pivotal factor is retinal image size, for that is the only fixed thing as far as the stimulus is concerned (Bartley, 1969).

When judged size and distance are contrasted with true size and distance, both on the surface and in the water, one finds a weak invariance. Both surface and submerged size and distance ratios change with distance. On land there is a decrease in the ratios, and in water there is an increase in the ratios. This relationship is illustrated in Figure 2-12.

Another meaningful relationship is obtained by comparing surface judgments with judgments made under water. Figure 2-13

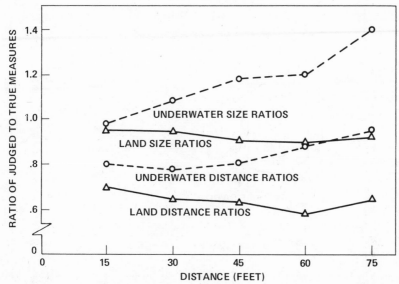

Figure 2-12.   The ratios of judged to true measures as a function of distance. (Ross, 1967.)

illustrates the land-to-underwater size ratios and distance ratios, along with the optically corrected distance ratios. The close correspondence between the optically corrected ratios is noteworthy. Ross (1965) concluded that this is possibly due to the diver's learning to compensate for the optical effect. The last assertion is in need of additional support.

The overestimation stems in part from the loss of contrast under water, due to the scattering of light by particles. Fry, Bridgman, and Ellenbrock (1949), and Ross (1967), have reported similar effects of reduced contrast in air, and the fact that overestimations increase as turbidity increases lends further support. According ot Luria and Kinney (1970), overestimations are, however, more severe than would be expected solely on the basis of loss of contrast, for they do occur under conditions of fairly high contrast.

Luria and Kinney (1970) reported a control experiment performed in air to determine whether or not the *Ganzfeld* characteristics of underwater viewing were influential in depth perception as they were in stereoacuity. Subjects estimated the distance to a target in three different environments. The first environment was an

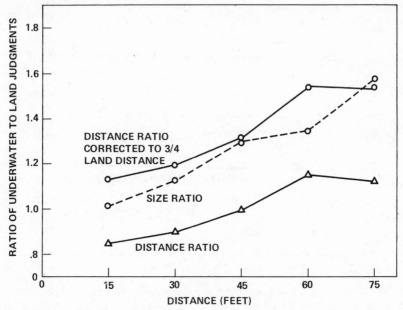

Figure 2-13.   The relative increase in size estimates under water as related to the relative increase in distance estimates. (Ross, 1965.)

ordinary, well-lighted room about 6 m² with all the usual apparatus and furniture in full view. Under these conditions the median estimates of distance were quite accurate. When the experiment was repeated in the center of a large, well-lighted, empty gymnasium, the median estimate at every target distance was higher than in the first room; moreover, every estimate, except in the case of the shortest distance, was greater than the actual distance. Finally, the same procedure was carried out in a completely dark room with nothing visible except the target, at a constant, dim illumination. The distance of the target was now even more markedly overestimated, increasingly so as the actual distance increased. Thus, as fewer cues of distance were available, observers tended more and more to overestimate distance.

Luria and Kinney concluded that both relative and absolute depth perception are less acute under water. Various changes in the physical characteristics of light under water are responsible. Loss of contrast, which increases with increasing turbidity, and the typical lack of stimulation under water cause increasingly larger errors in stereoacuity and increasingly larger overestimations of distance. Refraction results in underestimation at very short distances.

Polarized Light as a Tool in Underwater Vision

In 1967, Lythgoe and Hemmings made an attempt to find out whether the ability to distinguish the plane of *polarized* light has any effect on the distance an object can be seen under water. A polarizing screen (a lens from a pair of polarizing sunglasses) was taken under water during a scuba dive off Malta. When the screen was rotated in front of the eye, it was evident that the plane of maximum polarization (*e* vector) lay at right angles to the sun's rays in the expected way. But when the screen was oriented to exclude the maximum space light, it was observed that the apparent brightness of the small fishes present was reduced less than the background space light. Hence fishes stood out in greater contrast against their background. Furthermore, there was a strong subjective impression that more distant individuals, although invisible to the naked eye, became visible when the polarizing screen was used. The investigators made an experiment using four rectangles painted black, white, and combinations of both to produce two shades of gray. They found that in the relatively clear waters off Malta the ability to analyze the plane of polarized light indeed was an advantage (Lythgoe & Hemmings, 1967).

The use of polarized light as well as devices such as television and pulsed lasers can increase markedly the visibility range over the value of 5.82 attenuation lengths given for the eye. These devices, although less sensitive, tend to enhance object contrast and therefore provide greater penetration through the media. The polarized light device described by Lythgoe and Hemmings (1967) provides the greatest benefit when there is considerable polarization associated with backscattered light.

Dark Adaptation in the Undersea Environment

Brightness sensitivity, or the ability to detect a dim light, is of great importance in the detection of objects in the undersea environment. Below certain intensities and luminances, the eye does not respond at all, that is, the light source is invisible. As the amount of light is increased, a threshold value is obtained at which the eye is just able to detect that light is present. It has been found that the threshold value depenls upon various preexposure variables, such as how much light the subject has been exposed to before the test and how long he has been exposed to that light. Obviously, the eye's sensitivity to a light stimulus depends upon its state of prior adaptation to light. Thus absolute thresholds for light intensity can be measured either to find the maximum brightness sensitivity of the fully adapted eye, or to determine the degrees of adaptation to darkness or to any level of brightness as a function of related variables (Wulfeck, Weisz & Raben, 1958).

Whenever a diver submerges and has to obtain information through vision, some degree of dark adaptation may be required. Whether or not rod and/or cone vision are required (or available) depends on the level of illumination at the site (Kinney, personal communication). When very distant, dim objects must be located, or when large outlines are to be spotted, such as the hull of a wrecked ship, rod vision is required (rods respond to a range of brightness from 0.004 to 0.00004 mL). However, if details or color must be seen, cone vision is required (cones respond to a range of brightness from 0.004 to 10,000 mL).

Very little information is presently available on the effects of high-pressure environments (wet or dry) on dark adaptation. One study by Hemmings and Lythgoe (1965) suggested predive dark adaptation for divers who are to operate in deep or turbid water where the level of illuminance is very limited. This proposition appears reasonable and merits further investigation. Such a pre-dark adaptation procedure could be very useful for excursions from sea bottom habitats.

Kelley et al. (1968) did some preliminary work on the effects of hyperbaric environments on dark adaptation but found no significant results. Their study, however, was limited in scope, and a more extensive project seems most definitely needed.

COLOR DISCRIMINATION UNDER WATER

A major factor in determining which colors are visible under water is the type of water. It has been mentioned earlier (Chapter 1) that water selectively absorbs electromagnetic energy, and that the degree of this absorption varies with the body of water.

Luria and Kinney (1970) have pointed out that, since a long column of water is one of the best monochromators that can be devised, the relative visibility of different colors can be expected to vary greatly with the body of water in which the colors are immersed. Kinney, Luria, and Weitzman (1968a,b, 1969) have mentioned that distilled or exceptionally clear water has its highest value of transmisison at 480 nm, in the blue-green region of the spectrum, and absorbs to a greater extent wavelengths on both sides of this peak. As the water becomes more turbid with suspended material such as algae, plankton, and silt, or as greater depths are obtained, there is a selective absorption of the short wavelengths along with greatly reduced total transmission. The peak of the transmission curve is moved from 480 nm toward the long wavelengths. Because of this selective absorption the relative visibility of different colors can be expected to vary considerably with the body of water in which they are viewed.

A test of color and form perception was conducted during the U.S. Navy's Sea Lab II experiment off the coast of California. This project approximated an actual operational setting at a depth of 62.5 m (205 ft). In the visual experiment, as described by Miller, Radloff, Bowen & Helmreich (1967), the divers swam down a visual detection range on which were located four targets: a black circle, a white square, a yellow triangle, and a white cross.

The divers both detected and identified the black circle at greater distances than either the white or yellow targets. This is particularly interesting, considering that the black circle was the smallest of the four targets in area. The differences between the means of the black circle and white square shown in Table 2-4 are statistically significant at the .01 level. These workers conclude that the early detection of the black target was due to the high object-to-background contrast.

During the debriefing interviews after the Sea Lab II experiment, the divers indicated: "The white habitat was far more visible than the reddish-orange personnel transfer capsule (PTC)." In many

Table 2-4 Detection and Recognition Distances for
the Form / Color Study (Miller, Radloff, Bowen,
and Helmreich 1967) ($N = 20$)

Measured Parameter	Targets (ft from subject)			
	Black Circle	White Square	Yellow Triangle	White Cross
Detection	24.4	18.3	16.7	16.5
Recognition	20.0	14.2	13.5	13.4

cases the habitat was said to be visible at two or three times the distance of the PTC (Miller, Radloff, Bowen & Helmreich 1967).

Anderson, Pesh, and Allen (1967) investigated diver versus submersible operator visual capabilities at a depth of 15 m (50 ft) and at distances of 15, 12, and 9 m (50, 40, and 30 ft). The findings revealed a form of color confusion between divers and vehicle observers. The highest incident of error occurred for the colors red and black. However, while divers confused red with black, vehicle observers identified red as blue or green. The other colors that created problems were black and green. The colors blue and yellow were identified correctly nearly 100% of the time at all three distances.

Behan, Behan, and Wendhausen (1972) experimented with 12 scuba divers who were divided into three groups of 4, one group descending to 10 m (33 ft), another to 20 m (66 ft), and another to 30 m (98 ft). They examined 13 plates of a standard diagnostic color perception test. In clear water under conditions of low illumination, colors in the full range of the visible spectrum were detectable at 30 m (98 ft). In a few instances low-saturation greens and reds were not identified. All colors seemed somewhat faded due to reduced contrast and low illumination.

The most effective colors in air are the oranges which combine the advantages of a great deal of energy conversion, the great sensitivity of the human eye, and good color contrast with natural backgrounds of blue or green. Kinney, Luria, and Weitzmen (1969) found that under water the colors of best visibility are as follows.

A. For murky, turbid water of low visibility (rivers, harbors, etc.).
  1. With natural illumination:
    a. Fluorescent yellow, orange, and red.
    b. Regular yellow, orange, and white.
  2. With incandescent illumination:
    a. Fluorescent and regular yellow, orange, red, and white.
  3. With a mercury light source:
    a. Fluorescent yellow-green and yellow-orange.
    b. Regular yellow and white.
B. For moderately turbid water (sounds, bays, coastal water).
  1. With natural illumination or incandescent light source:
    a. Any fluorescent in the yellows, oranges, or reds.
    b. Regular yellow, orange, and white.
  2. With a mercury light source:
    a. Fluorescent yellow-green or yellow-orange.
    b. Regular yellow and white.
C. For clear water (southern water, deep water off shore, etc.).
  1. With any type of illumination fluorescent paints are superior.
    a. With long viewing distances, fluorescent green and yellow-green.
    b. With short viewing distances, fluorescent orange is excellent.
  2. With natural illumination:
    a. Fluorescent paints.
    b. Regular yellow, green, white.
  3. With incandescent light source:
    a. Fluorescent paints.
    b. Regular yellow, orange, white.
  4. With mercury light source:
    a. Fluorescent paints.
    b. Regular yellow, white.

According to Kinney, Luria, and Weitzman (1969), the most difficult colors to see at the limits of visibility with a water background are dark colors such as gray and black. This applies to incandescent, mercury, and natural illumination. In addition, any factor causing the major spectral components of a color to be lost results in poor visibility. Such a factor may be absorption by the water, or lack of appropriate wavelengths in the light source. Among regular paints, they mentioned the following examples of poor visibility against a water background:

A. Blue and green in turbid water.
B. Orange and red in clear water.
C. Blue and green with incandescent sources.
D. Orange and red with mercury sources.

These workers have an explanation of the superiority in visibility of fluorescent paints over regular paints under water. Fluorescent paints convert short-wavelength energy into wavelength energy to which the eye is more sensitive. The converted energy is added to the reflected light, thus increasing the brightness and contrast of the painted object. In this way reflectance in excess of 100% of the incident visible energy is often possible (see Figure 2-14).

The exciting energy for fluorescence is in the shorter wavelengths of visible energy. These wavelengths are well transmitted in clear water and produce good fluorescent oranges. The longer wavelengths that are thus produced, however, are poorly transmitted. The result is that, in clear water, the fluorescent oranges are brilliant at short distances but decrease rapidly in visibility as distance is increased.

Kinney, Luria, and Weitzman (1969) and Luria and Kinney (1970) provide the following explanation concerning the changes introduced by artificial lights. "For a given color to be visible, the wavelengths reflected by the paint must be present in the light source. Moreover, to activate the fluorescent paint, there must be short wavelengths present in the source, and they must be transmitted through the water to the target." These investigators found that with a mercury light, which is rich in short-wavelength energy, fluorescent paints were far superior to nonfluorescent paints in every kind of water tested. With a tungsten light, the advantage of the fluorescent paints was lost in turbid water. They concluded that there was too little short-wavelength energy. While the yellow and oranges were most visible with the tungsten light, yellow-green was most visible with the mercury light.

Luria and Kinney (1970) concluded: "Visibility can be predicted from a knowledge of the spectral sensitivity of the eye and the spectral distribution of energy reaching it. To specify the latter, we must

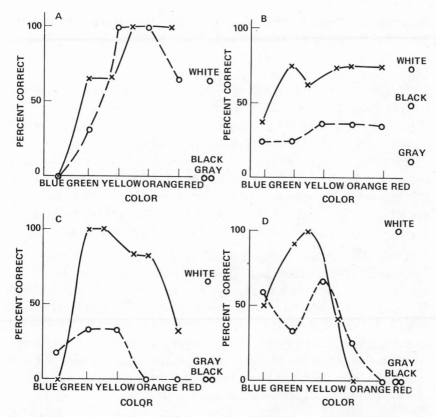

Figure 2-14. The visibility of various colors. These tests were performed in (A) Thames River, Connecticut, (B) Long Island Sound, (C) Gulf of Mexico, and (D) Morrison Springs, Florida, for fluorescent paint (solid line) and nonfluorescent paint (dashed line). Scuba divers viewed the colored targets one at a time at distances near the limits of visibility; these ranged from 1.8 m in the Thames River to nearly 30 m in Morrison Springs. The divers reported whether or not the target was visible, and if so they attempted to identify its color. The two open circles shown on the abscissas of A, C, and D under "gray" and "black" indicate that these two colors were never visible. (Luria & Kinney, 1970.)

know four special distributions: (i) the energy reaching the target, (ii) the reflectance of the target, (iii) the absorption of the water from the target to the eye, and (iv) the background. From these values, both the brightness and the color contract can be calculated" (p. 1457).

It is important to distinguish between the visibility of colors and their absolute identification. The question of which colors to employ for color coding is an equally important problem, but one that is quite different from the question of visibility. White, for example, while always highly visible, tends to adopt the color of the water; for this reason it is the easiest to confuse and should not be used for color coding (Luria & Kinney, 1970).

In general, it is hard to distinguish a given color from the colors closest to it in the spectrum. Luria and Kinney recommend that, where correct discrimination is important, it is best to use only two colors, one from each end of the spectrum, with black as a possible third choice. They also emphasize that the choice of colors depends upon the body of water and the type of illumination. Kinney, Luria, and Weitzman (1968a) give the following recommendation.

"For color coding, use only three or four colors. Green, orange and black are easily discriminable in natural and incandescent illumination. With a mercury source, change to green, yellow and black. To add a fourth color in natural illumination, use blue in clear water, substitute yellow and red for orange in turbid water. With artificial sources it is difficult to add a fourth color that will not be confused with one of the other three. Nothing appears acceptable for the mercury source. For the incandescent source substitute yellow and red for orange in all bodies of water" (p. 8).

PERCEPTUAL LEARNING IN THE UNDERSEA ENVIRONMENT

In water, the visual distortion that afflicts the diver is extensive. However, human beings possess the remarkable ability to adapt to changes in all kinds of stimulus conditions such as illumination, color, and a wide variety of optical distortions.

Habituation of divers to the distortion of size and distance under water has been studied a great deal. Ross (1967) found a trend, although not statistically significant, which indicated that more experienced divers are better at underwater estimation of size and distance than are naive divers. Another encouraging factor was reported by Ross (1965). She discovered that a submerged observer is not affected by different orientations of himself or the target. A land observer is often confronted by visual illusions because of his or the target's relationship to the rest of the environment. Under water, however: "There appears to be an absence (or marked reduction) of the usual visual and postural cues to orientation" (Ross, 1965).

Ross, Franklin, and Weltman (1969) found that, in a series of five experiments, three were successful in demonstrating visual learning. Two techniques were used:

1. The method of adjustment in which a diver adjusted the size of a horizontal line, set in the frontal plane at a fixed distance, to a length of 30 cm.

2. The method of estimation in which the diver recorded his judgments of the size and distance of a series of targets which varied in these dimensions.

In Experiment I the method of size adjustment was used by experienced and novice divers in air and in water before and after a 20- to 40-min period of underwater exposure. Significant differences between pre- and postexposure indicated that adaptation to size distortion (in the amount of about 20%) occurred during the underwater exposure period.

Experiment IV examined, by the method of estimation, size and distance adaptation in experienced divers. Before and after 20 min of underwater exposure in a swimming pool, divers estimated the size and distance of an array of targets in air and in water. A comparison of pre- and postexposure showed that a small but significant amount of adaptation to size occurred during the exposure period.

In Experiment V, the effect of previous diving experience on underwater size estimation was investigated by the method of adjustment. Divers and nondivers were asked to adjust an expandable line to 30 cm (12 in.) both in air and in water, with the water settings being made from outside the diving tank looking in through a viewport. The result suggested that objects appeared less enlarged for divers than for nondivers. While nondivers seemed to respond on the basis of immediate optical stimulation, divers applied corrective measures as a function of their diving experience. The results indicated that the more experienced the diver the more accurate his estimate of the size of an underwater object. Both groups of divers showed significant aftereffects in air, indicating that some size adaptation had occurred. The aftereffect declined rapidly and was significant for only the first two trials. (See also Ross, Franklin, Weltman & Lennie, 1970.)

The underwater environment provides a unique opportunity to study adaptation to perceptual distortions under natural conditions. Many subjects are completely unaware that distortions exist. A diver's response to the visual distortions under water at first resembles the responses of a subject wearing distorting lenses. For instance, when asked to pick up an object, subjects often fail on the first attempt. Their errors in reaching are gradually reduced, however, on successive attempts, until they can make motor responses appropriate to the distorted display. When the distortion is removed, subjects make errors in the opposite direction (Luria & Kinney, 1970).

In an excellent study, Kinney, Luria, Weitzman, and Markowitz (1970) made extensive measures of hand-eye coordination of subjects with various amounts of underwater experience. The apparatus used was simply a table, and the subjects were directed to make a mark on the underside of the table directly under a given point on the top. The test situation is shown in Figure 2-15.

The amount of theoretical optical displacement averaged 5.6 cm (2 in.) toward the subject. The amount of apparent displacement was measured empirically by relating the marks made on the underside of the table in the water to those made in air. A value of zero indicated perfect correspondence between the two sets of marks.

Table 2-5 shows a compilation of the data from many subjects tested by Kinney et al. from 1968 through 1970.

As is evident from this table, there is excellent agreement between the amount of prior underwater experience and the amount of compensation for distortion. Only inexperienced subjects showed complete reliance on the optical image; the average amount of displacement for them was the theoretical maximum of 5.6 cm (2 in.) toward the subject. For the others there was increasing correspondence between their determination of the apparent location of the object and its actual location.

According to Luria and Kinney, these differences in the test results for experienced and inexperienced subjects suggested that considerable adaptation occurs naturally as a consequence of underwater experience. They tried to measure this adaptation and its time course,

Figure 2-15. Testing for hand-eye co-ordination under water. The subject is directed to make a mark on the underside of the table directly under a given point on the top. (Luria & Kinney, 1970.)

Table 2-5   Amounts of Underwater Experience and Original Distortion (Luria and Kinney, 1970)

Subject	N	Amount of distortion (cm)
Never used snorkel, mask	42	5.59
Occasionally used snorkel, mask	69	5.00
Frequently used snorkel, mask	20	3.30
Scuba class		
No scuba experience	14	3.23
Some scuba experience	12	2.64
Navy diver	8	2.03

a Group average.

and gave a battery of underwater visual tests every week for 4 weeks to the men in a class undergoing daily scuba training. However, at the end of 4 weeks of testing under water, the divers exhibited an amount of adaptation that was surprisingly small, an amount sufficient to compensate for only 20% of their original visual distortion.

These investigators concluded that this result was in sharp contrast to the results obtained with prisms in air and concluded that it resulted from two factors:

1. Visual stimulation under water is minimal.
2. Distortion in water is symmetric, rather than all in one direction.

They also postulated that specific activities should be provided for inexperienced scuba divers to facilitate their adaptation. Therefore, they conducted several experiments to determine the most effective way of training novice subjects.

Different groups of subjects were assigned different activities under water and were tested for hand-eye coordination before and after these activities both in air and in water. The difference between the two sets of underwater measures gave the measure of compensation, and the difference between the measures in air gave the size of the aftereffect.

The results of these experiments were quite clear. Three to four minutes of underwater activity yielded about 20% compensation, which was a significant amount. The type of activity made no difference; all subjects achieved the same compensation, as long as they were in the water for that length of time with their eyes open.

Fifteen minutes in the water, however, produced not only a greater amount of compensation, but distinct differences among the groups of subjects as well. Subjects who participated in various games under water for three 5-min intervals performed significantly better than subjects in any other groups, achieving 60% compensation on one test and 100% on another. Explaining the distortions to subjects and then allowing them to practice placing the test objects did not help. Figure 2-16 illustrates the results.

These workers concluded that the factors underlying the success of this underwater activity in promoting adaptation included:

1. The active placing of the test object.
2. The use of spaced rather than massed trials.

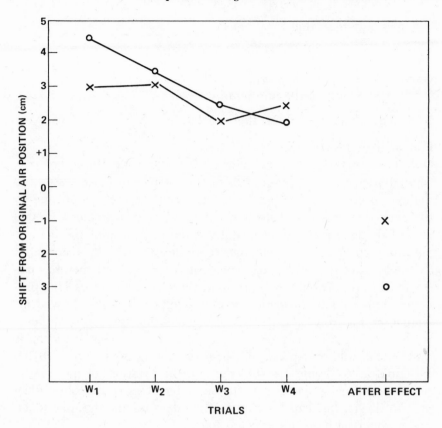

Figure 2-16. Changes in the apparent position of targets with repeated testing underwater (test W_1 to W_4) and on final testing in air (aftereffect). Positive values indicate a shift in apparent position toward the subject; negative values, a shift away from the subject relative to the apparent position of the object in air on the preliminary test. The total time in the water during the course of the experiment (W_1 to W_4) was 3 weeks for the scuba class (X); for the inexperienced subjects (open circles) to total time in the water was 30 min, which included three 5-min periods of practice and four test periods of about 4 min each. (Luria & Kinney, 1970.)

3. The holding of the interest and attention of the subjects by the activity. Luria and Kinney predicted that further refinements and more time in the water should result in complete compensation for all subjects.

When an object is viewed obliquely, or subtends a large angle, further optical distortion occurs.

Snell's law states that:

$$\sin i/\sin r = \text{a constant}$$

where i = angle to the normal in air
r = angle to the normal in water.

In the case of air and water, the constant is 1.33,

For small angles $i/r \approx \sin i/\sin r$.

Objects of small angular size viewed through a face plate are perceptually located at three-fourths of their actual distance, assuming the eye to be at the face plate and ignoring any refraction due to the glass. There is less distortion if the eye is at a greater distance behind the face plate. Rays of light at the periphery of the field of view must strike the face plate more obliquely in order to be accepted by the lens. They make a large incident angle, and are therefore refracted disproportionately more than those at the center. This produces "pin-cushion" distortion, a square appearing to be bowed inward (see Figure 2-6d). In the third dimension the center appears further away than the extremes (see Figure 2-6c). This distortion is quite noticeable on square tiles in a swimming pool (Ross, 1970). In addition to being nearer, the optical location of peripheral points is imprecise, causing a blurred image. This is scarcely noticeable to divers, but can be seen in the edges of photographs taken under water with an uncorrected lens.

Ross (1970) expected that divers would exhibit some adaptation to the curvature distortion during the course of a ½-hr dive. She suggested that as a diver moves his head or body the shapes of objects are transformed consistently. It is not necessary that straight lines be visible in the environment. According to Ross, sufficient information to determine the type of transformation is available from an object of any shape, even if the diver is not consciously aware of the distortion.

To determine whether adaptation occurred during the course of a dive, and then to determine whether experienced divers showed greater initial adaptation than novices, Ross performed two experiments on the apparent curvature in depth of the central line.

She studied seven divers in air and in water before and after a ½-hr dive by means of a specially designed Perspex box. Approximately 25% of full adaptation to the optical distortion occurred during the dive, with a corresponding negative aftereffect in air.

Ross also measured the apparent curvature of the line for 16 novices and 15 experienced divers both in air and immediately upon entering the water. The experienced divers showed some initial adaptation, while the novices showed none. These results suggested that the experienced divers had acquired a "situation-contingent" visual response.

Ross, in her discussion of the results, points out that curvature distortion is a fairly minor aspect of the change in image size and distance under water. Since curvature adaptation occurs, one might expect adaptation to more noticeable changes in size and distance. Most experiments on size and distance judgments have compared and contrasted judgments in air with those in water without considering the length of time subjects had been in the water. According to Ross, it is highly likely that some adaptation occurred during the course of the experiments. Ross proposed that this may account for some of the high variability found in the underwater data. She also suggested that the effects of perceptual adaptation are not confined to one diving session, which is usually referred to as perceptual learning rather than adaptation. The diver learns a new set of perceptual responses to which he resorts to only under water. This seems to be a more complicated process than adaptation during one session, according to ·Ross.

Blind And Blindfolded Divers

Recently, experiments have been made with blind and blindfolded divers. In Sweden, a group of blind students has been trained to work underwater as divers; and in Los Angeles, California, novice diving students have been trained from the beginning to perform underwater work blindfolded. Both of these groups of divers are reported to have been used in very turbid waters without any sight at all and with great success. They are not handicapped by the inability to see what they are doing, and they have no feeling of disorientation and claustrophobia. However, as far as is known, no comparative scientific study has yet been conducted on sighted versus blind or blindfolded diver performance. Leonard Greenstone, who works with the Vocational Diver Program for inmates at Chino

Prison near Los Angeles and who has developed a blindfolded diving training technique, has reported great success with his men who work on pipeline repair jobs and other mechanical failures in an outfall system. All these jobs were performed in relatively shallow water with no visibility (Bergman, 1970; Greenstone, personal communication). There is no doubt that these interesting facts must be scientifically investigated in order to evaluate their importance for future diver traning programs.

ENVIRONMENTAL STRESS AND VISUAL PERCEPTION

Factors other than energy attenuation affect visual performance. Several researchers have reported the presence of psychophysiological stress in the underwater environment. Most of the disabling effects have been observed in human cognition and psychomotor performance. [See, among others, Adolfson (1967) and Bennett & Elliott (1969).] Weltman, Christianson, and Egstrom (1970) have recently reported that experienced divers showed essentially unchanged performance between a diving tank and the ocean. Novice divers performed slower than experienced divers in the tank and showed a marked decrement in both assembly time and problem-solving accuracy in the ocean. These investigators suggested that diving experience improves underwater motor skills rather than work strategy, and that psychological stress was a significant factor for novices even at shallow ocean depths. There are, however, two studies reporting the effects of stress on tasks heavily weighted in visual performance.

The first of these studies was made by Weltman and Egstrom (1966). It involved novice divers monitoring a peripheral light while performing a central addition or dial-watching task. They found that some of the subjects exhibited markedly increased response times to the peripheral light. These workers hypothesized that the stressful underwater environment caused perceptual narrowing in subjects who were inexperienced divers.

The second visual study demonstrating a possible underwater stress factor was made by Christianson (1968), and was actually designed as a visual acuity study. As a part of this study, the subjects performed a self-paced Landolt acuity task. It was found that the response times for the subjects under water were much longer than those on land. As a check on this observation, the experimenter administered a forced-paced Landolt acuity task to two of the subjects in the water. The results showed a marked reduction in acuity, but no firm conclusions could be drawn due to the small sample. Christianson suggested that the diver's response process was apparently impaired when under water. Confirmation of this hypothesis must wait for a more complete study.

SUMMARY

A major advantage of vision over the other senses is its ability to obtain precise information on distant objects very quickly, a factor that can often be of life-saving importance for a diver in the sea. When a diver lives in an underwater laboratory or habitat, which means that he is living in a dry hyperbaric environment, it has been found that there are no essential changes in human visual functioning at ambient pressures to as much as 26 ATA, providing that a low-density nonnarcotic breathing mixture is used. However, hyperbaric air at very high ambient pressure (13 ATA) has been shown to cause changes of a psychosensorial character in human vision. During long saturation dives in small habitats, there is also the possibility of an increase in myopia and loss of visual acuity due to the constant accommodation for near distances.

The underwater environment is usually not very transparent, and vision is consequently quite restricted. When the cornea of the vertebrate eye interfaces water rather than air, it loses a great deal of its refractive power because the index of refraction of the cornea is nearly the same as that of water. It has been found that visual acuity, measured under water without face masks, is exceedingly poor. Under the most ideal conditions, it is reduced to the level found for night vision. Now face masks are used to replace the air at the corneal surface and restore normal refraction of the eye.

An alternative to face masks are contact lenses, but it has been found that this device has many disadvantages and that a face mask most often is preferable. However, a face mask reduces the field of view on an average of about 50% and is often "fogged up" during a dive.

Distance and size perception are greatly affected under water. Underestimation as well as overestimation of distance takes place, and it appears that at some point distance estimation changes from underestimation to overestimation. The crossover point seems to be dependent upon the clarity of the water; the more turbid the water, the less the object-to-background contrast, and the further the perceived distance.

Underwater objects appear to be both larger and closer than they really are. Overestimation of size underwater is common. Both surface and submerged size and distance ratios change with distance. On land there is a decrease in the ratios, and in water there is an increase in the ratios. There are also indications that overestimation stems in part from loss of contrast under water, due to the scattering of light by particles, and that the *Ganzfeld* characteristics of underwater viewing are influential in depth perception.

The values of polarized light as a tool in underwater vision and dark adaptation in the undersea environment are discussed in the chapter, and it is suggested that both may have some advantages. However, very little information is presently available on the effects of polarized light and predive dark adaptation.

A major factor in determining which colors are visible under water is the type of water. In general it can be said that fluorescent paints are far superior to regular paints in all kinds of water. It is also important to distinguish between the visibility of colors and their absolute identification. In general, it is hard to distinguish a given color from the color closest to it in the spectrum.

Perceptual learning plays a vital role in the undersea environment. Considerable adaptation seems to occur, and there is a marked difference in the test results between experienced and novice subjects as measured by means of visual tests. Psychological stress has been shown to be a significant factor even at shallow ocean depths for novices. Habituation to the stressful environment could be one important factor in explaining the complicated process of visual perceptual learning under the surface of the ocean.

III

AUDITION

The peripheral components of the auditory system function with greatly reduced efficiency when man is exposed to increased ambient pressure, and in the water additional acoustic impedance phenomena are of special importance. A diver suffers hearing difficulties which may partially be explained by increased ambient pressure causing disturbances in sound conduction through the middle ear. The loss in air conduction capability is marked, while bone conduction is nearly unaffected. The influence of hyperbaric air intoxication on a diver's consciousness and wakefulness has been shown to cause a delayed response, thus preventing a sound pattern from being immediately identified.

The human auditory system is constructed to function optimally in a terestrial environment. A very large impedance mismatch exists between the air and the tissues of the head. Under water only very weak diffraction effects occur at the head, since the acoustic impedance of the head and the water are similar.

Under water man either totally loses his natural sound localization capabilities, or they are seriously impaired. The binaural time difference, as well as the intensity differential, is changed, which operates to reduce underwater sound localization.

INTRODUCTION

Acoustic communication mutually conducted between one diver and another and between a diver and surface personnel has long been a problem of importance. The feasibility of using acoustic communication in an undersea system is dependent upon transmission fidelity and reliable reception. "The human ear is a multi-component non-linear acoustic detector embedded in a quasi-spherical baffle, the head" (Smith, 1969). The sensitivity of the ear is dependent upon the following characteristics:

1. The transmitting medium.
2. The sound reflections around the head.
3. The convolutions of the pinna.
4. The patency of the canal.
5. The compliance of the tympanic membrane/middle ear system.

The peripheral components of man's auditory system may be expected to function with greatly reduced efficiency when he is exposed to increased ambient pressure (Smith, 1969). Increased pressure not only affects the conductivity of the hyperbaric gas, but the increased partial pressures of the different components of the breathing mixture also affect the consciousness of the diver (Behnke, Thomson & Motley, 1935; Case & Haldane, 1941; Kiessling & Maag, 1960; Adolfson, 1965, 1967). In the water environment additional acoustic impedance phenomena are of special importance.

AUDITION IN A DRY HYPERBARIC ENVIRONMENT

Changes in sound transmission velocities are quite important for the formation and generation of sound by humans in hyperbaric environments, but their effects on sound reception seem to be easily corrected simply by raising the volume of sound. The conductive hearing loss, demonstrated by Fluur and Adolfson (1966), in air and suggested in Thomas', Summitt's and Farmer's (1973), data for helium–oxygen, is most likely related to two major factors:

1. Changes in the mechanical and acoustic impedance of the tympanic membrane and middle ear structure.
2. Changes in the resonance frequency of the external canal and

middle ear (Summitt, Personal communication).

The latter should be directly related to the change in sound velocity in the medium, and thus to the density of the gas mixture.

As early as 1898, Lester and Gomez observed diminution in auditory acuity in eight subjects in a caisson during construction of the East River Bridge in New York. They concluded that both air and bone conduction of sound were considerably reduced while under pressures of 3.0 and 3.5 ATA. This diminution was proportional to the rise in atmospheric pressure. The effect persisted for 24 to 48 hr after the men left the caisson.

Other investigators have also found diminished hearing acuity in divers (Bijlsma, 1901; Poli, 1959; Almour, 1942; Kos, 1944).

Human auditory functioning is affected by several factors in the hyperbaric environment:

I. Hazards—temporary or permanent injury to the ears.
    A. Noise and vibration.
    B. Barotrauma.
    C. Decompression sickness.
    D. Ear infections.
II. Sensory-Perceptual alterations—temporary changes due to the environment.
    A. Normal conductive hearing deficit.
        1. Change in acoustic impedance.
        2. Change in resonance characteristics.
    B. Inert gas narcosis.
    C. Water immersion.

These are discussed in more detail below.

Intense Noise Levels

It is easy to agree with Summitt and Reimers' (1971) observations that, although high-pressure gases and associated systems can obviously produce intense noise, quantitative information on sound levels inside compression chambers, diving bells, and diving helmets is almost nonexistent. Furthermore, very little seems to be known of the sensitivity of the inner ear to noise injuries under conditions of high pressure. Summitt and Reimers found that many divers accept tinnitus and muffled hearing as normal sequalae to helmet

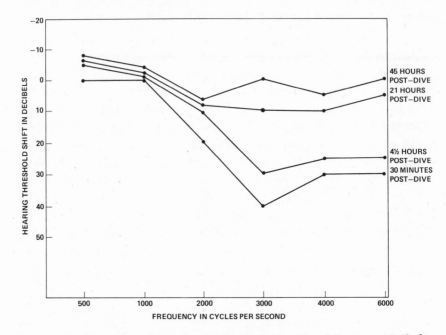

Figure 3-1.   Temporary shift in hearing threshold in a diver following a 190-ft dive using an air helmet. (Summit & Reimers, 1971.)

diving, provided the subjective symptoms disappear within a few hours.

In a study at the U.S. Experimental Diving Unit, Washington, D.C., whose primary purpose was to test decompression schedules and to evaluate diving helmets, Summitt and Reimers found a temporary bilateral hearing loss of the sensory-neural type, which is illustrated in Figure 3-1. There was no evidence of barotrauma by otoscopic examination. These investigators also reported that divers had difficulty with communication because of background noise, and they suggested that acoustic trauma was a possible cause. Table 3-1 shows the noise levels during the different conditions to which the divers were exposed.

In the helmet studies two positions of the air-supply valve were used. The lower valve setting simulated the air supply a diver normally would use near the surface. As can be seen from Table 3-1, there is little if any difference between the noise produced at the

Table 3-1   Diving Helmet and Hyperbaric Chamber A—Weight Sound Pressure Levels Obtained with Different Supply Valve Settings and/or Environmental Conditions (Summitt and Reimers, 1971)

Description of the Environment	Gas Supply Valve Setting (If Appropriate)[a]	Depth of Seawater (ft)				
		0	50	100	150	200
Diving helmet A	$\frac{1}{4}$ turn	93	101	99	99	100
	Full open	92	100	100	99	101
	Full open (exhaust chatter)	106				
Diving helmet B	$\frac{1}{4}$ open	110	113	111	113	112
	Full open	109	112	113	112	111
Diving helmet C	$\frac{1}{4}$ open	96	95	96	100	102
	Full open	97	95	96	99	103
Diving helmet D	$\frac{1}{4}$ open	98	93	94	94	98
	Full open	95	94	96	97	99
Diving helmet E	$\frac{1}{4}$ open	95	96	97	100	102
	Full open	95	96	98	100	102
Quiet hyperbaric chamber	N.A.	43				
Hyperbaric chamber with life support system on	N.A.	68				
Hyperbaric chamber (ventilating)	Full open	116	121	118	118	116
Hyperbaric chamber	Compression rate of 60 ft/min		116	114	110	107

[a] N.A., not appropriate.

lower setting and when the valve was fully open. In both cases the sound levels were well above the 90 dBA considered to be the upper limit of an 8-hr occupational exposure on the surface. dBA refers to the sound pressure level measured with an A weight hazard scale according to the International Organization for Standardization.

Figure 3-2 illustrates the allowable noise exposure limits currently accepted for hearing conservation programs in the U.S. Navy. Superimposed on the limit curve are the highest noise levels recorded in individual helmets and in compression chambers as measured by Summitt and Reimers. Obviously, diving and chamber personnel

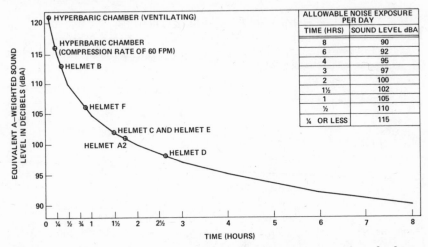

Figure 3-2. Highest noise levels recorded in individual helmets and in the hyperbaric chamber superimposed on a curve describing the allowable industrial noise exposure per 8-hr day currently accepted by the U.S. Navy. (Summit & Reimers, 1971.)

frequently are exposed to noise that can injure the unprotected ear in a relatively short period of time.

However, as Harris (1969) has pointed out, a group of divers can be formed by careful selection and training, which can continue to perform well for years, even though they may undergo constant auditory rigors. Schilling and Eversley (1942) showed that the mean audiogram for divers who have had no special exposure to intense noise was not appreciably worse than for controls. Coles (1965) examined 57 very experienced divers and found their hearing perfectly normal except for those who had experienced "much" gunfire or small-arms noise. Harris (1969) concluded: "Evidently in a cadre of men who do not experience barotrauma and who are protected by proper procedures from bubble formation, hearing may remain perfectly normal. There is thus no suggestion that repeated compression-decompression cycles per se have any effect on auditory acuity." This is quite in accordance with the findings of Coles and Knight (1960) who evaluated the audiograms of 62 divers and submarine escape tank instructors. They concluded that there is no evidence that "the minor incidence of barotrauma associated with normal diving procedures impaired hearing."

Harris has pointed out that there are many individuals for whom pressure equalization across the eardrum is not semiautomatic, or even possible, and there are fairly frequent occasions when even experienced divers find it difficult to clear their ears with sufficient rapidity. Furthermore, there are those who have experienced sudden hearing losses during a dive. In summary, Harris states that, among those who are exposed repeatedly to compression–decompression cycles, a high incidence of otological symptoms including hearing loss is often reported. He adds that most of this can be attributed to the residual effect of repeated aerotitis media (so termed by Armstrong and Heim, 1937) caused by lack of ventilation of the middle ear. The onset of aerotitis media is not sudden, however, and so does not completely explain the sudden deafness that occasionally occurs during a dive.

Harris prefers the theory that decompression sickness is a main cause of sudden hearing loss during a dive. He reported 10 patients who experienced hearing loss during decompression. Two of them recovered completely during recompression, and three recovered only slightly. He assumed it likely that these five patients had sustained bubble formation in one or more branches of the internal acoustic artery. In the five patients not responding to recompression, but treated with decongestans, vasodilators, and so on, he suggested a possible microhemorrhage in the cochlea.

Recently, Nourrit (1970) carried out a series of experiments with guinea pigs in hyperbaric chambers. Histological examination of the animals' cochleas demonstrated vascular type injuries. Although the conditions of the experiments with the guinea pigs were not strictly parallel to diving conditions, they demonstrated, according to Nourrit, the fact that the structures of the inner ear are extremely sensitive to pressure variations. Nourrit could not explain the pathogenic mechanism of sudden deafness.

Change in Conduction of Sound through the Middle Ear

Normally, air pressure on both sides of the tympanic membrane is equal. The balance is maintained by the passage of air into and out of the middle ear via the Eustachian tube. Ordinarily, equalization functions independently of the magnitude of the ambient pressure, thereby preventing unequal pressure from restricting the mobility of the tympanic membrane, which usually results in decreased hearing acuity. A considerable change in air pressure imbalance could be expected to affect sound perception in other ways. This could either be through changes in the characteristics of the middle ear mechanism for transmitting sound energy across the middle ear, or by affecting the round window membrane, which might change the endolymph movement in the cochlea.

In 1966, Fluur and Adolfson made an investigation to determine the effects of increased ambient pressure on the hearing acuity of divers. To permit a more precise evaluation of psychoacoustic measurements, an investigation of changes in the transmission characteristics of the transducers as a function of air pressure was performed. Air and bone conduction pure-tone threshold audiograms were made on 26 experienced divers in normal air (1 ATA) and in hyperbaric air at 4, 7, and 11 ATA. After correcting for transmission changes in the earphone characteristics (5 to 10 dB), the hearing threshold curve for air conduction at 11 ATA was elevated 30 to 40 dB in the middle-frequency range of hearing. For the two highest frequencies tested, threshold elevation was less marked, generally only 10 dB. The subjects who showed good hearing acuity at these frequencies at 1 ATA demonstrated only insignificant changes at high test frequencies at elevated atmospheric pressures, in most cases within ±5 dB (Figure 3-3). Contrary to the observations of Lester and Gomez (1898), bone conduction thresholds were unaffected by changes in ambient pressure in the Fluur and Adolfson experiment (Figure 3-4). In two subjects at 12 ATA breathing oxygen–helium, Olivier and Demard (1970) observed a hypoacousis of transmission of the entire range of frequencies tested, increasing toward the lower frequencies.

Fluur and Adolfson suggested that, apart from physical changes in the transmission characteristics of the communication system, divers' hearing difficulties may partially be explained by the increased ambient pressure causing disturbances in sound conduction through the middle ear. The unaffected bone conduction thresholds indicate that no loss of sensitivity appears in the sensory-neural function (Fluur and Adolfson, 1966; Fluur, 1970).

However, a smaller loss in bone conduction has been found recently. Miller (1971) has described an experiment in which he meas-

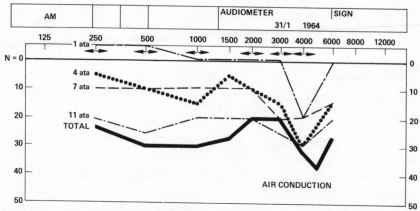

Figure 3-3.   Audiogram. Air conduction threshold at 1, 4, 7, and 11 ATA. Subject A.M. Total hearing loss at 11 ATA after compensation for transmission changes in the earphone. (Adolfson & Fluur, 1965.)

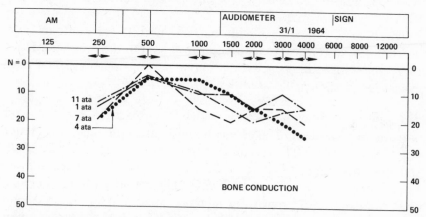

Figure 3-4.   Audiogram. Bone conduction threshold at 1, 4, 7, and 11 ATA. Subject A.M. The deviation shown has to be accepted as insignificant for this mode of measurement. (Adolfson & Fluur, 1965.)

ured cochlear potentials in cats at eight frequencies from 0.5 to 20 kHz at 10 ATA. A 15- to 20-dB loss in sensitivity was found at 2, 4, and 8 kHz, with a variable response at the higher and lower frequencies. He also observed that the loss at 5 ATA was about half that at 10 ATA. A smaller loss in bone conduction (average 7 dB) than in air conduction (average 14 dB) at 1.5, 2, 4, and 8 kHz was recorded.

These results agree with those of Fluur and Adolfson (1966) but, as Miller (1971) points out, comparison with that study is limited for at least two reasons:

1. Audiometry is necessarily a subjective technique.

2. Inert gas narcosis is a very prominent factor, and its effect on a particular individual is unpredictable.

Miller suggests that the loss of sensitivity may be at several sites. First, the tympanic membrane is less efficient under this pressure due to the greater density of gas on each side. The mechanical impedance is increased, reducing the amplitude of tympanic membrane displacement and therefore its efficiency. Second, the ossicular chain of the middle ear may be the site of the loss. Since the ossicles under normal conditions have their own characteristic resonance frequencies, altering air density to such a great extent may well modify their vibratory characteristics.

These sites, tympanic membrane and middle ear contents, may reflect a loss of sensitivity which is transferred to the inner ear. However, that a loss still occurred with bone conduction suggests a third causal locus, the cochlea (Miller, 1971).

The Influence of Inert Gas Intoxication

A common symptom of inert gas narcosis are prolonged associative reactions (Behnke, Thomson & Motley, 1935; Adolfson, 1965; Adolfson & Muren, 1965; Adolfson, 1967). Speech sounds reach the brain via the ear and its auditory pathways. The sound patterns probably are associated with preexisting memory images. Appropriate motor impulses are transmitted to the "organs of speech." This complex process may be rendered far more difficult if the essential mental processes cannot proceed unhindered. According to Liden (1954), retarded associative processes are manifested in poorer discrimination scores than those that might be expected on the basis of the pure-tone threshold audiogram.

To determine the extent to which hearing discrimination is influenced by inert gas narcosis while air is breathed, Adolfson and Fluur (1967) investigated 23 experienced divers using a speech discrimination test. The test was conducted in a compression chamber at normal air pressure (1 ATA), and at 4, 7, and 11 ATA, and presented to the subjects at an easily audible level.

The hearing discrimination test was based on phonetically balanced monosyllabic word lists originally constructed by Carhart (1951) and translated into Swedish by Liden and Fant (1954). The Swedish word lists, used in Adolfson's and Fluur's study, were presented by means of a tape recorder at the subject's most comfortable listening level, which meant that the intensity of the speech sounds was raised over the hearing threshold by about 30 to 55 dB. It was found that hearing discrimination ability decreased with increased ambient air pressure, and the changes were statistically significant at both 7 and 11 ATA. These workers suggested that the divers' hearing difficulties could not be explained fully by the fact that the increased ambient pressure causes disturbances of sound conduction through the middle ear. Even when the speech sound intensity was raised well above the hearing acuity threshold and the mechanical impedance changes in the middle ear were well compensated for, the divers had difficulties in comprehending simple common words. These misperceptions increased with increased ambient air pressure. They conclude: "The influence of hyperbaric air intoxication on divers' consciousness and wakefulness and prolonged associative reactions will prevent the sound pattern from being immediately identified when reaching the auditory center, and this will cause a delayed response" (p. 175).

By testing human pure-tone auditory sensitivity in a nonnarcotic helium–oxygen environment the problem of depth narcosis can be eliminated. Two studies have been reported on man's auditory response in this type of environment. The first of these studies by Farmer, Thomas, and Preslar (1973) investigated psychoacoustically the hearing of six divers during a chamber dive to an equivalent sea depth of 600 ft or 19.2 ATA. The researchers concluded from their data that (1) exposure to hyperbaric helium–oxygen conditions produces a reversible conductive hearing loss that is related to exposure depth and (2) sensorineural auditory function is not altered by hyperbaric helium–oxygen exposures down to depths of 19.2 ATA. Farmer et al. (1973) postulated that the conductive hearing loss is "due to an increased impedance of the middle ear transformer in the denser atmosphere plus an upward shift in the ear resonant frequency in a helium atmosphere" (p. 41).

The second experiment on auditory thresholds in a high pressure helium–oxygen environment was done by Thomas, Summitt, and Farmer (1973) at the U.S. Navy Experimental Diving Unit. This study reports the results of air conduction and bone conduction (sensory acuity level, SAL) on 33 different divers on eight different saturation dives in helium–oxygen. The dives included one saturation dive to 300 ft, four separate dives to 600 ft, two dives to 850 ft, and one dive to 1000 ft. A total of 400 air conduction and 300 bone conduction audiograms were gathered at 26 different depths during these dives, 11 during compression and 15 during decompression.

The results for the four saturation depths are shown in Figure 3-5. There is a rather uniform reduction in hearing threshold associated with increased pressure, the most prominent decreases being for 500, 1000, and 3000 Hz.

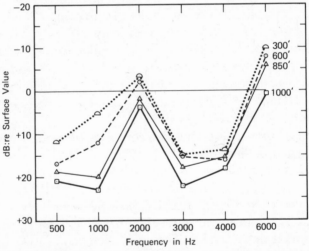

Figure 3-5. Mean threshold taken during bottom time at four different depths. All thresholds are relative to surface values. (Thomas, Summitt, and Farmer, 1973.)

Figure 3-6 shows a general trend during compression and decompression. For all but two of the frequencies there is a gradual reduction in hearing sensitivity associated with compression. During decompression there is a slow, steady return to normal surface baselines.

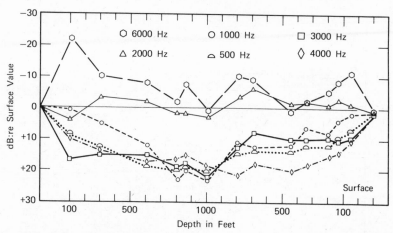

Figure 3-6. Mean thresholds for six different frequencies as a function of depth. All thresholds are measured relative to surface threshold. (Thomas, Summitt, and Farmer, 1973.)

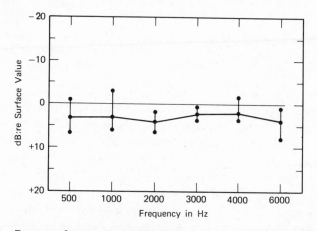

Figure 3-7. Bone conduction thresholds (SAL) as a function of frequency. Because of the similarity of the data for all depths, the mean thresholds averaged over all depths and the range from the highest to lowest scores are plotted. All measures are relative to SAL measures at the surface. (Thomas, Summitt, and Farmer, 1973.)

None of the 300 bone conduction audiograms showed significant differences at any of the depths tested. These results (Figure 3-7) tend to agree with previous research, indicating that the threshold shift represents a conductive hearing loss that is reversible, and to some extent, depth related.

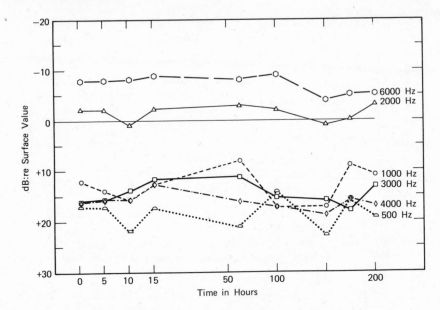

Figure 3-8. Mean thresholds for six different frequencies as a function of time at 600 ft. The figure shows thresholds upon arrival at 600 ft and at various times to 200 hr at this depth. (Thomas, Summitt, and Farmer, 1973.)

In Figure 3-8 the results of numerous tests taken over time at 600 ft are shown. "Ten audiograms were made on each of sixteen (16) divers during four saturation dives to 600 feet (183 m.). These audiograms ranged from the time of arrival at this depth to 200 hours later, just prior to leaving the bottom. There is no significant differences among any of the tests given over time during this isobaric exposure. It would appear that auditory thresholds neither improve nor degenerate as a function of time at saturation levels" (p. 48).

Thomas et al. (1973) reported that "the hearing losses noted in the helium–oxygen environment even at 1000 feet, failed to reach the 30 to 40 dB conductive hearing loss noted by Fluur and Adolfson at 330 feet. In the Fluur and Adolfson study, however, the divers were breathing the much denser hyperbaric air instead of helium, which may account for this difference."

Before moving on to a new topic it should be pointed out that the data gathered in the hyperbaric helium–oxygen environment are only an approximation of the true state of human auditory sensitivity. Thomas et al. (1973) indicated in their study that there is a great deal of variability between earphones and their response to pressure. They also pointed out that the same earphone responds differently during compression and decompression. They reported that "this variability would indicate that audiometric threshold data taken with standard earphones under hyperbaric conditions should be evaluated with caution. Although the data indicate a trend toward greater depth related hearing loss, the absolute values should be interpreted with care and are probably only close approximations because of the great variability in earphones."

AUDITION IN A WET HYPERBARIC ENVIRONMENT

Continued diving is not without hazards to the ear. Harashima and Shigeno (1965) observed many more otorhinolaryngological problems in diving women in Japan than in their nondiving counterparts. In fact, they found it to be the chief occupational disease of the Ama. Problems included chronic otitis media, opacity of the tympanic membranes, stenosis of Eustachian tubes, sinusitis, and rhinitis. Of the Ama in this study, 50% demonstrated severe hearing losses. These conditions improved during the nondiving season. The initial otitis was thought to be a sequela to irritation and subsequent occlusion of the Eustachian tubes by seawater (Strauss, 1970).

Sensitivity

How is the sensitivity of the human ear affected when it is immersed in water? According to Smith (1969), each component of the human auditory system has a role in determining the overall sensitivity of the ear, and each has so evolved that the system functions optimally in the terrestrial environment. According to Reysenbach de Haan (1966), the normal mammalian ear is almost totally unsuitable for underwater hearing.

In air the head is a relatively rigid obstacle in the sound field. According to Smith (1969): "At certain frequencies the sound pressure level (SPL) at the surface of the head is measurably greater than the SPL in a free sound field. This diffraction effect is due to the very large impedance mismatch existing between the air and the tissues of the head. Under water, however, only very weak diffraction effects occur at the head, since the acoustic impedance of the head and water are similar" (p. 1).

Also, the external auditory canal and the tympanic membrane become fairly useless in water. Smith, in his brilliant discussion of the function of the human ear when immersed in water, points out:

"In air, the external auditory canal exhibits the properties of a short, rigid-walled resonator. The dimensions are such that the sound pressure acting on the tympanic membrane, the medial terminus of the canal, is considerably higher over the frequency range 2.0 to 6.0 kilohertz (kHz) than at the entrance to the canal. This effect depends on the material that bounds the canal and on the wave lengths of airborne sound. Over the outer one-third to one-half of its length, the canal is cartilliginous, the inner portion is bony. If the ear canal is filled with water and the head submerged, then the outer portion of the canal is acoustically non-existent" (p. 1).

Normally, the air pressure on both sides of the tympanic membrane is equal, and balance is maintained by the passage of air into the middle ear via the Eustachian tube. According to Smith:

"The acoustic impedance of the tympanic membrane and the middle ear system is matched to the acoustic impedance of the ear canal in air. With the canal filled with water, there would exist a large impedance mismatch at the boundary, the tympanic membrane, with the impedance of the water-filled canal being considerably higher than the tympanic membrane/middle ear system impedance. Such a boundary is a pressure release boundary. That is, positive pressures are reflected as negative perssures and vice versa. When the ratio of the impedance is very large, the sound pressure at the boundary is at all times close to zero" (p. 1).

Smith suggested that characteristics of the medium, the head, the pinna (which in general is composed of soft tissues and can have no acoustic function under water), the canal, and the tympanic membrane/middle ear system may account for a reduction in sensitivity of about 84 dB at 2.5 kHz upon immersion. He also suggested that the loss of sensitivity may be less at higher and lower frequencies.

It is interesting to note here that, in whales and other cetaceans (e.g., dolphins and porpoises), the mammalian air hearing mechanism has been readapted to the underwater environment and has reached even greater perfection.

In several comparative studies Reysenbach de Haan (1957, 1957a) has pointed out that, in order to be optimal:

"Sound in water must be offered to the inner ear through a much more massive middle ear system. It must be adapted to the physical properties of the medium in which the sound is produced, which is water, and not to the air for which it was built. It has been calculated that, to produce the same intensity of sound, sound pressure in seawater has to be sixty times as high as in air. As, however, the maximum amplitude of particles from the equilibrium position in a sound wave in water is only one-sixtieth of that in air, a much heavier and more rigid middle-ear mechanism is required."

The skull of terrestrial mammals, vibrated by sound waves under water, no longer insulates the two ears from each other; thus, directional hearing is lost. The need for the animal to have two independent hydrophones at its disposal has been realized in the Cetacea. According to Reysenbach de Hann (1966): "The two ears have been acoustically insulated in the skull, in so far as possible, by foam—that is, air-filled paranasal sinuses which surround both the middle ear and the inner ear. Thus, sound in water can reach each of the two inner ears independently of each other only via the middle ear system."

In sea lions, Odend'had and Poulter (1966) noted three significant differences from the human middle-ear cavity. First, the ratio of the foot plate of the stapes to the tympanic membrane was 1:1, in contrast to the 20:1 ratio in man. Second, the mucous membrane internal to the tympanic membrane was attached only in the area of the epitympanic recess, which contains the middle-ear ossicles. In other places the membrane was attached only by the blood vessels perforating the temporal bone. Finally, the mucous membrane was composed of three layers, the middle layer consisting of a "complex network of venous channels and sinuses imbedded in a matrix of loose connective tissue." As a relatively negative pressure developed in the middle ear when the external pressure increased with descent, the venous sinuses passively filled with blood in order to eliminate the pressure differential. Distention of the mucosa and eventual obliteration of the middle ear cavity resulted. Consequently, further descent did not affect the tympanic membrane. The remaining air was compressed into the small epitympanic cavity. This permitted the tympanic membrane and ossicular system to transmit sound vibrations and make hearing more efficient. These investigators suggested that the reverse phenomenon occurred with ascent (Strauss, 1970).

Apparently, the peripheral components of the auditory system of man may be expected to function with greatly reduced efficiency as man dives. Transmission of sound by way of the ear canal and eardrum is not the only mechanism for stimulating the cochlea, however. An alternative mechanism is bone conduction hearing. Smith (1969) properly points out: "Without an understanding of the mechanism of underwater hearing, the development of communications and sensing devices for divers may not proceed in the most efficacious direction."

Bone Conduction Hearing and Hearing Thresholds under Water

Bone conduction hearing as a possible mechanism of underwater hearing is supported by several investigators. Three conditions might occur during underwater hearing and contribute to bone conduction sensitivity:

1. The external meatus is occluded by the water, and the resonance of the external meatus thus changed by the medium (Hamilton, 1957).

2. The mismatch of impedance between the ear and the water (Sivian, 1947; Wainwright 1958).

3. The possibility of mass loading of the eardrums and the middle-ear mechanism by the water (Reysenbach de Haan, 1957a).

Hamilton (1957) measured underwater hearing thresholds in four divers at frequencies of 250, 500, 1000, 2000, and 4000 Hz and found that the minimum audible tones under water were from 44 to 60 dB greater than the minimum audible tones in air, and that the shape of the threshold versus frequency curve was different. He suggested that the changed shape of the curve when the ear is immersed in water may be due to one of the following: changing of the resonant frequency of the external ear canal, the possible use of bone conduction for underwater hearing or, more likely, the two factors combined.

Hamilton found the bone conduction theory quite convincing. In air, occlusion of the external canals causes an attenuation of sound signals of about 20 to 30 dB. However, if the sound is transmitted by bone conduction, loudness is enhanced when the canals are occluded. It was also determined that, when the divers occluded their ears by inserting their index fingers in the external canals, the most common report was no change in loudness.

In a theoretical analysis, Sivian (1943b) concluded that a small bubble of air trapped in the external auditory meatus has no important effect on underwater auditory sensitivity. The impedance of the water-filled canal and the eardrum were shown to be so poorly matched that the sound pressure activating the eardrum was about 40 dB lower than the incident water-bone sound pressure at a frequency of 1 kHz. Thus the sound pressure level required to produce a just audible signal was at least 40 dB higher under water than in air. This theory has been confirmed experimentally by Hollien and Brandt (1969).

Sivian considered four additional secondary effects which could further alter underwater sensitivity. These were:

1. Decreased aural sensitivity caused by unbalanced hydrostatic pressure on the eardrum of the submerged observer.
2. The masking effect of noise in the water and the noise created by the submerged swimmer's propulsion efforts.
3. The effects of the diver's head and body upon the sound field in the vicinity of the eardrum.
4. Bone conduction in water; although this does not function to decrease the diver's sensitivity.

The effect of static pressure imbalance is known to be of great importance in air conduction, but may not affect bone conduction (Fluur & Adolfson, 1966). Ambient and propulsion noise levels were dismissed by Sivian as being unimportant in his experiments conducted in quiet water with a diver at rest. The effects of the diver's head and body on the sound field were thought to be of great importance. Sivian maintained that the head and body of man are much more compressible than water; thus the head exerts a pressure release effect and reduces the sound pressure level at the entrance to the canal. Finally, Sivian expected bone conduction to aid underwater hearing.

Sivian estimated that a sound pressure level in water of 43 dB is sufficient to set the mastoid process into vibration at an amplitude at which average bone conduction thresholds with occluded ear canals are reached in air. Neglecting secondary effects, which have similar magnitudes for both hearing via eardrum and bone conduction hearing, the two threshold estimates are similar. That is, for man under water an incident sound pressure level up to 40 dB produces a sensation of hearing through eardrum hearing, while a sound pressure level of 43 dB produces a sensation of hearing by bone conduction.

Sivian conducted an experiment in a swimming pool; however, it is hard to draw any definite conclusions from this experiment because only three subjects were employed (Sivian, 1943a). One of his divers had a substantial "aerial" hearing deficiency, and his underwater hearing thresholds deviated from those of the other two subjects by about the same amount as did his air conduction hearing. Sivian took this as evidence that underwater hearing is eardrum hearing rather than bone conduction hearing.

Wainwright (1958), in a study in which he compared hearing thresholds obtained in air and in water, supported the bone conduction theory. His subjects used closed-circuit scuba to avoid interference from bubble noise produced by open-circuit scuba. In accordance with the findings of Hamilton (1957), he found no effect on underwater hearing by occluding the ears with fingers. Wainwright also found that the greatest loss in hearing acuity in water occurred over the frequency range from 500 to 2000 Hz and amounted to approximately 20 dB, while below 500 Hz the threshold intensity in water was lower than that in air. He suggested that: "Evidence seems to indicate that hearing under water is primarily accomplished by bone conduction." However, Wainwright used only two subjects, thus it is impossible to draw any significant conclusions from his experiment.

A redetermination of underwater hearing thresholds was made by Montague and Strickland (1961), who used a fixed-frequency

Békésy technique to determine both air conduction and underwater thresholds. They tested a sample of four young men with normal or better than normal hearing acuity, and a sample of three men all of whom exhibited depressed air conduction hearing thresholds.

In discussing their results they pointed out that the loss of auditory sensitivity that accompanies water immersion is greatest at those frequencies for which hearing is most acute in air. They concluded that this effect may be due to the impedance mismatch of the ear and the water, or to the loss of ear canal resonances. Figure 3-9 shows composite results of five studies of underwater hearing sensitivity in man.

The data of Brandt and Hollien (1967, 1969) supported all the theories mentioned above. They pointed out that it is obvious that the situation is a complex one, and that changed resonance of the external meatus as well as the impedance mismatch between the ear and the water and a possible mass loading of the eardrum and the middle ear mechanism should be considered (Hollien, Brandt & Mallone, 1968). Hollien and Brandt (1969) studied the effect of air bubbles in the external auditory meatus on underwater hearing thresholds and found that the presence or absence of bubbles of air in the external auditory meatus was unimportant to underwater thresholds. These findings confirmed the statement of Sivian (1943) that a small bubble of air trapped in the external auditory meatus has no important effect on underwater auditory sensitivity. Hollien and Brandt speculated:

"If the middle ear mechanism (water-conduction) is functioning in underwater hearing, a change in the impedance characteristics of the external canal produced by the presence of a bubble of air should produce a change in the audibility threshold. In the present case, trapped air would be representative of a high impedance in series with the tympanic membrane and an increase in sound pressure level (SPL) for the audibility threshold would be predicted. This clearly is not the case."

Hollien and Brandt summarized their findings further: "The middle ear mechanism is not used in underwater hearing but, rather, is bypassed by the mechanism of bone conduction. If this is the case—and it appears to be—changes in the impedance characteristics

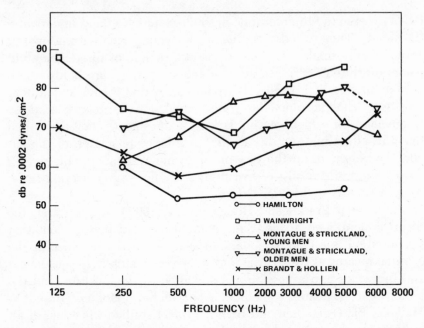

Figure 3-9. Composite results of five studies of underwater hearing sensitivity in man. (Smith, 1969.)

of the middle ear mechanism should not affect the audibility threshold underwater." Thus they suggested: "The bone conduction mechanism is, indeed, responsible for hearing underwater." The findings of Hollien and Brandt are illustrated in Figure 3-10.

Waterman and Smith (1970) altered the characteristics of the possible conductive paths and observed the effects of such alterations on underwater hearing sensitivity. According to these workers, it may be possible to alter the functioning of the middle ear apparatus by introducing helium–oxygen into the cavity. Since a mixture of 80% helium and 20% oxygen has an acoustic impedance about three times that of air, it is possible that the compliance of the middle ear cavity changes sufficiently to result in a change in hearing sensitivity. To test this possibility, Waterman and Smith measured hearing levels of three subjects at 125, 1000, and 8000 Hz in a soundproof room at ambient air pressure while the subjects in one situation breathed air and in another situation breathed the above-mentioned mixture of helium and oxygen. No significant changes in

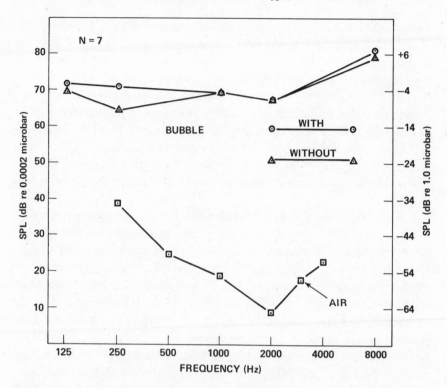

Figure 3-10. Mean threshold SPL (dB re 0.0002 microbar) as a function of test frequency in air and water (with and without air bubbles). $N = 7$ divers/listeners. (Hollien & Brandt, 1969.)

hearing levels, which could be attributed to the effects of the gas breathed, were detected during or following a 30-min period on helium–oxygen. They concluded that respired helium–oxygen at surface pressures has little or no effect on hearing sensitivity at 125 and 1000 Hz. A small decrement may occur at higher frequencies, but these investigators found that the effect, if any, was not of sufficient magnitude or generality to be of practical importance. However, they did not exclude the possibility that effects may be found at pressures greater than 1 ATA.

In addition, Hollien and Brandt recently completed a series of experiments in which the middle ear was filled with a helium–oxygen mixture. A comparison of these thresholds with those obtained for air-filled middle ears indicated no differences in threshold under the two conditions, which is quite in accordance with the findings of Waterman and Smith. As the impedance characteristics for the middle-ear cavity filled with the two gases are entirely different, they suggested that the middle-ear mechanism is not of prime importance in underwater hearing (Hollien, personal communication).

In an earlier report, Smith (1965) revealed that, for frequencies of 6 and 8 kHz, the greater the auditory sensitivity of a subject in air the greater the loss of a auditory sensitivity suffered by that subject upon immersion in water. These data were taken as evidence that underwater hearing may be predominantly bone conduction hearing.

However, Smith did not consider these findings conclusive. This led him to make a new series of experiments in conjunction with a study of the effect of sonar transmissions on the hearing of underwater swimmers. Underwater hearing threshold measurements were made on 16 male divers of which 11 had normal hearing (no hearing losses greater than 10 dB), 3 had air conduction losses at a single frequency (6 kHz), and 2 had mixed air conduction and bone conduction losses at more than one frequency. The testing conditions were such that the diver's head was 4.5 m (15 ft) below the surface in 23 to 24.5 m (75 to 80 ft) of water, and air conduction and bone conduction data were obtained by ascending-descending pure-tone audiometric methods. The diver was given a two-directional switch by which he could signal whether he did or did not hear the tones. Three series of experiments were run.

Smith found that the results of the first two experiments "were consistent with the hypothesis that underwater hearing is primarily bone conduction hearing." However, according to Smith: "The role of BC (bone conduction) in underwater hearing has been clearly demonstrated only for the frequencies of 6 and 8 kHz." He found evidence that: "Dependence of underwater hearing on bone conduction and the independence of underwater hearing from depressed air conduction, holds for frequencies as low as one kHz." In the absense of clearly contradictory evidence, he provisionally concluded that "underwater hearing is directly related to bone conduction."

Underwater Sound Localization in Humans

Under normal or ideal conditions, human beings are able to locate a narrow-beam sound source to an accuracy of about 1°. When several sounds arrive at the same time from different directions, the listener is able to sort them out and locate the source of any of them. However, in the underwater environment both theory and empirical evidence predict either that humans will totally lose their sound localization capabilities or that they will be seriously impaired.

Normal Sound Localization Conditions in Air

Are both ears necessary in auditory localization? Many experiments have attempted to quantify the conditions that would determine whether or not two ears are better than one. They have also sought to isolate and measure the strength of stimuli which are available and which a subject might use to make accurate sound localization. Thus, as early as 1901, Pierce demonstrated that plugging one ear in normal subjects impaired localization to a considerable extent. Several additional investigations have confirmed these findings. Starch (1908), for instance, found that individuals who were completely deaf in one ear demonstrated poor localization immediately after their loss. Although the loss was followed by some improvement, they were still subnormal and liable to right-left confusion, a rare occurrence among individuals having normal binaural hearing. Engelmann (1928) showed that similar experiments with animals gave comparable results. Butler and Haunton (1967) plugged one ear of normal-hearing subjects and found that localization improved as loudness increased. They attributed this to the increasing influence of interaural time differences.

Harris and Sergeant (1970) performed an experiment to furnish a more complete quantification of the monaural/binaural comparison. Three men, highly experienced in listening, judged whether a sound source moved left or right of (1) the horizontal midline, or (2) a point 60° off midline. The subjects made the judgment under two different conditions: (1) with both ears open, and (2) with their ears plugged, muffed, and masked by noise. These investigators found that the monaural minimum audible angle at either azimuth condition was as good as the binaural minimum audible angle, but only for white noise and for the lowest tone at 0° azimuth. Judgments were distinctly less accurate elsewhere. They concluded that there is much usable directionality for the monaural mode, even in the most inaccurate azimuth.

It seems clear from all investigations made that two ears yield more efficient auditory localization, although one ear is usable to some extent. In binaural hearing the main difference between the two ears is the fact that a sound usually has to travel farther to reach one of the ears, resulting in a binaural time difference in signal. The sound waves that reach the farther ear have been reflected by some part of the head, while those that reach the nearer ear are not so affected. Hence this "sound shadow" allows the stimulus to be more intense at the nearer ear, and there is a binaural intensity difference. Thus, quoting Hollien (1971) "Directional perception of sound in air is based on the utilization of phase (time-of-arrival) and/or intensity information provided by the arriving signal of the auditory mechanism."

Let us now investigate the elements of the so-called binaural time difference. Sound travels in air at a speed of 344 m/sec, or 34.4 cm/ msec. For each centimeter difference of binaural distance, there is a time difference of $1/34.4 = 0.29$ msec. Hence a distance difference can be reduced to a time difference (Woodworth & Schlosberg, 1960).

The binaural time difference is a physical fact that holds good for a sharp impulsive sound or an abrupt onset of any sound. But what about a continuous sound? If the source is a continuous pure tone rather than a click, the condensation phase, or the "crest," of the component sound waves are likely to arrive at different times at the two ears. The sound reaching each of the two ears will be out of phase. This phase difference between the sounds at the two ears will vary with the position of the source, just as the time-of-arrival difference does. Phase differences are expressed in angles. When two sounds are in phase, the phase angle is 0°; when the crest of one coincides with the trough of the other, they are 180° out of phase (Howard & Templeton, 1966).

When the difference between time of arrival at the two ears exceeds half the period between one crest and the next, the sounds at the two ears will begin to come into phase again as the sound source is moved into a more lateral position. There will be a certain frequency of sound for which half of the intercrest period is equal to the time difference introduced attributable to the separation distance between the ears. This frequency has been calculated for the average head and is about 1000 cps. (Howard and Templeton, 1966). In theory, for higher frequencies, the phase difference cues should become ambigous, since the interval between successive crests both between the left ear and the right ear, and vice versa, is short enough to be compatible with a source on the left or with a source on the right. Thus the phase-difference cue becomes less effective for high-frequency pure tones (Howard & Templeton, 1966). According to Hollien (1971), the arrival of sound at one ear versus its arrival at the opposite ear can vary up to 0.6 to 0.7 msec.

The "sound shadow effect" is a binaural cue. The result is that the sound stimulus is more intense at the nearer ear. If the source is anywhere in the median plane (directly ahead, above, or behind), the ears will be stimulated equally. Equal intensity of the sound in both ears thus indicates a source lying somewhere in the median plane, and greater intensity in one ear indicates a source somewhere toward that side. Thus the amount of binaural intensity difference indicates the direction angle. The same "cones of confusion" apply to the intensity difference as to the time difference (Woodworth & Schlosberg, 1960).

The intensity difference produced by the shadowing effect of the head varies with the frequency of the sound. High-frequency tones have a shorter wavelength than low-frequency tones and therefore cast a sharper "shadow" when they encounter an obstacle. The longer waves of the low-frequency tones "get around" the obstacle to some extent, which means that they are diffracted more than short-wavelength high-frequency tones. From this physical fact it may be predicted that laterally placed high-frequency sounds produce larger intensity differences between the ears than low-frequency sounds. The localization cues of intensity differences should be more effective for high-frequency than for low-frequency tones (Howard & Templeton, 1966). According to Hollien (1971), this shadow effect, which produces a marked high-frequency intensity difference between the two ears, is approximately 15 dB at 5 kHz and increases with increased frequency.

Abnormal Conditions under Water

In water a quite different situation from that in air exists. First, sound velocity is approximately five times greater than it is in air. The velocity of sound increases with the temperature, pressure, and salinity of the water. Other differences are that the acoustic imped-ance of air is 42 g/cm^2 sec, and that of water is 150,000 g/cm^2 sec. Therefore, for a given intensity of sound, the particle velocity in air is 3570 times as great as the particle velocity in water, and the sound pressure in water is 60 times as great as the sound pressure in air (Albers, 1970).

Because of these physical facts, the time interval of an arriving signal across the head is correspondingly shortened, virtually elimi-nating the directional perception attributable to time delay (phase). Hollien (1971) states: "It is as if, in the air environment, the indi-vidual's head had shrunk to the size of a golf ball." The time-of-arrival data available for processing at the cortex are dramatically reduced once the head is immersed in water.

The second factor that operates to reduce underwater sound localization concerns the intensity differential, the "sound shadow effect" which permits the auditory processing in air of the direc-tionality of higher frequency signals. As mentioned earlier, this rela-tionship does not hold in water, as the impedance of the head is similar to that of the fluid. The skull, vibrated by sound waves under water, no longer effectively separates the two ears from each other, and directional hearing is severely impaired. Bauer and Torick (1966) observe that, when an individual is submerged: "Sounds appear to arrive from nowhere. The location of a friend, or foe be-comes a matter of dangerous conjecture, and reverberant sounds mix with direct sounds into an unintelligible jumble."

Brandt and Hollien (1967, 1969) and Hollien and Brandt (1969) found additional confirmatory evidence. This resulted from a series of experiments during which underwater auditory acuity was being investigated. These studies generated an hypothesis that man's underwater hearing sensitivity is *normal*, with the following restric-tions. The external and middle ear do not function (or only minimally contribute to sensation), and submerged hearing is accomplished by transmission of the acoustic signal from the water to the cochlea via the skull (Hollien, 1971). Hollien conjectures: "If this contention is correct—and the evidence in this regard now appears overwhelming—one must begin to think of underwater auditory function in totally new and different terms. For most practical purposes, man must be considered to be 'one eared' underwater; such terms as 'bone conduction' acquire new meaning; 'air (water) conduction' as used in Audiology now has little or no validity . . . and the implications relative to underwater sound localization are substantial."

Thus arguments appear strong against any effective underwater sound localization abilities in man. However, informal reports by many divers continue to emerge wherein they claim that they feel as if they can make at least some gross localization of sound. More importantly, Feinstein (1966) has reported contrary research evidence; and Hollien, late in 1967, undertook a pilot study designed to be definitive. According to Hollien (1971), before the experiment he believed the results would support the no-localization position. Instead, the data were in sharp contradiction to that position, which subsequently led to an extensive series of experiments.

Hollien used sinusoids of 250, 1000, and 6000 Hz, and a thermal noise, as experimental stimuli. The stimulus presentation consisted of five pulses of the experimental frequency set up as 500-msec bursts whose level was 40 dB (110 dB SPL) above the underwater hearing thresholds for the poorest hearing subject. The research was carried out on 10 males and 7 females. They were all at least reasonably competent divers with experience in taking hearing tests in air and had participated in underwater projects of this general nature. During the experiment the subjects were free to move their heads but not their bodies. Their tasks were to localize the underwater sound sources presented at reference angles of 90°, 45°, 0°, 315°, and 270° at a water depth of 12 m (40 ft). Table 3-2 shows the percentage of correct localization responses to each of the four stimuli.

Inspection of Table 3-2 reveals that the overall performance accuracy was clearly above the chance level of .20. Hollien concluded that humans show some ability to localize sound under water, and that localization is best for low-frequency and broad-band signals.

Table 3-2   Percent of Correct Localization Responses to Each of Four Stimuli by 17 Subjects (Hollien, 1971)[a]

Subject	250 Hz	1000 Hz	6000 Hz	Noise	Mean
			Stimulus		
1	40	52	76	68	59
2	72	52	32	68	56
3	64	36	64	44	52
4	56	52	52	48	52
5	56	48	40	56	50
6	72	48	28	36	46
7	44	52	24	56	44
8	60	20	12	84	44
9	40	52	32	48	43
10	64	36	28	40	42
11	44	40	52	40	41
12	68	16	16	64	41
13	40	24	40	56	40
14	44	28	20	56	37
15	36	40	24	44	36
16	36	36	28	40	35
17	24	28	24	32	27
Mean	50.6	38.8	33.4	52.5	43.8
Standard deviation	14.0	11.9	16.3	12.9	

[a] All stimulus presentations were at 110 dB SPL; the diver was located at an ear depth of 40 ft.

Hollien's results were quite in accord with those of Feinstein (1966), who reported data demonstrating that human subjects were able to localize sounds successfully within the quadrant from which they originated. As early as 1944, Ide reported that divers were successful in localizing an underwater sound source. In Ide's study several blindfolded men swam a distance of approximately 275 m to an ammonia jet which acted as the sound source. Anderson and Christensen (1969) repeated Feinstein's experiments and obtained essentially the same results. Leggiere, McAniff, Schenck, and van Ryzin (1970) reported that their six subjects demonstrated some localization ability, especially at the low frequencies of 600 and 800 Hz.

Hollien then proceeded to analyze his basic localization data. He wished to determine the extent to which subjects' responses were distributed over the five possible sound-source locations in his investigation. This was accomplished by measuring the magnitude of error for each of the stimulus conditions and for all conditions pooled. He found the errors were distributed roughly in bell-shaped curves around the actual location. Localization ability, within a quadrant, was 78% for the 90° projector, 86% for the 45° projector, 73% for the 0° projector, 90% for the 315° projector, and 81% for the 270° projector. The data show that the scores were highest for the thermal noise and the 250-Hz sinusoid. Table 3-3 shows pooled correct responses for the 17 subjects and four stimuli relating actual projector location to perceived location.

Hollien arranged his quadrant data from Table 3-3 in still a different manner. In this case the position array was "collapsed." The mathematical rotation of that data relevant to sidedness is presented in Table 3-4. Only the data for the left side (270 and 315° positions) and right side (45 and 90° positions) were considered; 0° data were ignored.

As can be seen, the incidence of correct localization is surprisingly high, and accuracy is superior for both the low-frequency signal and broad-band noise.

Table 3-3 Pooled Correct Responses for 17 Subjects and Four Stimuli Relating Actual Projector Location to Perceived Location (Hollien, 1971)

	Source				
Response	90°	45°ᵃ	0°	315°	270°
90°	*44*	23	10	4	2
45°	34	*43*	14	6	5
0°	15	20	*39*	18	12
315°	4	7	20	*48*	38
270°	3	5	17	24	*43*

ᵃ This column does not add to 100% due to rounding.
ᵇ Values in italic type indicate the percentage of correct responses for each projector source location.

Table 3-4   Mean of Correct Responses by Quadrant and
with Respect to Sidedness. (Hollien, 1971)

	Quadrant		Sidedness[b]	
Stimuli	Mean	Range	Left	Right
250 Hz	87	76–98	82	76
1000 Hz	80	66–90	70	66
6000 Hz	74	68–82	64	64
Noise	90	72–96	90	85
Mean	83		76	73

[a] Data are percent correct levels for 17 subjects and four stimuli presented 25 times each from four positions each separated by 45°.
[b] The 450° and 90° positions were to the right of the diver; the 270° and 315° to the left.

Hollien (1971) has pointed out that this ability is demonstrably poorer in water than in air. The general patterns among the data, with respect to subject variability, show increased accuracy scores for broad-band noise and low frequencies. This suggests a type of processing for water similar (but impaired) to that for air.

From all the data available it seems to be quite appropriate to agree with Hollien's statement:

"The mechanism for underwater hearing is bone conduction, hence, the two 'ears' cannot operate to provide differential auditory information to the cortex. Further, sound in water operates in a manner detrimental to the usual localization mechanism. Specifically, because the head does not operate as a sound barrier underwater as it does in air, the intensity difference at each ear should be eliminated by the water and because sound in water travels approximately four to five times faster than in air, phase or time-of-arrival cues also are greatly reduced. In fact it can be expected that sound would arrive at one cochlea only microseconds before it arrives at the other. Actually, however, it would appear that it is these small arrival time differences (0 to about 67 microseconds at angles of 0° and 90°, respectively) that may provide at least part of the information utilized by an individual to localize underwater sound sources as it has been reported that the ear is able to resolve time differences in the order of only 7 microseconds (Tobias & Zerlin 1959). Thus, if the two cochlea can resolve time differences of less than 50 microseconds, say, the type of processing described above, would permit some sound localization" (p. 8).

According to Hollien, an alternate, or possibly coordinate, system which may enter into underwater sound localization has been suggested by J. F. Brandt. Brandt's proposed mechanism incorporates a difference in loudness at the two cochlea produced by the differential sensitivity of the skull to free-field sound sources. However, Zwislocki (1957) and Nixon and von Gireke (1959) were unable to obtain differential threshold shifts as a function of sound source location while stimulating subjects in air by a free sound field bone conduction stimulus. To prevent the sound from entering the ear through the ear canal, these investigators used ear plugs and ear muffs. From a contrary point of view, Isele, Berger, Lippy, and Rotolo (1968) reported differential sensitivity as a function of five different placements of a bone conduction oscillator. The results of this study suggest that a subject may be able to localize a skull-conducted stimulus on the basis of intensity differences alone. Hollien comments: "Such a relationship should hold for underwater hearing also. That is, a loudness difference may result (for underwater sound sources of equal intensity) because of the differential sensitivity of a subject's head to bone conducted stimulation. In the case of this experiment, if an auditory stimulus struck the head at a different location for each of the five different angles and Brandt's postulate held, localization on the level experienced could occur" (p. 9).

Recent evidence suggests that an auditory phi may be useful in underwater sound localization. Hollien (1972) has reported some data suggesting that the movement of a sound from point A to point B might aid in localizing an underwater sound. This may have practical applications for diver navigation.

Thus, there seems to be growing evidence that humans show at least some ability to localize sound under water. It is also clear that localization studies utilizing amphibious marine mammals such as the common harbor seal (*Poca vitulina*) and the California sea lion (*Zalophus californianus*) have shown that these animals are able to localize sounds in fluids (Gentry, 1967). The fact that these amphibious mammals have been able to adapt to the demands of an underwater environment may be relevant to man's potential adjustment. According to Hollien, who quotes from Feinstein, these animals "appear to have adjusted to sensory demands of hydrospace without the benefits of acoustically isolated ears or specialized relationships between the bones of the middle ear." In cetaceans, as mentioned earlier, the two ears have been acoustically insulated in the skull as the result of a readaptation from air to underwater hearing. This anatomical isolation is not true in pinnipeds. Nonetheless, these mammals do have directional hearing. Thus Mohl (1964) reported well-developed auditory localization ability in the harbor seal, and Gentry (1967) showed that the California sea lion can localize sounds in most of the frequency ranges in which it vocalizes. Table 3-5 shows comparative results of auditory localization tests with three marine mammals.

From the data obtained there are several indications that human auditory localization ability under water might be better than pure theory predicts. Variability, for instance, as mentioned by Hollien (1971), follows the general pattern that would be expected of a similar study in air, a relationship suggesting that no unusual mechanisms are needed for operation in the underwater milieu.

It is apparent, then, that man can localize underwater sound sources at a more accurate level than previously suspected. This capability is less effective than it is in air. Underwater localization ability is best for low-frequency tones and broad-band noise.

Table 3-5 Comparative Results of Auditory Localization Tests with Three Marine Mammals (Mohl 1964; Busnel, Dziedzie and Anderson, 1965; Gentry, 1967)

Marine Mammal	Frequency (kHz)	Auditory Angle	Correct Responses
Porpoise	3.5	11°	68
	6.0	8°	84
California sea lion	5.5	15°	71
	6.0	10°	70
Common harbor seal	2.0	1.5°	71

SUMMARY

The demonstrated conductive hearing loss in hyperbaric environments is most likely related to (1) changes in the mechanical and acoustic impedance of the tympanic membrane and middle-ear structure, and (2) changes in the resonance frequency of the external canal and middle ear. Diminished hearing acuity, proportional to the rise in atmospheric pressure, has been generally found in divers.

A temporary bilateral hearing loss of the sensory-neural type has been found while testing decompression schedules and evaluating diving helmets. It is no doubt that diving and chamber personnel frequently are exposed to noise that can injure the unprotected ear in a relatively short period of time. Those who are repeatedly exposed to compression-decompression cycles also suffer a high incidence of otological symptoms including hearing loss. A considerable change in air pressure imbalance could be expected to affect sound perception either through changes in the characteristics of the middle ear mechanism for transmitting sound energy across the middle ear, or by affecting the round window membrane, which might change the endolymph movement in the cochlea.

The hearing threshold pure-tone audiometry curve for air conduction has been shown to be markedly elevated in the middle-frequency range of hearing at high ambient pressures, while bone conduction is nearly unaffected. It has also been found that inert gas intoxication is a very prominent factor; its effect on a particular individual is unpredictable.

The human auditory system has so evolved that it functions optimally in the terrestrial environment, and the peripheral components of this system function with greatly reduced efficiency as man dives. Fortunately, man has an alternative mechanism for stimulating the cochlea, and this is bone conduction hearing. It has been shown by many investigators that the middle-ear mechanism is not used in underwater hearing, but rather is bypassed by the mechanism of bone conduction.

When several sounds arrive at the same time from different directions, a listener normally is able to sort them out and locate the source of anyone of them. Not so in the underwater environment, where humans either totally lose their sound localization capabilities or they are seriously impaired. In air, directional perception of sound is based on the utilization of phase shift (time of arrival or binaural time difference) and intensity information provided by the arriving signal of the auditory mechanism (binaural intensity difference). Because of the physical properties of seawater, the time interval of an arriving signal across the head is correspondingly shortened, virtually eliminating the directional perception attributable to time delay, and as the impedance of the head is similar to that of the fluid, the skull under water no longer separates the two ears from each other and directional hearing is severely impaired. However, because the mechanism for underwater hearing is bone conduction, there are indications that human auditory localization ability under water might be better than pure theory predicts, although this capability is less effective than it is in air. It has been found that sound localization is better for low frequency tones and broadband noise.

IV
SPATIAL ORIENTATION UNDER WATER

Introduction — The vestibular system — The haptic system — Influence of ambient pressure changes on the vestibular apparatus — Alternobaric vertigo — Effects of increased ambient pressure on nystagmus — Effects of increased ambient pressure on body sway — The free-floating diver — Problems in underwater movement — Orientation to the vertical under water — Geographical orientation under water — Kinesthesis — Summary

A brief summary of the proprioceptive system is given in the chapter, and the importance of sense organs for proper spatial orientation is outlined. The effects of pressure differentials in the middle ear and the toxic effects of various inert gases have been shown to cause postural disturbances of considerable importance. The ramifications of these effects for spatial orientation under water are discussed. It has also been found that there is a strong relationship between postural balance and increased ambient air pressure.

The postural cues for a free-floating diver are much reduced. Therefore he has some difficulties in his orientation to the vertical in the liquid environment. His geographical orientation under water is much worse than that on land. The effects of immersion on the human kinesthetic sense that have been found apparently can be overcome by appropriate training.

INTRODUCTION

The sensory systems that provide us with information on our position in space are the visual, the auditory, the tactile, and the proprioceptive. The sensory structures associated with the discrimination of body posture and movement are collectively referred to as proprioceptive systems, and this aspect of perception is referred to as proprioception.

Special proprioceptors are the nonauditory parts of the right and left labyrinths inside the skull: the vestibular system composed of semicircular canals, utricles, and saccules. They relay data concerning the position and movement of the head relative to the body axis and, even more importantly, concerning the movement and change of position in space of the body as a whole.

General proprioceptors are the sense receptors found in muscles, tendons, joints, and deep connective tissues. They provide information which enables the central nervous system to:

1. Sense movement and the position of the body in space, including the position of the limbs relative to the body.

2. Control muscle tonus and thus the maintenance of posture and the regulation of movement.

Muscle tonus is the slight tension of a muscle, which is particularly evident in the antigravity muscles. In man the extensor muscles have to maintain erect posture against the pull of gravity.

The receptive cells and units of the proprioceptive systems are classed as mechanoreceptors. They occur nearly everywhere in the body, the only obvious exception apparently being the brain itself.

The terminals are of many sorts:

1. Free nerve endings, the bare branches of the afferent fibers.

2. Encapsulated nerve endings with tiny corpuscles, bulbs, spindles, and cylinders, which are found both in the skin and below it.

3. Microscopic hair cells which seem to be confined to special organs like the inner ear.

According to Gibson (1966), these receptors are particularly associated with regions or organs indicated:

1. They are thickly distributed in and below the skin. They cluster at the base of each hair, and they are present in hairless regions. They are even found in the sheathing of bones.

2. They supply the joints and connecting ligaments between all the movable bones of the body.

3. They interpenetrate all the muscles and the tendons attaching muscle to bone.

4. They are wrapped around the blood vessels, even the smallest, which dilate or constrict.

5. In the form of hair cells, they supply the flexible structures of the semicircular canals, the utricle and sacculae, and the cochlea of the inner ear.

The Vestibular System

Static receptors are those responding to gravity and to comparable mechanical field forces. In vertebrates the vestibular apparatus is located in the bony labyrinths of the head. Since many readers may be unfamiliar with the elements of the vestibular system, a detailed, nontechnical description follows.

The vestibular mechanism of the inner ear consists of three semicircular canals (similar to clear plastic tubes in a bony labyrinth). Within each canal is fluid, known as endolymph, and a swinging-door arrangement called a crista. When the skull turns, the fluid lags behind and causes the swinging door to open. Hair cells in the crista signal how much movement has occurred. The canals lie in three planes approximately at right angles to each other.

The semicircular canals are the chief receptors for rotational movements and have been likened to angular accelerometers. Physiological stimuli typically involve acceleration, followed immediately by deceleration. One is usually not aware of these movements, although most of them can be perceived if so desired (Kennedy, personal communication).

On the floor of the utricle lies a thin, gelatinous pad within which are calcium carbonate concretions, the otoliths. This gelatinous pad, containing the otoliths, underlying hairs, and hair cells, serves as another type of transducer for gravity and linear accelerations. Thus, as the head is oriented in different positions relative to the direction of gravity, the otoliths are displaced and provide a shearing force to the hair cells at their base. The otoliths, being of density different from that of the surrounding endolymph, are an efficient detector of linear acceleration. Therefore the vestibular system is responsive to changes in position relative to the direction of gravity, and to different accelerations.

The classic term for information about both linear and rotary components of physical movement is kinesthesis, which means sensitivity to body motion. Kinesthesis cuts across the functional perceptual system. There is articular kinesthesis for the body framework, vestibular kinesthesis for the movements of the skull, cutaneous kinesthesis for movement of the skin relative to what it touches, and visual kinesthesis for perceptive transformations of the field of view (Gibson, 1966).

The connections of the vestibular system and its proposed cortical projection area are very diffuse and include the autonomic system and the motor system, to name just two. Some main connections of importance for spatial orientation are schematically shown in Figure 4-1.

There are several useful summaries of research on the vestibular system. The interested reader is directed to Money (1970) or Clark (1970), who both give excellent reviews of the latest literature.

The Haptic System

The vestibular system is presumably as sensitive to gravity under water as it is in air, while the postural stimuli for a free-floating diver are much reduced. The whole system of general proprioceptors that controls the sensory-motor system is termed by Gibson (1966) the haptic system. The haptic system operates, according to Gibson, "when a man or animal feels things with his body or its extremities. It is an apparatus by which the individual gets information about both the environment and his body. He feels an object relative to the body and the body relative to an object. It is the perceptual system by which animals and men are *literally* in touch with the environment."

The haptic system, unlike the other perceptual systems, includes the whole body, that is, most of its parts and all of its surface. Gibson has summarized the perceptual systems as in Table 1-5.

There seems to be no doubt that the haptic system plays a major role in orientation under water. Spatial orientation may be looked upon as a phenomenon of perception which represents an individual's interpretation of stimuli originating in various organs of special sense. Graybiel (1951) discussed the relative importance of the various sense organs considered in terms of a task designed for pilots. His discussion is summarized in Table 4-1 with a modifica-

CORTICAL VESTIBULAR PROJECTION AREA

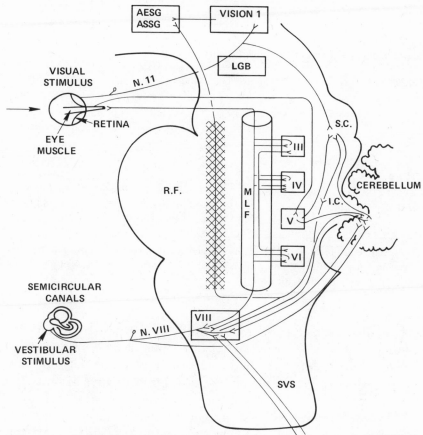

Figure 4-1. Cortical vestibular projection area. (Kennedy, personal communication.) AESG, anterior ectosylvian gyrus; ASSG, anterior suprocylvian gyrus; VISION 1, primary visual cortex; N.11, optic nerve; LGB, lateral giriculate body; S.C., superior collicular; III, oculometer nucleus; IV, trochlear nucleus; V, trigemiral nucleus; VI, abducers nucleus; R.F., reticular formation; I.C., inferior collicular; MLF, medial longitudinal facicular; VIII, vestibular nerve; SVS, spiral vestibular system.

tion suggested by Kennedy for conditions under water.

THE INFLUENCE OF AMBIENT PRESSURE CHANGES ON THE VESTIBULAR APPARATUS

Do changes in the ambient pressure have any influence on the vestibular apparatus? If so, what is the effect of the pressure, as

Table 4-1   Importance of Sense Organs for Proper Spacial Orientation[a]

Perceptual Environment	Eye	G Receptors		Semi-circular Canals	Acoustic Labyrinth
		Otolith Organ	Other		
Aircraft	Very important	Moderate importance	Moderate importance	Nil	Very slight importance
Earth	Essential	Occasional slight importance	Occasional slight importance	Nil ?	Very slight importance
Objects in space	Essential	Nil	Nil	Nil ?	Very slight importance
Under water	Frequently not usable	Essential	Important but might be distorted	Essential	Often not usable

[a] The relative importance of the various sense organs in spatial orientation are considered in terms of a pilot's or a diver's task. [Modified after Graybiel (1951) by Kennedy, personal communication.]

such, in different parts of the labyrinth? Is the pressure effect a continuum, or does it occur only after disruption of labyrinthine structures? Do changes in the ionic composition of the endolymph and perilymph occur before membrane disruption occurs? How is the pressure increased?

A growing interest in these problems stems from an apparently increasing incidence of auditory and vestibular derangement, an incidence that seems to parallel the burgeoning of deep diving in recent years (Rubenstein & Summitt, 1971).

Alternobaric Vertigo

When researchers first start to explore the underwater vertigo problem, they inevitably select caloric irrigation as the primary causitive factor. It seems reasonable that, when man enters cold water and immerses his head, the cold stimulation of the tympanic membrane will cause vertigo. Caloric stimulation, after all, is a standard test of vestibular function. However, the results from diver surveys such as those of Lundgren (1965) and Vorosmarti and Bradley (1970) indicate that hyperbaric pressure and changes in pressure may account for many of vestibular problems in divers.

Vertigo following exposure to increased ambient pressure was first reported by Curnow (1894) and Alt (1896). Frequently, episodes of vertigo have been reported since then both in the presence and absence of decompression sickness. In addition to decompression sickness, other possible causes of vertigo are oxygen toxicity, carbon dioxide excess, nitrogen or inert gas narcosis, caloric stimulation, sea sickness, alcoholic hangover, sensory deprivation, hyperventilation, hypoxia, hypoglycemia, autosuggestion, and impure breathing gas. It should also be mentioned that, according to Pinto (1966), the use of current mouthpieces by underwater swimmers eliminates contact of the posterior teeth and causes development of extra pressure within the temporomandibular joints. These pressures can also produce nausea and loss of equilibrium in the diver.

Lundgren (1965) coined the term alternobaric vertigo, defined as vertigo involving a pressure differential between the middle and/ or inner ear and the environment. He found that 26% of the Swedish sport divers he questioned had experienced alternobaric vertigo while diving. Vorosmarti and Bradley (1970) reported that, of 143 questioned subjects, 11.9% had experienced one or more occurrences of vertigo while diving. One of the divers reported vertigo during a dry chamber dive; all the other episodes, however, occurred during wet dives, particularly while scuba diving. No vertigo was experienced during helium–oxygen diving. Nine of the subjects reported vertigo during ascent, and four stated that it occurred on descent. The greatest depth at which vertigo was experienced was about 45 m (147 ft), while most of the subjects reported vertigo as occurring between 20 and 40 m (66 and 131 ft).

However, some of the subjects in a series of dry chamber dives to 120 m (394 ft) in air, as well as in helium–oxygen, conducted by Adolfson (1967), spontaneously reported dizziness and vertigo, often at about 70 to 80 m (210 to 240 ft) and most often during the descent. One of the subjects developed pronounced nausea at 13 ATA which culminated in vomiting. No mouthpiece was used in this investigation.

Vorosmarti and Bradley suggested that overpressurization of the middle ear may be relatively more important than a decreased pressure. They considered it a confirmation of their suggestion when 27% of Lundgren's and 38% of their own divers who had experienced alternobaric vertigo reproduced it by performing a Valsalva maneuver. This is also in accordance with the findings of Lundgren and Malm (1966) in a study of alternobaric vertigo in pilots. Among 108 pilots of the Royal Swedish Air Force, they found 18 (17%) who had experienced alternobaric vertigo, and some of the most severe incidents were described as occurring in connection with the rapid pressure increase in the middle ears achieved when the Valsalva maneuver was applied against the clamped nose.

Rubenstein and Summitt (1971) have pointed out that true rotary vertigo usually is labyrinthine in origin and is characterized by discrete attacks, nystagmus, nausea, vomiting, ataxic gate, pallor, and sweating. Central vestibular vertigo often involves a constant sense of imbalance, and disproportionate or absent accompanying symptoms (Shambaugh, 1967).

Henriksson, Gleisner, and Johansson (1966) reported a series of experiments on the effects of pressure variation in the membranous labyrinth of the frog. They demonstrated the elasticity of the membranous labyrinth by showing a linear relationship between changes in volume and pressure, and consistent rupture of the frog saccule at applied pressure exceeding 5 to 8 cm of water. In some of their preparations they showed an effective block between the utricle and the saccule, and made use of this block to show that, at pressures below the rupture point, the intact utricular membrane does not permit passage of fluid. Where the utriculosaccular connection was intact, the rise in pressure for a given increase in volume was followed by an exponential decline due to loss of the added volume from the system. Fluid staining techniques and applied pressure below the rupture point showed fluid uptake in the capillaries surrounding the endolymphatic walls, a small amount exiting into the cranical cavity via the endolymphatic duct, and no leakage through the membrane into the perilymph. Subsequently, again with pressures below the rupture point, they showed a transient rise in ampullary nerve activity in response to increased pressure, and suggested that more persistent nerve activity would result from membrane disruption (Henriksson, Gleisner & Johansson, 1966; Henriksson & Gleisner, 1966). Also, changes in the partial pressure of oxygen may change activity in the vestibule, just as in the retina; both are areas of higher metabolic activity.

Rubenstein and Summitt (1971) postulated several ways in which such changes might occur either transiently or with enough force to create membrane disruption during decompression:

1. Bubble formation in the endolymph.

2. Decreased circulation perhaps due to hemoconcentration or to autonomic responses involving the supplying vessels and resulting in decreased resorption of endolymph.

3. Rapid build-up release of middle-ear pressure as suggested by Lundgren.

4. Pressure differences within the membranous labyrinth because of blocks in the endolymphatic circulation. Additionally, osmotic gradients from dissolved gases, as suggested by Kylstra, Longmuir, and Grace (1968), could raise endolymphatic pressure by causing fluid shifts.

A new slant to the vestibular problem came to light during a 1200-ft (366 m) saturation dive conducted at the Institute for Environmental Medicine at the University of Pennsylvania in 1970. During physiological studies designed to evaluate human respiration of dense gases, three of four subjects became ill, showing symptoms of nausea, vomiting, dizziness, nystagmus, and disorientation. These clinical signs of vestibular dysfunction were produced in a dry-chamber environment while the hydrostatic pressure was held constant. The cause of these symptoms is still undetermined and has stimulated a lively debate among researchers in the area (Wright, 1970).

Fortunately, it seems that the overall incidence of alternobaric vertigo or vertigo is rather low in diving. Vorosmarti and Bradley (1970) believe that the incidence of this problem among military divers is lower than among sport divers. However, when it occurs while diving, it may be catastrophic. Disorientation may cause a diver to swim downward instead of upward, or a vertiginous diver may panic and return to the surface, missing decompression stops or incurring an air embolism. Vertigo-induced vomiting into a mouthpiece or mask may be fatal.

While alternobaric vertigo can be defined as vertigo involving a pressure differential between the middle and/or the inner ear and the environment, there is evidence that the narcotic or toxic effects of an inert gas in the breathing medium act on the central nervous system and cause postural disturbances of considerable importance for spatial orientation under water.

Effects of Increased Ambient Air Pressure on Nystagmus

An attempt was made to localize possible sites and mechanisms of action underlying observed and reported balance disturbances in divers under water. Adolfson, Bjerver, Fluur, and Goldberg (1970) studied possible influences of hyperbaric conditions on nystagmus in 10 experienced divers from the Royal Swedish Navy by means of electronystagmography. A new type of rotation device was constructed which very closely imitated the normal movements of the head. The head of the subject was accelerated at about $30°/sec^2$ and was prevented from exceeding 90° by means of a switch. The rotation device is illustrated in Figure 4-2.

No changes were found in the reaction pattern of the vestibular-ocular reflex arc to graded movements of the head, nor to acceleration and retardation during rotation. Nor were any differences in activity between the left and right labyrinths observed during exposure to an ambient air pressure of 10 ATA. Figure 4-3 shows a typical nystagmogram recorded at 10 ATA.

It was suggested by these investigators that exposure to increased ambient air pressure of 10 ATA does not cause significant changes in the reaction pattern of the vestibular–ocular reflex arc. However, some of the subjects reported a sense of imbalance during the exposure, which led to further investigations of body sway under hyperbaric conditions.

Effects of Increased Ambient Air Pressure on Body Sway

Nashner (1970) has treated the basic functional properties of the posture control system as a multiloop system in which several specialized feedback sensors contribute to the generation of commands. Neural processing at the lowest levels permit crude but fast-acting responses based on information from body-centered proprioceptive sensors. "Inertial" sensors and higher-center processing provide

Figure 4-2. Rotation device for evaluating visual nystagmus (Adolfson, Bjerver, Fluur, & Goldberg, 1970.)

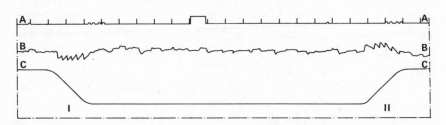

Figure 4-3. Nystagmus during rotation. *I*, rotation to the left. *II*, rotation to the right. *A*, Time indication; *B*, nystagmus; *C*, rotation speed. (Adolfson, Bjerver, Fluur, & Goldberg, 1970.)

145

more accurate, adaptable control but with longer processing delays. Hence, according to Nashner, postural control is a highly nonstationary process in which responses to transient disturbances are initiated at the lowest levels. Allocation of control then "radiates" upward to the higher centers where successive corrections, based on more complete information, fine-tune the initial response. Nashner summarized the properties of the postural control sensors as in Table 4-2.

It has been found that, during quiet standing on a rigid, flat surface, ankle stretch reflex gains are about one-third that necessary for posture stability (Goldberg, 1943; Bjerver & Persson, 1957; Nashner, 1970). According to Nashner, small "stiction" forces acting between both intra- and extrafusal muscle fiber supplement this reflex gain, and together they provide a gain adequate for complete stability for very small ankle deflections. The kinesthetic cues associated with changes in pressure distribution of the feet are the first signals of postural divergence. These signals trigger a multiplicative increase in the reflex loop gain proportional to the disturbance amplitude. Because deep-pressure sensation habituates, as do all sensations, an additional sense, either visual or utricular otolith information is necessary to provide drift stabilization.

In the central nervous system the task of sensory processing and generation of muscle commands is multilevel. The lowest level of coordination is located at the spinal ventral roots, and subsequent levels extend upward to the highest brain centers (Eldred, 1960). Nashner has pointed out that body sway motion represents the critical mode in control of body posture because of the inherent unstable "inverted pendulum" characteristics of the body. It seems possible, then, that changes in body sway can be used as a measurement of the degree of influence on body posture of various drugs (especially alcohol), gases and gas mixtures at ambient and raised pressures.

Preliminary results from a pilot study by Adolfson, Bjerver, Fluur, and Goldberg (in press) showed that body sway increased during exposure to 10 ATA while air was breathed in the same proportion in sagittal and lateral directions, eyes open and eyes closed. The device used, a so-called statometer (Goldberg, Bjerver, & Goldschmidt, in press), recorded and evaluated changes in body posture or body

Table 4-2 Properties of the Posture Control Sensors (Nashner, 1970)

	MUSCLE RESPONSE REFLEX RESPONSE	EXTERO-CEPTIVE	SEMICIRCULAR CANALS	VISION	UTRICLE OTOLITHS
INPUT	ANKLE DEFLECTION	ANKLE DEFLECTION AND PRESSURE ON THE FEET	ANGULAR ACCELERATION OF THE BODY	BODY MOTION	BODY ANGLE AND ANGULAR ACCELERATION OF THE BODY
OUTPUT	PROPORTIONAL TO θ_A AND $\dot\theta_A$	APPROXIMATELY PROPORTIONAL TO ANKLE DEFLECTION	BODY ANGULAR RATE	BODY ANGLE AND ANGULAR RATE	BODY ANGLE
DYNAMIC CHARACTERISTICS	$(0.1S+0.80)$ $$\frac{0.4\,(2S+1)}{(0.1S + 1)}$$ "STICTION"	$$\frac{1}{(1 + 2/S)}$$	$$\frac{s^2}{(8.3S+1)\,(0.1S+1)}$$	≈ 1	$$\frac{-0.16S^2 + 1}{(5.3S+1)\,(0.66S+1)}$$
THRESHOLD	≈ 0	0.10^0 BODY ANGLE	0.05^0 /SEC^2	≈ 0	0.29^0 BODY ANGLE
TIME DELAY	≈ 10 MSEC.	≈ 100 MSEC.	225 MSEC.	425 MSEC.	225 MSEC.
FUNCTION IN POSTURE CONTROL	RESISTS CHANGES OF THE ANKLE ANGLE (POSITION CONTROL LOOP)	CONTROLS THE REFLEX GAIN DURING TRANSIENT DISTURANCES	DETECTS SWAY DIVERGENCE AND INITIATES ANKLE TORQUE COMMANDS	CORRECTS SLOW DRIFT OF BODY ANGLE	CORRECTS SLOW DRIFT OF BODY ANGLE
	PHASIC CONTROL (MODE 1)		PHASIC CONTROL (MODE 2)	STATIC CONTROL (MODE 1 OR 2)	

sway. This apparatus is comprised basically of three main sections: a rigid, flat, circular balance stand; a recording and storage unit; and an evaluation and data analysis unit.

Adolfson, Goldberg, and Berghage (1972) studied the effects of increased air pressure on standing steadiness at 2.2, 4, 7, and 10 ATA, as compared with results obtained in two control situations at ambient air pressure (1 ATA). In a simple Romberg test, body sway was recorded by statometry in a sagittal direction, and in a lateral direction with eyes open, and with eyes closed.

It was found that:

1. There is a strong quadratic relationship between balance and depth.

2. Deterioration in balance increases at a much faster rate for the eyes closed condition than for the eyes open condition as depth is increased.

3. There are highly significant individual differences.

4. Performance at depth is related to performance at the surface.

5. There seems to be no habituation or other adaptation to the test device.

6. There seem to be no essential aftereffects to the exposure to increased ambient air pressure under the conditions used.

Figure 4-4 shows actual recordings of standing steadiness in the lateral direction with open and closed eyes at normal air pressure and at 10 ATA.

Figure 4-5 shows the relation between body sway (in statometer units) and pressure level.

Perhaps one of the most interesting findings in the analysis of the results obtained by Adolfson et al. was the interaction between the condition of the eyes (open/closed) and the depth of the dive. The results indicated that deterioration in balance increased at a much faster rate for the eyes closed than for the eyes open condition as depth increased. Balance was severely disturbed, but the subjects were able to compensate at least in part for the deterioration as long as a visual reference was present.

In diving to deep depths or in turbid or amorphous water, visual references are lost along with many other orientation cues. The decreased visibility, as well as the reduced illumination occurring dur-

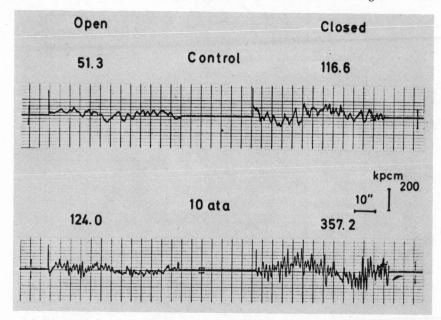

Figure 4-4. Actual recording of standing steadiness (body sway). Open eyes (left) closed eyes (right). (Adolfson, Goldberg & Berghage, 1972.)

ing a dive, reduce the effect of visual stimuli and add to the impairing effect of exposure to increased ambient air pressure. The combined effects of 10 ATA breathing air and the absence of visual cues caused body sway to increase to an average of 453% of the normal (1 ATA) with open eyes.

Under these conditions it seems reasonable to suspect that man will have a great deal of trouble in orientation under water. As mentioned above, the vestibular system is as sensitive to gravity under water as on land, but postural stimuli for a free-floating diver are very reduced because of his neutral buoyancy. When these losses of sensory information are coupled with man's decreased ability to process information while breathing high-pressure air (Adolfson, 1965, 1967; Adolfson & Muren, 1965), it is not difficult to understand the subjective reports of divers swimming down instead of up during open-sea deep air scuba dives.

The findings of Adolfson et al. seem to correspond well with the results of an investigation of the effects of hypoxia on standing

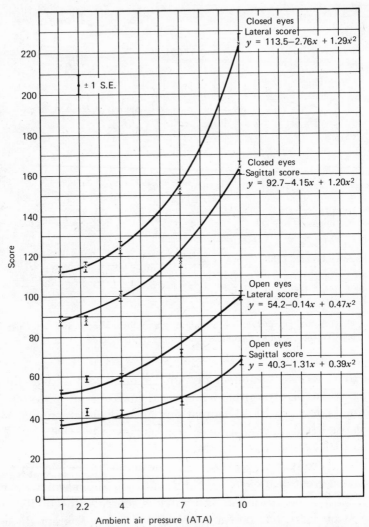

Figure 4-5. Standing Steadiness (body sway). Relation between standing steadiness (body sway) in statometer units (score) and pressure level (depth). Means of 10 experienced divers when air was breathed. Curves are best-fit curves significant at the $P < .0001$ level, implying a quadratic relationship. (Adolfson, Goldberg, Berghage, 1972.)

steadiness by Bjerver and Persson (1957). They found that, after 1-min inhalation of 10% oxygen and 90% nitrogen at ambient air pressure (1 ATA), an increase in statometer values was recorded, these values increased successively during inhalation of the gas mixture. They also found a rather large variation among subjects. However, no carbon dioxide measurements were made in the investigation, and it is suggested that differences in carbon dioxide tension in the tissues cause disturbances in body sway. There is a great need for further investigations of this type.

The role of carbon dioxide in depth narcosis is still obscure and might be of great importance for the diver. Rebreathing studies by Friberg, Muren, and Rogberg (1971) have recently shown a very fast carbon dioxide build-up when air was rebreathed at ambient pressure and at 10 ATA. They also found that the rebreathing time was considerably shorter at 1 ATA than at 10 ATA (3.9 and 5.4 min, respectively). After air was rebreathed at 1 ATA, the pO_2 value was reduced to 70 mm Hg, while the pCO_2 value was raised to 60 mm Hg. The pCO_2 values obtained during one experiment are plotted in Figure 4-6.

These investigators noted that the pronounced air hunger experienced in the control experiments at 1 ATA did not occur at 10 ATA. Instead, an increasing euphoria developed, together with quasi-hallucinatory symptoms of different kinds in most of the subjects.

THE FREE-FLOATING DIVER

Problems in Underwater Movement

A diver is free to move in any direction in three-dimensional space, and can therefore perform many more maneuvers than on land. But he may have to learn perceptual stability for these new situations. In darkness or low visibility, the visual frame of reference is ill-defined, providing the type of situation in which autokinetic apparent movement may occur. In addition, the diver may be moved passively by turbulence or currents or changes in buoyancy, and it is not clear whether he can be expected to compensate for this. During slow, passive drift due to currents, he has no information about his movement unless he can see some fixed object such as the sea-

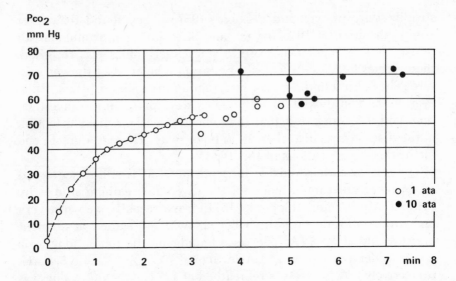

Figure 4-6. Series 1. Carbon dioxide partial pressure in the spirometer at breaking point after air rebreathing at 1 and 10 ATA. The circles connected by the dotted line show the gradual increase of $_pCO_2$ in one experiment. Time is given in minutes. (Friberg, Muren & Rogberg, 1971.)

bed. During slow rising and sinking, he may obtain visual information from fixed objects or from changes in brightness, and he may also obtain information from pressure changes in his ears (Ross & Lennie, 1968).

Orientation to the Vertical under Water

Even when neutrally buoyant, a diver is never totally deprived of the postural stimuli necessary for his knowledge of the vertical, although some of these cues are severely reduced. Knowledge of the vertical normally depends partly on visual stimuli, partly on the gravitational response of the vestibular system, and partly on postural stimuli from the haptic system. Underwater man-made geometry is generally absent, reducing the precision of visual stimuli. In dark, murky, or "empty" water, there may be no cues except the brightness gradient; normally, the closer to the surface one is, the brighter the surroundings appear. Also, the postural cues for a free-floating diver are much reduced.

However, the different parts of his body are of different densities, so that the diver's legs tend to sink and his chest to float, hence allowing him to attain a vertical position. His diving apparatus provides an additional example of varying densities: his weight belt tends to sink, and his breathing apparatus may either float or sink, depending upon its particular density. He may also notice the direction in which his exhaust air bubbles float to determine the vertical position (Ross, Crickmar, Sills & Owens, 1969). Also, his center of gravity is different than when on earth, because of all the additional equipment which can range widely in size, shape, and weight depending on the diver's mission. It may consist of a variety of small hand tools, underwater cutting torches, explosive charges, scientific apparatus, or photographic equipment. All these items together can change the center of gravity, and so may be important to the diver.

As early as 1912, Stigler attempted to measure the orientation of swimmers after they had been rotated on a bar while completely submerged. Their eyes and ears were covered to eliminate visual and auditory stimuli, and they were instructed to point in an upward direction upon termination of rotation. Apparently, they were seldom able to do this accurately. The experiment was terminated by the unwillingness of the subjects to repeat the procedure after one trial. They found the experience most unpleasant and anxiety provoking and, perhaps because of their anxiety, they were unable to hold their breath long enough for adequate observations to be made. The problem of breath holding was eliminated by use of underwater breathing equipment. The subjects were stretched out on a board under water. The board was turned back and forth on fixed bearings and then set in one or several terminal positions. The subjects subsequently attempted to point in the upward direction. Their attempts were usually in error by approximately 15°.

Whiteside (1960) also tested orientation in subjects immersed in water up to their necks. Some loss of directional sense was found in this situation. Loss was attributed to altered muscle balance, absence of visual information, and reduced proprioceptive stimuli.

Brown (1961) investigated the extent of possible disorientation in a liquid environment when visual, tactual, kinesthetic, and buoyancy stimuli were eliminated. Approximately neutrally buoyant, blindfolded subjects at a depth of either 5.5 or 7.5 m (18 or 25 ft) were rotated in a tucked position on a horizontal rod through three,

four, or five revolutions. Rotation was terminated with the head in
one of four positions: upright, or inclined forward, down, or back.
Upon termination of rotation the subjects were directed to point in
an upward direction, to nod the head and correct the direction of
pointing if necessary, and finally to swim toward the surface. Brown
found errors in direction of initial pointing of as much as 180°.
Errors were greatest with the head down or back, and least with the
head up or forward. Nodding of the head was followed by consistent
improvement in the direction of pointing. There was little indication
of any difficulty in swimming in the upward direction. Greater
density of the legs as compared to the trunk resulted in fairly rapid
vertical orientation of the body with feet downward and head upward upon release of the rod. According to Brown, it is evident that,
with a moderate amount of disorienting motion, subjects tend to
lose their orientation to the vertical when immersed to depths of
5.5 to 7.5 m. In addition, there appears to be a relation between the
position of the body at the termination of rotation and the extent of
error in orientation as indicated by pointing.

Schöne (1964) confirmed the findings of Brown and stated:

"(a) The perception of the vertical depends mainly on the function of the statolith apparatus, whereas tactile and other sensory
clues seem to play no important role; (b) the precision of perceiving the vertical decreases with increasing inclination: in positions
in which the head hangs downwards the notion of the vertical is
very vague. Accordingly the deviations of the single values from the
mean increase gradually from 0° to 120° of actual inclination and
rapidly from 120° to 180°" (p. 771).

To estimate the sensitivity of the vestibular (otolithic) sense,
Nelson (1968) measured the accuracy with which human subjects
could sense the gravitational vertical when deprived of nonvestibular
cues, and how this accuracy varied with varying positions of the
head with respect to the vertical. He used seven experienced Navy
divers from the U.S. Navy Experimental Diving Unit. The immersed
subjects were required to position themselves, within a time limit
of 1 min, in one of six standard positions. An attending diver positioned the tilt-table as directed by the subject. The subjects were
secured to the tilt-table by three body restraints designed to limit

buoyancy cues. Visual cues were eliminated by use of a blackened face mask.

The major finding of the Nelson study was that submerged human subjects are relatively insensitive with respect to body position. Nelson stated: "The group responses showed some large and significant constant errors, most notably a pitch-forward bias shared (unequally) by all of the medial-plane positions exceeding 30° in the normal head-down position." This is in agreement with the classic finding of reduced sensitivity in the head-down position, but the results also indicated marginally useful sensitivity in all positions.

Ross, Crickmar, Sills, and Owen (1969) seem to be the only investigators who have studied orientation to the vertical in free divers in the open sea. They tested scuba divers in clear water off Malta. The divers were required to turn a somersault with their eyes closed, and then orientate their bodies and point up or down with or without vision. Two other divers photographed the subject simultaneously from the side and back, while another diver held a weighted rope behind him to mark the vertical. The subject's maximum angular deviation from the vertical in any plane was calculated from the paired photographic measurements. Results for five subjects showed that performance was worse when inverted than upright, and worse when blind than with vision. Another experiment in which the subject looked through a roughened Perspex (Plexiglas) faceplate showed that "distorted" vision produced worse performance than no vision.

Geographical Orientation under Water

The geographical orientation of a person is the direction the person is facing with respect to objects on the earth's surface (Howard & Templeton, 1966). A scuba diver is free to move in any direction in space, but to maintain knowledge of his position under water he must monitor the distance he has traveled, his orientation to the gravitational vertical, and his orientation to the points of a compass (Ross, Dickinson & Jupp, 1970). Vision is clearly man's most important modality for orientation, and so to study the other modalities it is necessary to blindfold the subject (Howard & Templeton, 1966).

Veering tendencies in blindfolded subjects have often been reported, and it is common knowledge that people who lose their way in a mist or in a snowstorm find that they have walked in a complete circle. Animals, too, have been reported to show this behavior (Guldberg, 1897). Some investigators have found that their subjects veered to the right, others to the left. Schaeffer claimed that right-turning was more frequent for most methods of locomotion but that left-turning predominated in swimmers. Anderson (1968) noted right-turning (easterly) bias in divers who attempted to swim north on a compass.

Three types of explanations have been put forward to account for these consistent trends:

1. A fundamental circling mechanism, "spirokinesis," existing in all animals (Schaeffer, 1928).
2. The asymmetry of the body (Guldberg, 1897).
3. Slight asymmetry of vestibular "tonus" (Howard & Templeton, 1966).

However, all these explanations are only theories, and it is easy to agree with Howard and Templeton that: "It cannot be said that the study of veering tendency has yet thrown much light on the role of kinesthetic and vestibular mechanisms in orientation."

The role of visual experience in geographical orientation has been studied by several investigators by comparing the performance of sighted subjects with that of subjects who have been blind for varying periods of time. But these studies have produced highly contradictory results. Using human maze-learning tasks, Koch and Ufkess (1926) and Duncan (1934) found that sighted subjects were superior, whereas Knotts and Miles (1929) found sighted subjects inferior on a stylus maze although they were just as good as blind subjects on a finger-relief maze. Worschel (1951), using a triangle completion task, found sighted subjects superior, whereas they were inferior on a pegboard task in which they had to replace sets of pegs in an orientation that they had tactually inspected earlier (Howard & Templeton, 1966).

The triangle completion technique has been used by Ross, Dickinson, and Jupp (1970) in a test of geographical orientation under water. Geographical orientation problems under water are similar to those on land, except that the subject is swimming rather than walking. Both on land and under water, man has to rely on proprioceptive knowledge or on visual cues such as familiar landmarks and the direction of the sun. Ross et al. pointed out that visibility is usually very poor under water by aerial standards. Visibility of 100 ft (30 m) is considered very good under water, but this is equal to a fairly thick mist on land. A diver rarely has an opportunity to view more than a small part of the diving site at one time. He can easily become disoriented and may fail to recognize even familiar landmarks. In darkness or with very low visibility, he must rely entirely on knowledge of his own body movements. This is complicated by the fact that he may be subjected to passive drifting due to currents or turbulent water. Even if the diver is aware of passive movement, he may have some difficulty integrating it with his knowledge of active movement (Ross & Lennie, 1968). The use of a compass eliminates gross directional errors, but even after practice divers may show errors of a few degrees.

Thus Andersen (1968) determined navigation accuracy by the extent to which divers deviated from a magnetic compass course over a range of 235 m (760 ft) at a depth of 10 to 12 m (33 to 39 ft). He found that the results obtained for this measure showed an overall average deviation from the required compass course of ±21.5 m (±71 ft), or an error of 5.21° in the compass heading. Individual performance improved with practice. Andersen's test range arrangements are shown in Figure 4-7.

Andersen concluded that perhaps the most significant fact derived from the course accuracy data was that improved performance resulted from practice on the test range. But, even with the significant improvement, the average performance accuracy was ±16 m (53 ft) from the center line of the measurement array, or 3.86° in compass error. According to this investigator, only conditions of excellent underwater visibility, or the presence of underwater topographical cues, would promote successful diver performance in underwater navigation.

Andersen found that the source of errors made by a diver in underwater navigation originated with either the diver or the environment. Diver errors are related to the diver's ability to read his compass and accurately follow a compass heading. A common error in following a compass heading results from not holding the compass parallel to the longitudinal axis of the body, and direction of motion

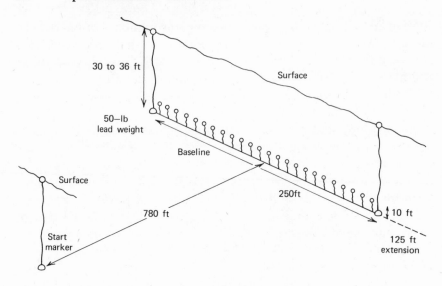

30 to 36 ft

Surface

50—lb
lead weight

Baseline

Surface

250ft

780 ft

Start
marker

10 ft

125 ft
extension

Figure 4-7.   Test range. (Andersen, 1968.)

when the heading is being read. He also found that once divers were aware of their errors, an appropriate correction in arm position could be made on subsequent trials.

A second error came from looking down instead of sighting over the compass to establish a compass heading. When looking at near objects, like a compass, there is a tendency for a diver temporarily to lose his orientation and attitude until he looks up and focuses on a more distant reference object.

Ross, Dickinson, and Jupp (1970) erected two triangles, one on land and one under water at a depth of about 7.5 m (25 ft) where there was no current. Guide ropes were tied on land to pickets about 1.2 m (4 ft) above the ground and under water to stones at a height of 1.8 m (6 ft), so that divers could swim along them without touching the bottom. The ropes connected two sides of each triangle.

The subjects were led blindfolded to the starting post and were told to expect some type of triangle. They held the rope in their left hand and walked or swam around the outside of the triangle. When they came to the end of the rope at the third post, they attempted to walk or swim back to the starting point, thus completing the third side of the triangle. They were told to stop when they thought they were at the starting point.

The routes taken by the subjects on land and under water are shown in Figure 4-8.

The results suggested that on land most subjects walked for about the right distance but tended to make angular mistakes, generally finishing outside the triangle. Under water the subjects tended to swim too far. They were also inclined to make a smaller angle around the outside of the third post, thus finishing farther outside the triangle than on land.

In a second experiment 16 divers were required to walk or swim a prescribed distance holding a rope in their hand, with and without vision, on land and underwater. It was found that novice divers tended to swim too far under water and to show high variability. More experienced divers usually swam for the correct distance. Estimates on land were fairly accurate for all subjects. Little difference was found between blindfold and visual performance, and it was pointed out that subjects must rely on proprioceptive rather than visual stimuli in this type of judgment. Counting the number of steps on land or kicks under water, or estimating the time taken, made no difference in performance.

Divers sometimes have to carry out a "circular search" under conditions of low visibility. They hold a rope attached to a central post and swim in a complete circle while searching the ground for a lost object. They then lengthen or shorten the rope and swim in another circle, systematically covering a large area. To examine a diver's ability to estimate circles or sectors of circles when under water, an experiment was conducted in which 14 divers attempted to walk or swim blindfolded in a complete circle or part of a circle. Ross, Dickinson and Jupp found that the subjects traveled too far on land, and too short a distance under water. Further, they found that errors were not a simple function of the angle made, but increased with the radius of the circle. The underwater experiments were performed at a depth of 15 m.

In 1970, Leggiere, McAniff, Schenck, and van Ryzin studied several divers for their ability to point to or locate a transducer emitting a sinusoidal, pure tone 40 ft away in shallow water. Various frequencies, signal strengths, and pulsing formats were tried, and experiments were run with the skull masked by a neoprene hood. Slight improvement in pointing performance was detected at the low frequencies, but none of the trials revealed any large improvements

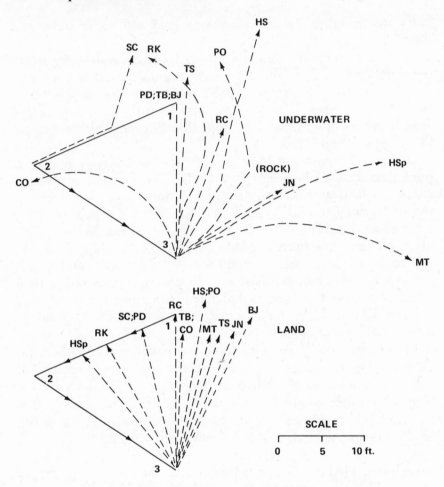

Figure 4-8. Routes taken by blindfolded subjects under water and then on land when attempting to complete the third side of a triangle. (Ross, Dickinson, & Jupp, 1970.)

in the binaural effect. In 350 trials a standard deviation of pointing error of 58° was found.

In 20 homing trials the subjects swam to the transducer 12 times. The divers noted that, when they were oriented to the bottom plane, homing was always possible. It is concluded that a weak binaural ability exists in scuba divers, and that a sonic, scuba emergency beacon can be constructed and probably would be practical.

Kinesthesis

The two general psychomotor abilities that seem basic to almost all control activities are:

1. The ability to position the arm and hand accurately.
2. The ability to judge the magnitude of forces exerted during the control manipulation (Morway, Lathrop, Chambers & Hitchcock, 1963).

Operation of any system in which there is little or no visual feedback, such as a wet submersible in turbid water, requires the operator to rely heavily upon his kinesthetic senses. Beckman (1959) listed "proprioceptive defect" as one of the factors limiting successful escape from a ditched aircraft underwater. He observed that subjects had difficulty in finding the emergency oxygen flow release when submerged, although they had had no previous trouble while in air.

The accuracy of arm movement in submerged subjects has been investigated in two different projects. The first study, by Chambers, Morway, Beckman, DeForest, and Coburn (1961), did not use completely submerged subjects, but the results they obtained are worth noting. They used two different tasks related to human positioning ability. In what they called a "target-aiming" task, the subjects, with their eyes closed and arms extended, attempted to mark a bull's eye with a grease pencil. All the subjects, when immersed in water to their neck, aimed too high with respect to the x coordinate ($P <$ .01). No significant tendencies were found with respect to left or right positioning. Figure 4-9 illustrates individual subject error means for the target-aiming task.

In a second task, called "positioning," Chambers et al. measured the time required for subjects to find and depress one of five pushbutton switches on a panel. Each button was numbered, and its location learned by the subjects so they could respond upon verbal command. The results of this study, shown in Figure 4-10, indicated that the time required to locate and depress buttons was consistently longer (20%) for the underwater condition than for the abovewater condition.

Another study dealing with the positioning ability of submerged

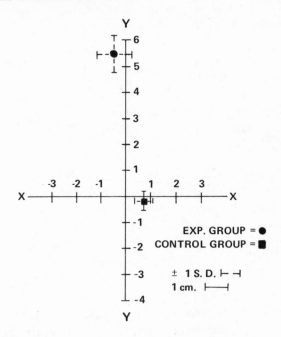

Figure 4-9.   Individual subject error means for the target-aiming task. (Chambers, Morway, Beckman, DeForest, & Coburn, 1961.)

humans was carried out by Morway et al. (1963). The experimental design used was very similar to that employed in the target-aiming experiment cited above, and the results obtained were also similar. Instead of using a grease pencil to mark positions, the Morway group used small magnets on a metal target. The subjects' placement errors were displaced upward during the immersed trials. There was, however, an indication that the subjects were learning over repeated trials, and that accuracy can be greatly improved with practice.

The second kinesthesis-related ability that seems important in human control activities is the ability to judge the magnitude of force exerted. In the Morway study described above, a measure of human force judgment was obtained. The subjects pulled on a handle connected via cables to a spring scale. In training sessions the subjects learned to produce a 15-lb force, and during the immersion experiment they were given four blocks of five trials each to reproduce it.

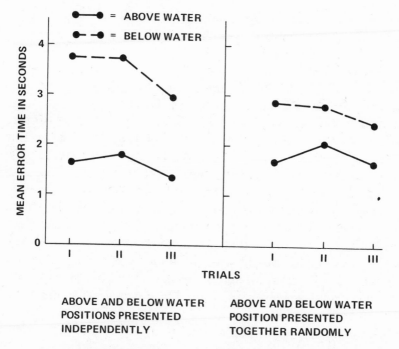

Figure 4-10.   Mean response times for positioning task. (Chambers, Morway, Beckman, DeForest, & Coburn, 1961.)

The experimenters had expected to find an underestimation in force of about 3.5 kg (the average weight of water displaced by the arm and hand of the experimental subjects). Although the deviation from surface trials was found to be of the expected magnitude, it was in the opposite direction. To explain this finding, Morway and his associates offered the following hypothesis:

"The act of raising the arm to the position required in the present study involves not only the biceps of the arm, but also the triceps, deltoid and other muscles of both the arm and the whole right side of the body. The kinesthetic feedback of all these responses establishes a zero point, about which the learning of a given force takes place. When immersed in water, the action of these muscles is significantly less. To raise the total feedback to the previously learned level, a greater downward force must be exerted, resulting in a greater actual force." (p. 19)

Unlike the positioning task, force estimation did not improve over the 18 hr the subjects spent submerged. Morway et al. suggested that underwater ambient pressure systems should be designed to tolerate overjudgment of muscular forces.

Hanna (1964) had five Navy enlisted men compare a series of weights and judge whether they were heavier or lighter than a standard weight. The task was done on dry land, and in a swimming pool with the subjects completely submerged (Figure 4-11). By using a modified constant-stimulus psychophysical technique, Hanna compared the discrimination threshold for land and water.

He found that marked decrements in performance did not appear in the underwater sessions when compared with the land sessions, as one might expect. It is important to note here that the standard weight against which the subject compared the various test weights was in the same medium, that is, when judgments were made under water, the standard weight was also under water, which involves a different experimental design than that used by Morway et al. Hanna did find, however, that variability was greater under water than on land.

In summarizing the available data on the effects of immersion on the human kinesthetic sense, one could say:

1. There is a constant error in human positioning in the vertical plane.

2. Positioning improves with practice.

3. Time to locate a given object using only the kinesthetic sense increases.

4. Force estimation may or may not be affected.

The key factor with respect to all these findings seems to be the location of the training phase of the experiment. If the training is carried out on the surface, and then the subject is tested in the water, a performance decrement is usually found. It is doubtful that the decrement would persist over any length of time, or that it would appear at all, if the initial training were carried out in the water.

SUMMARY

The sensory structures associated with the discrimination of body posture and movement are collectively referred to as the propriocep-

Figure 4-11. Immersed subject evaluating various weights against a standard weight test. (Hanna, 1964.)

tive system. The vestibular system is formed by special propriocep-tors, and the haptic system by general proprioceptors which control the sensory-motor system. The vestibular system is responsible for the perception of changes in position relative to the direction of gravity and acceleration, and the haptic system for an individual's feeling an object relative to the body and the body relative to an object. Kinesthesis is the term for sensitivity to motion.

Alternobaric vertigo, defined as vertigo involving a pressure differential between the middle and/or inner ear and the environment, is common among divers. Vestibular dysfunction may be caused in several ways by increased ambient pressure, which is discussed.

Body sway has been shown to increase with increased ambient air pressure, and balance disturbances are severe at 10 ATA. The deterioration in balance increases at a much faster rate when visual references are lost.

There is some loss of directional sense of the vertical under water, but the deterioration in geographical orientation is much worse. Veering tendencies in blindfolded subjects on land have been found by many investigators. Under water these tendencies are expressed more. Also, the kinesthetic sense has been found to be affected under water, but these affects can apparently be overcome by appropriate training.

V

CHEMICAL AND SOMESTHETIC SENSES, AND EFFECTS OF COLD UNDER WATER

Chemical senses — Taste — Somesthetic senses — Tactile sense — Thermal factors and diving — Physiological effects of water temperature — Respiratory heat loss — Acclimatization and tolerance to cold — Performance capabilities of divers in cold water — Use of insulation to counteract cold — Summary

The chemical senses seem to be of less importance for man in the underwater world. Among the somesthetic sense the tactile sense is the most important. The tactile sense appears to be fairly unaffected under water. Under cold conditions, however, there are indications that the tactile sense does undergo some changes.

The physiological effects of cold are discussed in the chapter. Respiratory heat loss is of very great importance to a diver breathing extremely cold air or a gas mixture in which the inert gas used possesses qualities of high heat conductivity. This and what it means to the performance of the diver are discussed in the chapter, so also acclimatization and tolerance to cold and how to protect the diver by using various forms of insulation.

CHEMICAL SENSES

The relative role of the chemical senses in the total sensory experience of man is a difficult question with which to deal. It is common knowledge that taste and smell play important roles in the functioning of lower organisms, but in man their roles are not so clear. It has been shown that both taste and smell can influence man's general health through their effects on food and water intake, but little has been done to determine their role in other phases of man's life.

In a closed ambient-pressure system, such as a sea floor habitat, man may be isolated for weeks or even months at a time. During Sea Lab II it was noted that the helium–oxygen atmosphere affected the aquanaut's sense of smell. Carpenter (1967) observed that there was a dulling of all odors, but that the aquanauts still enjoyed their food. If there are any adverse effects of the environment on any of the sense modalities, the efficiency of the total system could be compromised. Subtle changes in the taste and smell of food, for example, could be important morale factors for missions of long duration.

For the future expanded use of the underwater environment, it is important that an accurate picture of man's *total* perceptual experience be obtained. Any significant variation in man's perceptual experiences should be identified and considered in the design of equipment and mission profiles.

Taste

A variety of factors has been demonstrated to alter taste thresholds, including temperature, smoking, and various disease states. Chronic exposure to elevated concentrations of carbon dioxide (1.0 to 1.5%) and carbon monoxide (25 ppm) have been implicated in slight but significant decreases in taste thresholds for sour (citric acid) and bitter (quinine sulfate) solutions during submarine patrols (Hutchinson & Shiller, 1968; Nesson & Shiller, 1968). Also, changes in taste sensitivity to various compounds have been reported during exposure to helium–oxygen.

Teeter (1970) conducted a study designed to examine the effect of chronic exposure to increased *nitrogen* pressure and increased atmospheric density on subjective taste sensitivity. The subjective taste intensity of sweet, sour, salt, and bitter solutions was scaled by the method of magnitude estimation in which subjects assign numbers to designate the apparent strength of the stimulus concentration. Using this procedure the apparent perceptual intensity of stimuli S was shown to increase as a power function of the physical intensity I for over two dozen perceptual continua, including taste (Stevens 1960, 1969; Moskowitz 1968, 1970). This power function may be expressed as $S = KI^n$, or $\log S = n \log I + \log K$. The exponent, n governs the rate at which sensory intensity increases with physical intensity, and is independent of both the position of the stimulus on the physical scale and the subject's choice of scale units. An exponent greater than 1.0 indicates that sensory intensity accelerates with physical intensity, an exponent less than 1.0 indicates a decelerating relationship, and an exponent equal to 1.0 indicates a linear relationship between the increase in sensory intensity and the increase in physical intensity. The intercept K is a scale factor and may change without altering the value of the exponent.

Moskowitz also adds, along with Meiselman (1968), that each taste modality (sweet, sour, salt, and bitter) appears to be governed by a different exponent, and within a single modality different substances such as saccharin and sucrose give different exponents.

In another test in the Teeter (1970) study, subjects were asked to identify five differently flavored, sour lozenges, first while blindfolded and then while both blindfolded and wearing noseclips. The subjects were expected to identify correctly the lozenges at only a chance level while wearing the noseclips, but to perform better than chance while wearing only the blindfold. This was found to be the case during the preexposure trials.

The overall test data were analyzed with a computer program called Psycho-fit (Panck & Stevens, 1965), which provided statistics on the distribution of the magnitude estimates, as well as least-squares estimates of the exponent and intercept of the power function fitted to the empirical geometric means.

Results indicate that taste intensity increased as a power function of the stimulus concentration. However, no significant differences were detected in subjective intensity of taste sensation or olfactory sensitivity as a result of the exposure period. These results suggest that increased pressure and density alone have no effect on the subjective intensity of taste or olfaction. It must be noted, however, that these results were achieved in a nitrogen–oxygen environment and that no other environments were involved.

In 1968, Nesson and Schiller tested the effect of the atmosphere in a submerged submarine on the bitter modality threshold. Taste thresholds for quinine (bitter) were determined while the submarine was in port and were used as a base line. Subsequent taste tests were performed during the patrol at 2-week intervals. A borderline statistically significant decrease in taste threshold for quinine was noted.

Vanderwalker (1971) has detailed the events of a rather curious study initiated by NASA to determine the behavior of scientists working in rigid isolation. The study involved a mission called Tektite II, in which several teams consisting of five men each were sent to the bottom of the sea off the southeast shore of St. John, U.S. Virgin Islands. There, each team spent about 20 days living together in an underwater habitat.

Of note here is the eating routine. NASA supplied the five men with the same packaged diet furnished to Apollo astronauts in their quarantine van following splashdown. Although quite nourishing, it consisted of a monotonous supply of frozen dinners. As perhaps expected, the men were displeased with the food and on occasion complained of its generally unappealing nature.

It has already been noted that, at normal barometric pressure, oxygen and nitrogen are tasteless. According to Case and Haldane (1942), and the experience of many divers, if air is breathed at 6 to 7 ATA, it has a sweetish, acid taste due to oxygen; at 10 ATA a metallic taste is noticed which is stated to be due to nitrogen under pressure. This taste is not detected if the nitrogen is replaced by helium.

In view of these subjective observations, the sense of taste may be useful in recognizing an impurity in a breathing mixture, such as oil vapor from a compressor, but of course it cannot give any indication of the presence of carbon monoxide (Miles, 1969). Before the sense of taste can be used, however, it must be experimentally evaluated and efforts must be extended to quantify the sensations.

SOMESTHETIC SENSES

The skin senses of pressure, pain, warmth, cold, and touch are all vital for the diver if he is to maintain himself in the undersea environment. Of the studies measuring the ability of a diver to tolerate and perform in cold, wet environments, only a few are concerned with perception of the environment. It is doubtful that sensory input via these skin receptors change very much from dry surface values, but experimental evidence is needed to verify this assumption.

Tactile Sense

From the point of view of a systems engineer concerned with how man performs, perhaps the most important somatic sense is that of touch. Touch provides feedback from many manual operations. The improved performance, particularly for remote-control situations, resulting from tactile feedback is explained by Bliss, Hill & Wilber (1971). But the tactile sense has been virtually neglected as a possible predicting variable for job performance. One of the reasons for this neglect may be that use of the tactile sense is not as obvious to most investigators. Furthermore, a test for measuring individual differences in tactile sensitivity is difficult to design and hard to standardize.

Pollack (1965) developed a test to measure tactile sensitivity. He investigated the tactile sense by using different grades of emery paper. Subjects rubbed their fingertips over the papers, presented one at a time, and then estimated roughness on a scale. He found a fairly stable rating scale was achieved by the subjects. However, it was found that in such a test, unless a different set of emery papers was prepared for each subject, the skin and dirt on a subject's hands would rubbed off, rendering the texture of the emery paper noticeably different later in the test than it had been for the first subject.

Another test, conducted by Poock (1967), involved a metal plate (Figure 5-1) with 16 holes grouped in four sets of 4 holes each. The holes, of varying diameters, were tandomly positioned in each set. During the test, subjects felt the sets of four holes, one set at a time, using their middle and index fingers and not looking at the apparatus. After feeling each set, they ranked the holes from largest to smallest. This was done a total of three times for the four different sets of holes, the plate being rotated at the beginning of each new set.

The parameter used was the total number of mistakes made in ranking during three trials involving the 16 holes. It is of importance to note that none of the persons studied in this investigation gave inconsistent answers; that is, no one reported a wrong ranking at one level and then consistently gave correct results at harder levels of the test.

Chan (1964) developed a C-ring test for measuring tactile acuity.

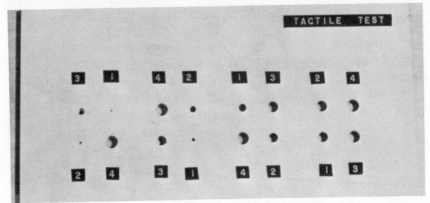

Figure 5-1.   Tactile sense testing apparatus (Poock, 1967).

The test employed 5-mm-diameter metal rings, some complete (O rings) and some slotted (C rings). The slots in the rings varied between 1 and 4 mm. The subjects reported whether they felt O or C rings when the stimuli came in contact with the pad of the index finger. Chan (1964) states that the C-rings test makes use of a technique based on the Landolt C-ring test developed to test visual acuity.

Training for the Tactile Sense

At the U.S. Navy's School of Diving and Salvage in Washington, D.C., one of the most valuable aspects of the training program is the exposure of student divers to a work task in the Anacosta River. Although the depth of the water is only about 10 m (33 ft), the visibility is zero and divers experience the complete absence of visual stimulation. To complete their work task they must rely entirely on their tactual sense. This experience is valuable, because in most actual underwater work situations the same type of visual conditions exist.

Studies concerning the Tactile Sense

Despite the fact that in most operational situations divers are obliged to rely heavily on their tactual sense, very little is known about the effects of water or increased barometric pressure on its functioning. However, we shall discuss certain studies that have been conducted relevant to these concerns. It must be noted, though, that the first four studies involved only gross measures of sensitivity since this was not their primary objective.

Behnke, Thompson, and Motley (1935) observed during a dry hyperbaric exposure at 4 ATA in air that tactile reception was not affected, but that response time increased. They did not, however, collect any empirical data to substantiate these observations.

The next three studies used the Mackworth "V" test as a measure of finger numbness during underwater performance experiments (Mackworth, 1953). The Mackworth "V" test includes the use of two straightedges clamped together to form a shallow "V." The subject places the pad of an extended finger at different distances from the point of the "V" and states whether he feels a single solid object or two closely parallel objects.

Baddeley (1965) measured tactile sensitivity in conjunction with a fine motor dexterity test in the open sea at depths of 3 and 31 m (10 and 100 ft). He found no significant change with either wetness or increased depth.

In an experiment by Bowen and Pepler (1967), a change in finger sensitivity was recorded during diver performance tests in cold water. In a more recent article, Bowen (1968) discussed the findings of the above cold-water test. He reported that just by submerging subjects in relatively warm water (21°C) he obtained a 23% reduction in tactile sensitivity. He terms this reduction a "water effect." Bowen also reports a reduction in sensitivity due to a "cold effect"; mean tactile threshold values increased significantly ($p < .001$) as a function of water temperature. During the low-temperature exposures in Bowen's study, divers reported that contact or pressure produced more pain in the hands than tactile sensations. It was also noted that there was reduced sensory feedback from the hands; consequently, manipulative actions required more visual monitoring. Table 5-1 illustrates Bowen's test results.

Another study that used the Mackworth "V" test as a measure of diver tactile sensitivity was conducted by Stang (1967). Stang, too, studied the effects of cold on diver performance. Unfortunately, he did not measure dry land sensitivity, so we have no confirmation of Bowen's "water effect"; he did, however, confirm Bowen's "cold effect."

Table 5-1   Mackworth V Test of Tactile Sensitivity: Average Thresholds for Four Divers across a Range of Water Temperature (Bowen, 1968)

Condition	Dry	70°F	61°F	54°F	49°F	44°F
Two-point threshold (in.)	0.13	0.19	0.19	0.21	0.31	0.33

Along the same lines Mills (1956) found that the tactile discrimination of the right index fingertips of men exposed to a cold environment decreased with the skin temperature of the same area. The measure of tactile discrimination consists of an individual sensing the separation of two edges. The logarithm of this separation was inversely proportional to the skin temperature between 0° and + 33°C. When the finger was rewarmed by spontaneous vasodilatation, which generally developed after about 15 min of exposure to −18 to −23°C, tactile discrimination recovered with the rise in skin temperature.

To prove that tactile discrimination is impaired under cold conditions, Provins and Morton (1960) immersed the index fingers of 10 subjects in water at 0.75°C for 40 min. Two-edge threshold discrimination was tested during cooling of the finger and subsequent spontaneous rewarming due to cold vasodilation. There was a marked deterioration in tactile discrimination at finger skin temperatures below 8°C. The wave showing the mean decrease in numbness with increasing skin temperature was displaced relative to the wave showing the mean increase in numbness with decreasing skin temperature.

Tactile discrimination was also tested on five subjects at each of six water-bath temperatures, 2, 4, 6, 8, 15, and 30°C (Provins & Morton, 1960). At each temperature the finger was immersed for 20 min and finger circulation arrested after the first 5 min. There was little impairment in two-edge discrimination after 15- or 20-min immersion of the finger at temperatures of 6°C or higher. At 4°C there was marked impairment, and at 2°C all subjects experienced complete numbness at the test site.

These studies, then, tend to indicate that the tactile sense undergoes some changes in a cold underwater environment. The effects of pure immersion (Bowen's "water effect") still remains a question.

A study designed to look at the effects of immersion (McKee, 1972) was conducted at the Navy postgraduate school for the U.S. Navy Experimental Diving Unit and involved a size discrimination test similar to that used by Poock (1967). The stimuli used were 3-in. squares of $\frac{1}{4}$-in.-thick hard acrylic plastic with holes of varying dimensions drilled through the center. There were seven different hole diameters, starting with $\frac{29}{32}$ in. and increasing by $\frac{1}{32}$ to $\frac{35}{32}$ in. One complete test consisted of 98 comparisons to a standard hole dimension of 1 in. Each stimulus size was presented to the subject 14 times during the test. The stimuli were presented to the subject in a stack of seven at a time. Each stack contained one stimulus of each hole size arranged in random order so that each size was presented as the top stimulus in the stack twice, second stimulus in the stack twice, and so forth. Four separate and randomly ordered tests were used. The number of correct or incorrect size discriminations for each hole dimension on each set were recorded. The percentage of correct responses was used as the test score. Figure 5-2 shows the results obtained by McKee using the method of constant stimulus.

Table 5-2 presents the test scores. The table refers to the tests performed on land in the open air, the test taken immediately upon the subject's entry into the water (full immersion), the test begun after 30 min under water (full immersion), and the test begun after 1 hr under water (full immersion). A principal finding of this experiment was that no "water effect" was noted; thus it failed to support Bowen's conclusions as discussed earlier. The practical diving experience of the authors indicates that for short dives in warm water—less than 2 hr—mere immersion has no quantitative effect upon tactile performance.

THERMAL FACTORS AND DIVING

The human body can maintain its thermal equilibrium only within very narrow limits. Both high and low temperatures represent human physiological limitations. In water above normal body temperature, fever develops even when one is in a restful state, and exercise accelerates its onset. In water below normal body temperature, an

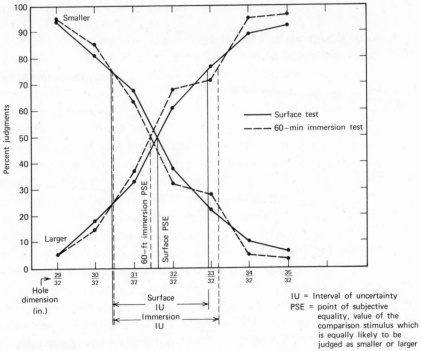

Figure 5-2. Tactile sensitivity determined by a method of constant stimulus. (McKee, 1972.)

Table 5-2 Scores for Manual Size Discrimination Test following Various Time Periods in the Water (McKee, 1972)

Subject Number	Test Score[a]			
	Open Air	Immediate	30 min	60 min
1	80	76	83	89
2	98	89	87	92
3	82	83	87	91
4	80	73	83	81
5	80	71	80	81
6	85	82	76	77
7	81	82	81	87
8	87	90	83	82
9	77	91	87	79
10	89	85	86	92

[a] Test scores are the percent correct.

unprotected man loses heat about 21 times faster than he does in normal air at the same ambient temperature. Metabolic heat produced by exercise extends man's tolerance to cold water, and the combination of insulation and work provides useful periods of time in water at temperatures as low as 10 to 15°C. Significant improvement in the degree of human temperature tolerance cannot be expected from the use of drugs or physiological adaptation.

Human temperature tolerance in water must be achieved by the use of insulating and external heating methods properly integrated with an understanding of physiological heat exchange. Such technical heating methods must also include preheating of the gas mixture to be breathed, because a significant amount of body heat is lost through the lungs when cold gas is breathed at high pressures. The temperature of gas inspired is normally equal to the temperature of the ambient water, and Hoke, Jackson, Alexander, and Flynn (1971) found that, at depths beyond 600 ft (180 m) and water temperatures of 40°F (4.4°C) or less, divers suffered a progressive negative thermal balance. They also found that the rate of heat loss increased as respiratory volume per minute increased at higher work rates. These investigators concluded that when respiratory heat loss exceeds about 350 W, a diver will soon be in danger.

Physiological Effects of Water Temperature

Few studies of the effects of water temperature on performance seem to have been performed. The results of experiments conducted on prisoners and internees during World War II on the effects of exposure to cold and on the value of rapid warming cannot easily be evaluated, since the scientific integrity of many of the workers concerned is open to serious question. There are, however, other investigations concerning the effects of immersion in cold water, which are of great importance to technicians in their effort to develop and evaluate diving suits and methods of thermal protection.

Greenbaum and Hoff (1966) have stated that the effects of immersion in cold water depend upon the condition of the individual at the time of immersion, the temperature of the water, and the duration of the exposure. In divers the effects of the breathed gas mixture and the ambient pressure must also be considered.

Newburg and Spealman (1943) pointed out that the complete curve of body cooling for the rat seems to be logarithmic in nature. The initial fall in body temperature of men immersed in cold water progresses in a linear manner. The rate of fall is approximately proportional to the difference between water and body temperature, with a tendency for body temperature to fall more rapidly than expected in the case of lower water temperatures. From experimental evidence gained by these investigators, it was inferred that survival time of men immersed in very cold water is very short. This inference is in agreement with various reports of the rapid death of men forced into the cold waters of the North.

In a study of cardiovascular responses of dogs to immersion hypothermia, Hegnauer, Shriber, and Haterius (1950) measured pulse rate, arterial blood pressure, and blood viscosity in relation to temperature within the right heart. In the early stages of hypothermia, the pulse rate reflects the algebraic sum of reflex excitatory and cold-depressor influences. In the lower temperature range (25 to 14°C), the reflex influence seems minimal or absent. Blood pressure regression with diminishing temperature follows a course independent of the pulse rate until a temperature of 24 to 23°C is reached, at which complete dependence on pulse rate becomes evident. Blood viscosity increases two- to threefold between normal body temperature and 20°C, hemoconcentration accounting in a large measure for the changes. Both systole and isometric relaxation are prolonged progressively with cold, there being a five- or sixfold increase at 18°C. It was suggested by these workers that the cause of death in hypothermia is predominantly cardiac, occasioned on the one hand by inadequate coronary blood flow, and on the other by diminished metabolic rate. The former stems from a fall in pressure head, increased blood viscosity, and prolongation of the tension phase of the cardiac cycle at the expense of the quiescent period. Developing respiratory inadequacy may influence the temperature at which terminal events occur, but does not affect their nature.

Penrod (1949) and Wolff and Penrod (1950) showed that oxygen consumption in the dog varied directly with shivering responses for rectal temperatures above 23°C. Below 25°C rectal temperature, shivering was no longer a factor, and the oxygen consumption of all dogs fell to approximately one-third of that of the precooling control level.

Hoff and Greenbaum (1954) found evidence in Spealman's statements (Spealman, 1949) that hypothermia may rank with asphyxia (drowning) as a cause of death following shipwreck in very cold water. The chief barrier to heat loss from the nude body in cold water is provided by the skin and other peripheral tissues. Heat is removed from the nude body more rapidly in cold water than in air at the same temperature; this fact applies equally well when only ordinary clothing is worn. The minimum water temperature in which nude men can maintain body temperatures at normal levels is about 32 to 33°C. Most men as well as dogs are chilled fatally in less than 1 hr in water near freezing. Glaser (1950) calculated that, in water at 0 to 5°C, the average body temperature in man would fall by about 0.18 to 0.14°C/min, which was also confirmed by experimentation.

Keatinge and Evans (1960) have reported on the effect of food, alcohol, and hyoscine on body temperature and reflex responses for men immersed in cold water. Neither 75 ml of alcohol, nor a heavy meal, nor 1/100 grain hyoscine taken 45 min before immersion significantly affected the rate at which men's rectal temperatures fell during 30 min of immersion in water at 15°C. It was found that under these conditions the blood flow in the fingers invariably decreased rapidly to low levels, and that the fall was significantly less rapid after the introduction of alcohol. Several of the subjects developed ventricular extrasystoles upon immersion, most of which were observed after hyoscine or a heavy meal, but not after alcohol. Alcohol greatly reduced subjective discomfort and sensation of cold in the water. Also, alcohol usually reduced both the rise in metabolic rate and the increase in heart rate during immersion. Hyoscine reduced the metabolic rate and abolished the increase in heart rate, but unlike alcohol it did not affect subjective sensation of cold.

The significance of the autonomic system in adjustment to cold and heat has been demonstrated rather clearly in Cannon's experiments with sympathectomized animal preparations (Cannon, 1939). According to D'Amato and Hegnauer (1953), one of the mechanisms involved in the autonomic response to initial exposure to cold is a rather extensive vasoconstriction with a concomitant decrease in plasma volume. The vasoconstriction brings about thermal insulation at the periphery, and conservation of body heat. Skeletal muscular activity (such as shivering and brisk movement) increase metabolic heat production, while the metabolic responses of philoerection and vasoconstriction decrease heat loss (Weybrew 1967). Moreover, Rubin (1957) showed that, when the skin temperature of the hand in cold air falls to about 10°C, a reflex vasodilation generally occurs which increases the peripheral blood flow and raises skin temperature a few degrees; sometimes this is followed by vasoconstriction and by vasodilation at an alternating sequence. This reflex vasodilation can also occur at much lower temperatures, for example, when fingers are immersed in ice water. Thus, in studies carried out by Greenfield and Shepherd (1950), immersion of a finger in a water bath at 0 to 6°C produced an initial, nearly complete cessation of blood flow. After a few minutes the blood flow increased notably. Similar but lesser changes in blood flow occurred at 6 to 12°C and at 12 to 15°C. There was no initial vasoconstriction, and the blood flow per minute was lower than in the colder ranges.

According to Bowen and Pepler (1967), the extent of reflex vasodilation and associated warming of the skin is greater if the rest of the body is at normal temperature. Vasodilation in the hands tends to be suppressed if the body is cooled also. In the absence of reflex vasodilation, an immersed part of the body cools rapidly until it attains the temperature of the surrounding water.

Calculations by Spealman (1949) show that the amount of water vapor evaporated from the skin in a cold environment may be as high as 19 g/hr in an uncomfortably cold environment, and approximately 4 g less than that evaporated in a comfortable environment. In cold conditions, with peripheral vasoconstriction, approximately 9 cal of heat per square meter of body surface per hour are transferred to the surface of the body for each degree of difference in temperature between deep body tissue and the body surface. Calculations indicate that the average blood flow in fully vasoconstricted skin is probably less than 15 cc/m^2 of surface area per minute. During moderate vasodilation, the flow may be 230 cc/m^2 of surface area per minute, and the figure may rise to 1200 cc/m^2 strenuous exercise.

Men immersed up to the neck in water at 20°C showed an average heat loss, after body temperature stabilization, of 198 cal/m² of surface area per hour. The difference between body and water temperature was 15.5°C. Therefore the heat transferred per degree of difference in temperature was 13 cal/m² of surface area per hour.

Spealman found blood flow values as low as 0.2 to 0.5 cc/min in hands and fingers during experiments in moderately cold environments. Extreme degrees of relative ischemia can be withstood for long periods without harm. Blood flow in very cold extremities (5 to 10°C) is many times greater than in moderately cold extremities (15 to 20°C).

Individuals differ in the consistency and rapidity with which they exhibit cold-induced vasodilation. According to Bowen and Pepler (1967), individuals who experience long delays or tend not to vasodilate in the cold appear to be highly or even overly aroused individuals in other aspects. This apparent relationship between arousal (or anxiety) and reflex response to cold could be significant for divers working in cold water under a combination of stressful conditions. Bowen and Pepler suggest that if an individual dives into cold water when he is very anxious or in some other way strongly aroused emotionally, he would probably work less effectively and would not be able to tolerate the cold as long as usual.

According to Hoff and Greenbaum (1954), several studies have suggested that hemodilution and hemoconcentration occur in hypothermia. This has been inferred from changes in the osmotic pressure or the plasma protein concentration of the blood. Rodbard, Saiki, and Malin (1950) found, for instance, that induction of hypothermia resulted in a shift of fluid from the plasma and the interstitial spaces to the intracellular space, and that blood cells and plasma proteins are removed from the circulating plasma and subsequently stored. Ström (1960) noted that the water-shifting response to cold stress in contingent upon the activity of the sympathetic nervous system and disappears after cervical spinal transection or after adrenalectomy. Ström concludes that the water-shifting response is at least partly evoked by the action of hypothalamic thermodetectors and is coordinated by anterior hypothalamic structures.

Respiratory Heat Loss

The effects of cold on the air passages and the lungs have been reported in papers by Moritz and Weisiger (1945) and Webb (1951). The former caused dogs to breathe extremely cold air for periods ranging from 20 to 130 min. The temperature of the air delivered to the larynx ranged between −50 to −28°C, and in no instance were the temperature readings lower than +18°C at the bifurcation of the trachea. Inhalation of cold air such that intralaryngeal inspiratory temperatures as low as or lower than −30°C were reached resulted in the development of localized sublaryngeal tracheitis. In some adults the disturbance was limited to unusual activity on the part of the mucussecreting glands, and in others there was focal destruction of the superficial epithelium. There was no evidence of injury to the lower part of the trachea, to the bronchi, or to the lungs. These workers suggested that the explanation of the rapid warming of inhaled cold air and of the occurrence of relatively mild and localized injury following inhalation of cold air is a simple one. Dry air has an extremely low heat capacity and the number of calories required to produce a great rise in the temperature of dry air can be provided by the heat derived from the cooling of a small amount of tissue by a few degrees. Long exposure to cold air, according to these workers, might result in obstructive edema.

Webb (1951) also measured air temperature in the airway with a thermocouple, and made air temperature tracings from the front, middle, and back of the nose from 18 resting human subjects. This was done in the following ambient air temperature ranges: 23 to 28°C, 5 to 8°C, and − 20 to − 31°C. Average minimum peak temperatures from these records demonstrated that the inspired air was rapidly warmed upon passing through the nose. It was noted that at the back of the nose inspired warm ambient air reached a temperature of 31.7°C, cool air reached a temperature of 30.0°C, and cold air reached a temperature of 25.4°C. Average maximum temperature peaks demonstrated that expired air at the back of the nose did not exceed 35.5, 34.9, and 31.9°C at warm, cool, and cold ambient temperatures, respectively. Measurements at the front of the nose showed that average maximum expired air temperature peaks had dropped to 34.1, 29.2, and 26.2°C under the same respective conditions. It should be added that Spealman (1949) estimated that heat loss from the respiratory tract may be as high as 50 cal/1000 liters of respired air in extreme cold.

The question of heat loss via the respiratory route is a critical one in low-temperature operations in which the inert gas used possesses high heat conductivity. The problem is greatly accentuated in modern deep diving, wherein greater and greater depths are involved. Webb and Annis (1966) have clearly demonstrated that a significant amount of body heat is lost through the lungs when cold gas is breathed at different pressure levels. They measured heat loss from the respiratory tract of resting and working subjects while they breathed air and different gas mixtures through an instrumented scuba mouthpiece at 1 ATA. Similar data were collected in a hyperbaric wet chamber with air and a mixture of 20% oxygen and 80% helium at 4 ATA, and a mixture of 4% oxygen and 96% helium at 8 ATA. It was found that heat loss was directly proportional to depth, respiratory volume per minute, and the product of density and specific heat of each gas mixture. With higher-density mixtures, respiratory heat loss was as high as 25% of the total heat production in either the resting or working condition. Individual values for respiratory heat loss ranged from 0.1 to 2.5 kcal/min. These investigators developed methods for calculating respiratory heat loss and the densities of different gas mixtures, which allowed a formula to be devised which made it possible to predict respiratory heat loss at any depth or water temperature for a given amount of pulmonary ventilation.

Using this formula, Tauber, Rawlins, and Bondi (1969) predicted that respiratory heat loss would exceed the body's ability to produce metabolic heat during dives to 850 ft (260 m) in 40°F (4.4°C) water. Tests by Hoke, Jackson, Alexander, and Flynn (1971) confirmed these predictions.

Their subjects breathed an oxygen–helium mixture at an inspired gas temperature of 32 to 35°F (0 to 1.7°C) in a warm, 88°F (31°C), dry chamber while working at various rates for the first 60 min; then one subject at each depth continued his cold gas exposure for a total of 4 hr. For control comparisons each subject underwent a 1-hr test run on warm, 88°F (31°C) gas at each depth. The data are plotted in Figures 5-3 and 5-4.

Figure 5-3 shows that when gas is breathed at the ambient

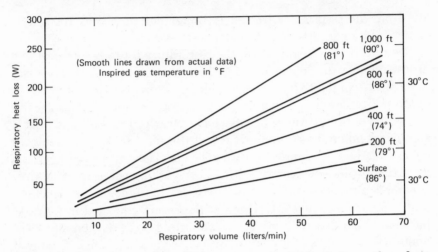

Figure 5-3.   Respiratory heat loss—warm gas controls. (Hoke, Jackson, Alexander & Flynn, 1971.)

chamber temperature (86°F, or approximately 30°C), the measured respiratory heat loss increases with depth and respiratory volume per minute. Respiratory heat loss during the warm control experiments at 305 m (1000 ft) was actually less than at 244 m (800 ft) because of a difference in the ambient temperature. The average inspired gas temperature at 244 m was 23°C, while at 305 m it was 31.5°C. At the surface the respiratory heat loss when subjects breathed warm, 30°C gas with a respiratory volume of 40 liters/min was 55 W, and 95% of this was due to humidifying the expired gas. With the same volume per minute, the respiratory heat loss at 244 and 305 m was between 150 and 200 W.

Figure 5-4 illustrates the respiratory heat loss, measured in watts, when subjects breathed a cold oxygen–helium mixture at various depths and respiratory volumes per minute. The experiments at the surface, at 60, 120, 180, and 244 m were conducted with an inspired gas temperature of 0 to 2°C. At 305 m the inspired gas temperature was 7°C. At a ventilation of 40 liters/min, the respiratory heat loss varied from 75 W at the surface to 490 W at 305 m. The highest measured heat loss, 780 W, occurred during heavy work at 1000 ft (305 m) with a respiratory volume of 64 liters/min.

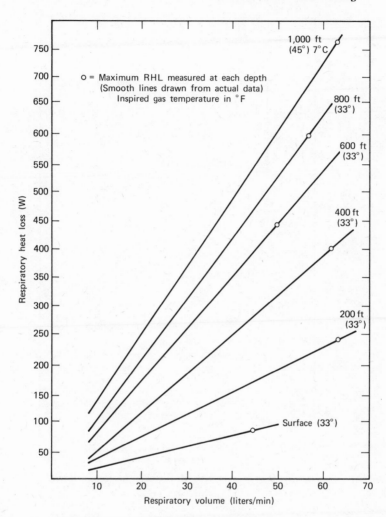

Figure 5-4. Respiratory heat loss—cold gas. (Hoke, Jackson, Alexander & Flynn, 1971.)

Figure 5-5 demonstrates the respiratory heat loss measured in 11 subjects at 244 m working at a steady, moderate work rate for 1 hr and breathing an oxygen–helium mixture at various temperatures. When warm, 16°C gas was breathed, the maximum heat loss was 250 W, whereas during cold gas (2 to 5°C) breathing, the respira-

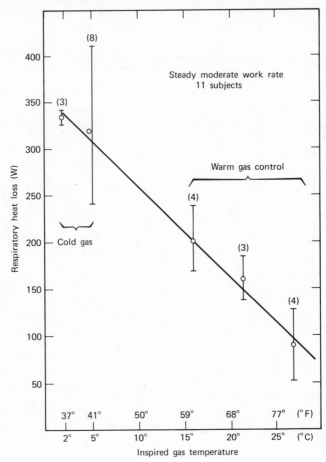

Figure 5-5. Respiratory heat loss at 850 ft. (Hoke, Jackson, Alexander & Flynn, 1971.)

tory heat loss ranged from 250 to 450 W.

Hoke et al. stated that their experiments showed conclusively that, at depths beyond 600 ft (183 m) and at water temperatures (i.e., inspired gas temperatures) of 40°F (4°C) or less, there is a progressive negative thermal balance. The rate of heat loss increases as respiratory volume per minute increases at higher work rates. When expiratory heat loss exceeds about 350 W, a diver is in danger. These workers have calculated some theoretical curves for respiratory heat loss at various depths and respiratory volumes per minute,

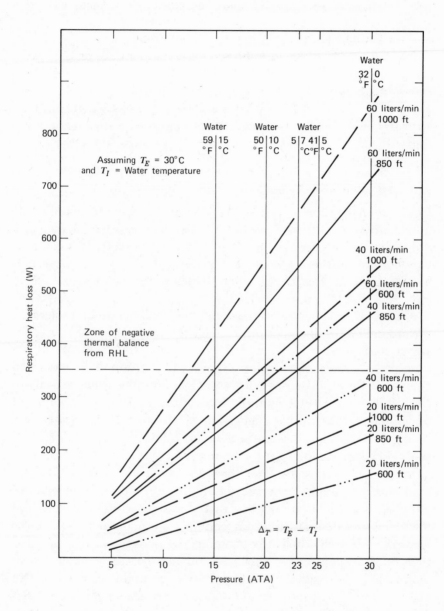

Figure 5-6. Theoretical respiratory heat loss in cold water at various depths and respiratory volumes (Hoke, Jackson, Alexander & Flynn, 1971.)

187

and for various water temperatures (Figure 5-6).

Inspired gas is assumed to be the same temperature as the water, and expired gas is assumed to be 30°C. Hoke et al. conclude that for safety, thermal comfort, and maximum efficiency, a diver's breathing gas should be heated for divers in excess of 152 m (500 ft). In fact, special, electronically regulated, breathing-gas heating devices are under development and seem to be very promising for the future (Agarate, 1971).

Acclimatization and Tolerance to Cold

Cold acclimatization is well-known among outdoor workers in arctic and subarctic cold. For example, the hands of outdoor workers do not seem to get as cold as the hands of indoor workers. It is common every winter in the northern part of the Gulf of Bothnia for fishermen to work on the ice with bare hands in temperatures down to −35°C (−30°F) for several hours.

Almost all investigations concerning acclimatization and tolerance toward cold have been performed with the subjects in cold air. Thus Bader and Mead (1949) and Bader, Mead, and Phillion (1950) observed a variety of vascular responses in a group of 24 men, and compared these responses with an evaluation of certain aspects of their individual cold tolerance. Individuals in whom reduction of finger blood flow during immersion of the feet in ice water was relatively transient showed, in general, a lower incidence of frostbite. They were able to work with unprotected hands in the cold for more prolonged periods than those in whom vasoconstriction was maintained through immersion of the feet in ice water. However, although a correlation between digital vascular response and cold tolerance was demonstrated for certain experimental groups, there were notable individual exceptions to the pattern. Hence the cold immersion response of a particular subject cannot be regarded as an absolute determinant of his performance under cold stress. No other physiological indices investigated were shown to have a significant relationship to cold tolerance.

Change in the circulation of blood in the extremeties as a factor in acclimatization to cold was also discussed by Bazett (1949). He pointed out that seamen undergoing prolonged exposure to cold weather at sea develop an ability to withstand immersion of the hands in cold water much better than do other individuals. Daniels, Fainer, Bommarito, and Bass (1951) emphasized that acclimatization to cold involves the role of many coordinated changes rather than striking changes in any one function. Animal studies of Sellers, Reichman, and Thomas (1951) and Sellers, Reichman, Thomas, and You (1951) have indicated that acclimatized rats manifest a greatly elevated metabolic rate in comparison with unacclimatized animals.

Dugal and Therien (1947) and Therien (1949) observed that acclimatization to low temperature involves large quantities of ascorbic acid. A direct relation was observed by these workers between adaptability to a cold environment and the quantity of ascorbic acid in the adrenal glands of white rats. Butson (1949) found an average increase of 10 mg % in the fasting blood-sugar level in men subjected to temperatures of -18 to $-37°C$ in the Antarctic. There was an increased sensitivity to adrenalin injection as indicated by blood pressure changes, respiratory rate, pulse rate, and subjective sensations. Frazier (1945) reported an increase in blood-sugar levels in men who took part in the United States Antarctic service expedition of 1939, and stated that a vital factor in cold acclimatization is an increase in epinephrine output.

LeBlanc (1956) observed that in acclimatized subjects the increased heat production caused by cold exposure is not as large as in unacclimatized subjects. Practical studies of Scholander, Hammel, Lange-Anderson, and Loyning (1957) involved the exposure of human subjects to conditions in the Norwegian mountains above the tree line. During the months of September and October, eight men lived in essentially summer clothing with "insufficient" night protection. Snow and sleet were common and night temperatures were usually between 0 and 5° C. The men had enough food and were kept busy hiking, fishing, and hunting. The nights were spent beneath a tarpaulin rigged as a rainproof shelter with one side open. The subjects slept naked except for socks and shorts in a single-blanket sleeping bag with a hydrophobic cover. After six weeks in the field they had acquired considerable acclimatization. Tests showed that they then stayed warm from head to foot all night and slept well. Heat production remained 50 to 60% higher than the basal production all night while they were asleep. Shivering occurred frequently during sleep which was either quite visible or detectable by electromyography. Control subjects had less elevated metabolic rates and were unable to rest and sleep because of chilling, especially of the feet (Greenbaum & Hoff 1966).

One investigation of acclimatization to cold in cold water has been performed by Skreslet and Aarefjord (1968). The authors studied three scuba divers, members of an archeological-biological underwater team, working in the Svalbard area north of Scandinavia, 79°N, who were shown to have established a short time adaptation to cold as a result of extensive diving in the cold sea. At intervals during a period of 45 days they were tested physiologically under standardized conditions in a cold bath. According to these workers, the results obtained from the tests seem to indicate a special pattern of successive acclimatization:

1. *Unacclimatized stage.*   Cold stress met with an elevated metabolic rate compensating for heat loss.
2. *Intermediate stage.*   There is a fall in the rectal (core) temperature as heat loss is not fully compensated for by the metabolism; this is believed to be caused by habituation of the central nervous system.
3. *Acclimatized stage.*   A constant rectal temperature is maintained, although a minor amount of metabolic heat is produced. Conservation of heat is attributed to lowered heat transfer from the blood to the body surface.

Adaptation to life in a cold climate undoubtedly involves psychological processes of habituation to the discomfort of cold, and learning to perform sensory-motor tasks with reduced or modified sensory feedback information (Edholm & Burton, 1955). Both these psychological processes are likely to be important for divers working in cold water.

Performance Capabilities of Divers in Cold Water

As stated previously, almost all investigations germane to the effects of cold seem to have been performed in cold air rather than in cold water. Most of them have been concerned with man's ability to use his hands, and the main problem seems to have been the immediate relation between the ambient temperature (sometimes wind and humidity also) and performance. Some of these studies have shown decrements in gross measurements of task performance, for example, fewer numbers of items handled per unit time, increased time to complete an assembly task, and reduced accuracy in manual tracking. They have also concerned losses of specific abilities such as tactile sensitivity, muscle strength, and speed accuracy of finger, hand, and arm movements. The general finding is that low temperature impairs manual performance, but only a small number of studies have related manual performance measurements to hand and body skin temperature.

Animal experiments by Dureuil and Ratsimamanza (1948) indicate that exposure to sudden temperature drops does not generally alter work output, and studies on human subjects similarly suggest that men may operate in the cold with unimpaired efficiency with proper protection. Horvath and Freedman (1947) exposed 70 men to ambient temperatures of -23, -26, and $-29°C$ with zero wind velocity. The subjects were sufficiently protected by arctic clothing. It was found that their reaction time to visual stimuli was not altered during continuous exposure to a low environmental temperature for periods of 8 to 14 days. In contrast, finger dexterity and hand strength were strikingly diminished by exposure to low ambient temperatures, even when the duration of such exposures was relatively short. The conclusion was that there is a need for extreme care in the design of equipment for cold-weather operations, a conclusion with which Forland (1950) also concurs.

According to Gaydos (1958) and Gaydos and Dusek (1958), manual performance is impaired when hand skin temperature drops to 13°C (and below) and the rest of the body is kept warm. Even when the surface of the body was cooled simultaneously with the hands to an average temperature of 26°C (78°F), no additional impairment of performance was observed. But in another study by Lockhart (1966), cooling the body surface to an average temperature of 20°C (69°F) impaired the performance of two manual tasks, even when the hands were kept warm. However, the impairment of manual performance associated with a body skin temperature of 20°C was less than the impairment resulting from a hand skin temperature of 13°C. The greatest decrement in performance occurred when the subject's body and hand skin temperature were simultaneously reduced to 20 and 13°C, respectively. The impairment in performance occurring at a hand skin temperature of 13°C was also observed by Clark (1961); in addition, the impairment increased up to 40 min, although no additional impairment was observed up to 60 min.

It has been demonstrated by LeBlanc (1956) that, when the fingers alone are cooled, the performance of tests involving little movement of a joint may be slightly enhanced, whereas impairment is great when joint movement is increased. This has been interpreted as evidence for the hypothesis that increased viscosity of the synovial fluid that serves as a lubricant for joints is a factor in decreasing finger dexterity in the cold (Edholm & Burton, 1955). However, since cooling of the arm, even when the hands are kept warm, also causes a large decrement in finger dexterity, this is apparently not the only factor. Edholm and Burton also state that, at low temperatures, blood becomes more dense and flows more slowly (even independently of vasoconstriction) and, at temperatures below 9°C, neural conduction is impaired.

The degree of impairment in performance at particular skin temperatures of the hand depends upon the rate of cooling, according to Clark and Cohen (1960) and Clark (1961). They found that, when the skin cooled very rapidly, the decrement was less than when the skin cooled more slowly. The implication, as advanced by Bowen and Pepler (1967), is that during exposure to severe cold the temperature of the skin falls much more rapidly than the temperature of deeper tissues, and that maximum impairment of manual performance occurs only when the deeper tissues have also had time to cool to a new steady state.

The manual tasks that have been performed less effectively in the cold have been relatively complex and involved numerous perceptual and cognitive elements. Among such tasks may be included the tuning and operating of radio and radar equipment, multidimensional tracking, and typing. It is possible that the cold exposures impaired not only the manual elements of these tasks, but also the organization of these elements into a complex activity involving the timing and coordination of responses to changing stimuli. Baddeley (1966a) found, for instance, that after diving in seawater at 4°C divers judgments of the passage of time were impaired. Notably, they judged a significantly longer period of time equal to 1 min than they did at normal temperatures. Bowen and Pepler (1967) conclude that an impaired sense of the passage of time might affect the timing of related elements in a complex task.

Carlsson (1960) has pointed out that cold may reduce performance speed by blocking tactile or kinesthetic nerve impulses (disturbed receptor function), inhibit muscular function or change the viscosity in the synovial fluid (disturbed effector function), and cause the general condition to deteriorate (disturbed central function). It is difficult to separate sensory performance from motor performance, because of the intimate connection between receptor and effector processes. It is very important, therefore, to choose the most sensitive test instruments when studying the effects of the cold.

Further, Carlsson (1962, 1963) found that cooling of the hand and arm reduced performance speed, especially when the subjects performed rotatory movements, and confirmed the statement of Edholm and Burton that deterioration of performance was accentuated when finger skin temperature was lower than 10°C. Also, it must be noted that Carlsson's experiments were made in air and with local cooling of the arm and hand.

Bowen and Pepler seem to have been the first to conduct experiments to examine the effects of diving in cold water on a representative sample of psychological functions. They hypothesized that all psychological functions would show some change or depletion, but that the effects would differ according to the type of function tested. In addition to the 72°F (22.2°C) dry land control condition, they operated at two water temperatures—warm—62°F (16.7°C) and cold—47°F (8.3°C). The tests were conducted in a diving tank and each diver, when prepared to dive, wore a $\frac{3}{16}$-in. neoprene wet suit.

In general, the five subjects who volunteered for the project made two dives per day, and the separation between dives was normally between 3 and 4 hours. Between dives, the diver took a hot shower, dressed in dry, warm clothing, availed himself of a heated rest room equipped with bunks, and consumed hot drinks and food as he might wish. Divers, after experiencing the cold test condition, found that they remained chilly for about 1 hr, were hungry and thirsty, and fell asleep easily.

The tests ranged across a representative sample of psychological functions and were designed to measure the depletions or changes in behavior that may occur as man dives in cold water. The functions tested were those often incorporated within normal living activities. Each trial lasted for 10 min. The experimenters used the following tests:

1. A tactile sensitivity test (Mackworth, 1953).
2. A manual dexterity test (screw plate test).
3. A manual movement test (peg and ring test).
4. A reasoning test (arithmetic).
5. A problem-solving test (set exception test requiring the subject to discover which one of five items differed from the other four).
6. A memory test (clock test requiring the subject to inspect a panel, remember what he saw, and record as much as he can remember).
7. A multitask test (two-hand tracking and audiovigilance test requiring the subject to perform a continuous tracking task and to listen for a specified signal in a continuous stream of signals at the same time).
8. A two-hand tracking test.
9. A listening vigilance test.

According to these investigators, the resultant data indicated that diving in warm water caused a loss in motor functions due, it was thought, to the changes and hindrances experienced in the diving condition. Diving in cold water increased motor loss and caused distraction and disruption in mental tasks; "blocking" of attention and lowered memory capability were found. An example of the performance decrement demonstrated by Bowen & Pepler (1967) is shown in Figure 5-7. There was considerable impairment in performance on the multitask test. It was hypothesized by these workers that cold-water stress, in addition to causing specific sensory and motor losses, causes a proportionally increasing loss of capability as the task becomes more complex and as it becomes more dependent upon sustained attention and memory functions (Bowen & Pepler, 1967).

In 1968, Bowen reported on a somewhat widened investigation of the effects of exposure to cold water. He confirmed the findings of Bowen and Pepler, and also found impairment in tactile sensitivity,

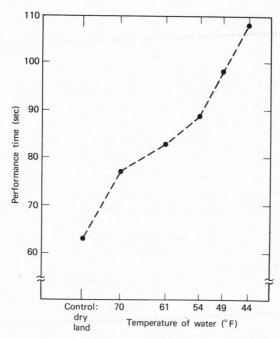

Figure 5-7. Preliminary experiment, screw plate test. Average performance time in seconds as a function of water temperature. (Bowen & Pepler, 1967.)

grip strength, and manual movement in the hand. These losses were proportional to the degree of cold and exposure time and followed a course similar to the skin temperature decrease. He also found psychomotor losses related to water temperature in manual dexterity, tracking and the group assembly task. Mental impairment occurred in cases in which the task required intense attention and involved considerable short-term memory. However, although he found that cognitive tasks were performed less well in water than in air, they were equivalent under warm and cold temperature conditions. Accuracy of performance in arithmetic remained constant regardless of the temperature, although cold appeared to affect the number of test items omitted. Bowen suggested that ability to perform tasks requiring intense concentration was subject to degradation by cold stress. The results of this expanded study are shown in Figures 5-8 and 5-9.

Stang (1967) also performed research on diver tactile sensitivity, utilizing the Mackworth "V" test (see p. 173). He wished to determine the effects of cold on diver performance. Since Stang did not measure dry land sensitivity, he was unable to confirm Bowen's "water effect." However, he was able to verify Bowen's "cold effect."

Later, in 1970, Stang reported on additional related investigations. Twelve experienced divers repeatedly performed several representative underwater tasks for 90-min. sessions at water temperatures of 10, 16, and 21°C. Time to complete the task (refer to Figure 5-10 for the tasks employed) was the primary performance measure; reaction time, with mental arithmetic as a loading task, and four physiological measurements were also recorded. The subjects worked in $6\frac{1}{2}$ ft of water, wearing full $\frac{3}{16}$-in.-thick wet suits and

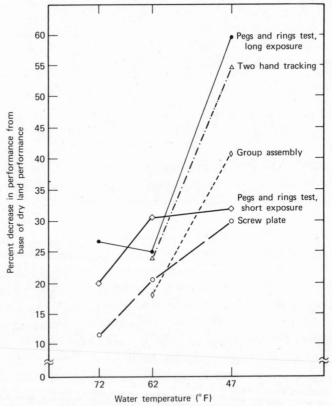

Figure 5-8.   Percent decrease in performance from base of dry land performance as a function of water temperature for manual performance. (Bowen, 1967.)

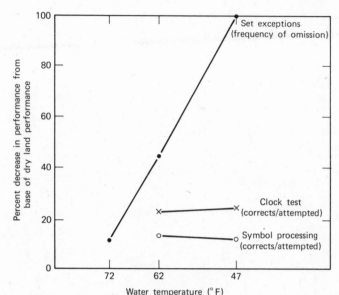

Figure 5-9.   Percent decrease in performance from base of dry land performance as a function of water temperature for mental performance. (Bowen, 1967.)

scuba equipment. Performance on all tasks except mental arithmetic tended to decrease as water temperature decreased. Most performance measures also showed a significant decrement over time and a significant time/temperature interaction. The general trend in performance was also reflected in several of the physiological measurements.

Bowen (1967) used exposure intervals of 30 min and estimated core temperature reduction by pre- and postdive measures of urine temperature. Average reduction in core temperature was only 0.28°C. Beagles and Coils (1966), however, found that when they exposed eight subjects to 0°C water skin temperatures fell rapidly, particularly at the extremities, and most of the dives were terminated due to diver complaints of painfully chilled feet. Therefore the performance degradation in Bowen's experiment was presumably a function of peripheral temperature decline.

The normal core temperature seems to be of very great importance to the mental performance abilities of a diver. Thus Beckman (1964), for instance, reported "general mental confusion and lack of contact with surroundings" in a subject whose rectal temperature

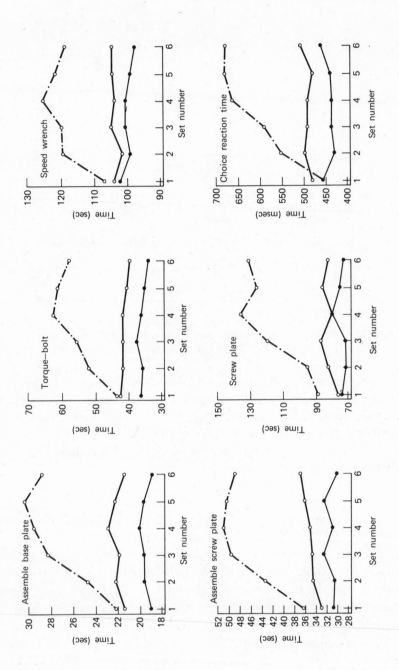

198

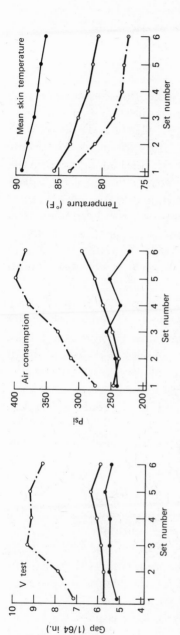

Figure 5-10. Performance measures versus set number for all tasks at 50° (—··—), 60° (o—o), and 70° (●—●). Each task (or measure) was performed once during each set. Each set had a duration of 15.25 min; therefore the six sets represent a total exposure of 91.5 min. (Stang, 1970.)

was 34°C, and Keatinge (1969) reported "general confusion and amnesia for recent events" in two subjects whose rectal temperatures were in the 33 to 35°C range (Vaughan & Matvor, 1972).

Use of Insulation to Counteract Cold

There exist for a diver various forms of insulation designed to protect him from the cold underwater environment.

According to Rawlins and Tauber (1971), Sea Lab III divers were provided closed-cell, foam neoprene wet suits for insulation. Many samples were tested to determine the best thermal insulation, the best resistance to compression, the best reexpansion in a high-pressure helium atmosphere, and the best resistance to tearing and abrasion consistent with good flexibility. However, the best foam neoprene available is by no means an ideal material for divers at depth. Indeed, the greater heat loads required at depth are largely due to the special properties of foam neoprene when it is exposed to pressure and helium.

The insulating properties of any given material are dependent on thickness and thermal conductivity. When a $\frac{3}{16}$-in. neoprene wet suit is placed in a hyperbaric chamber and slowly pressurized with helium over 24 hr to 19.2 ATA, the thickness decreases until at about 4 ATA it is 50 to 55% of the initial thickness, after which there is essentially no further change (Figure 5-11).

During compression helium diffuses into the neoprene, and oxygen and nitrogen diffuse out. Beyond 180 m (600 ft), diffusion of helium continues, as shown by the gradual reexpansion to about 65% of the initial thickness (Figure 5-12).

The cells of the neoprene are now filled with helium at 19.2 ATA, and when the diver enters the water, which of course has no dissolved helium, the gas diffuses out of the neoprene rapidly and it loses thickness (Figure 5-13). The pressure within the cells, however, is still 19.2 ATA helium, so that on return to the habitat there is no physical process to reexpand the neoprene, unless there is some sort of internal spring effect through which the neoprene cells tend to retain their volume and shape. Each subsequent dive results in further loss of helium, so that the Sea Lab diver is liable to end up with a very thin suit.

The thermal conductivity of a $\frac{3}{16}$-in. air-equilibrated foam neo-

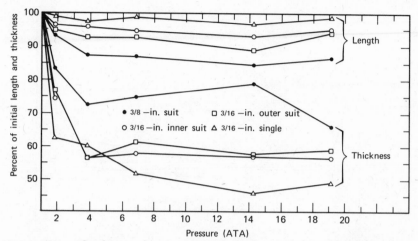

Figure 5-11.   Shrinkage and compression of neoprene wet suits during slow descent to 600 ft (19.2 ATA) (Rawlins & Tauber, 1971).

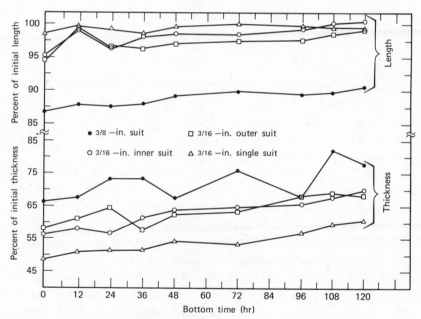

Figure 5-12.   Reexpansion of neoprene wet suits after slow compression to 600 ft (19.2 ATA). (Rawlins & Tauber, 1971.)

201

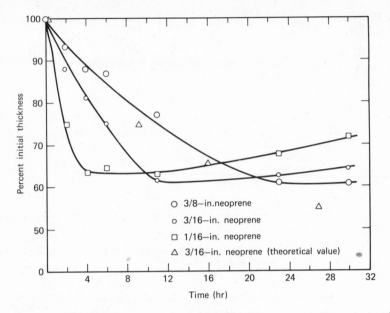

Figure 5-13. Thickness change in helium-exposed neoprene wet suits on immersion in air equilibrated 4°C water. (Rawlins & Tauber, 1971).

prene suit at the surface is about 0.045 Btu/hr ft °F. When helium-equilibrated under the same conditions the thermal conductivity is doubled, hence the insulation is halved. At 183 m (600 ft), after equilibration, the insulation is approximately one-fourth of the surface value, and decreases with each dive.

The obvious solution to the problem is a suit made of a noncompressible (syntactic) material. Rawlins and Tauber (1971) examined various samples, some containing small tiles of rigid foam plastic, and one consisting of glass microspheres suspended in a mineral oil base. The former delaminated on return to the surface from a simulated saturation dive in a helium atmosphere. The latter was an impressive technical achievement, but it was unacceptably stiff and bulky, weighing over 40 kg. Before attempting the construction of a suit along these lines, it is necessary to carry out thermal conductivity tests in air and when the material is saturated with helium at pressure. The effect of decompression on the helium-saturated material should also be investigated.

Rawlins and Tauber suggest that the decision to reject dry

suits was premature. Dry suits have an advantage in that cold water does not come in contact with the body. If a dry suit is inflated with a gas with low heat capacities, such as Freon or Carbon dioxide, the insulation at depth is not too different than that provided at the surface. Carbon dioxide has the advantage that it can easily be cleaned, hence prevented from contaminating the atmosphere in the PTC or habitat.

With conventional underwear and air inflation, insulation at the surface is not quite as good as with $\frac{3}{16}$-in. neoprene since 1000 W is needed to maintain heat balance in a tank at 40°F (4°C). But there is little change with depth, and it is simply a matter of supplying enough heat.

A better gas-trapping undergarment is required, because for a 6-ft diver upright in the water there is a 0.2 kg/cm² (3 psi) pressure gradient between the top of the head and the soles of the feet. Hence conventional insulating garments are compressed around the lower legs, while the insulating gas tends to inflate the upper part of the suit. What is required is a $\frac{3}{8}$ in. material that is flexible yet resistant to compression, with fine-diameter interconnecting cells or interstices.

SUMMARY

Increased ambient pressure and gas density seem to have no effect on the subjective intensity of taste or olfaction in a nitrogen–oxygen environment. Very little is known about the effects of water or increased barometric pressure on the functioning of the tactile sense, despite the fact that divers very often have to rely entirely on their tactual sense because of the complete absence of visual stimulation in murky waters. It is doubtful that there is a "water effect." In cold water, however, a marked deterioration of tactile discrimination has been noted.

In water below normal body temperature, an unprotected man loses heat about 21 times faster than he would in normal air at the same ambient temperature. A combination of insulation and work extends man's tolerance to cold water. Cold acclimatization in air is a well-known experience, however, very few investigations of acclimatization to cold in cold water have been made. One study seems to indicate a short time adaptation to cold as a result of extensive diving in the cold sea, and also a special pattern of successive acclimatization. Much more research has to be done in this area.

Physiological effects of cold and water temperature are discussed in the chapter. The effects of cold on the air passages and the lungs are of very great importance to the diver, especially when the inert gas used possesses high heat conductivity, and the problem is strongly accentuated in modern deep diving wherein greater and greater depths are involved. Respiratory heat loss has been measured and increases with depth and respiratory volume per minute. The greatest measured heat loss, 780 W, occurred during heavy work at a depth of 305 m (1000 ft) with a respiratory volume of 64 liters/ min and with an inspired gas temperature of 0 to 2° C.

It has been shown that diving in cold water increases motor loss and causes a disruption in mental tasks. Impairment in performance on multitasks is considerable. The losses are found to be proportional to the degree of cold and exposure time, and seem to follow a course similar to that of skin temperature decrease.

Various forms of insulation designed to protect divers from the cold underwater environment are discussed in the chapter.

VI

COMMUNICATION UNDER WATER

Introduction — Visual communication — Tactile communication — Verbal communication — The sender — The message — Transmission equipment — The receiver — Summary

Because of the hazardous and unusual nature of the undersea environment, a great deal of attention must be directed to the development of reliable underwater communications. The optical transmission of water sets an unavoidable limit on the ranges over which visual methods can be used. However, such systems exist today, and the most useful form is the hand signal. Also, tactile communications systems are discussed in the chapter.

It seems obvious that providing a diver with the ability to communicate verbally with his associates will improve his performance on complex tasks under water. Many problems concerning underwater verbal communications systems are discussed in the chapter. Speech production is severely distorted because of increased pressure, or rather the changed gas density and the changed velocity of sound for a particular gas mixture. A message is hard to understand unless it is short and precise. The transmission of electromagnetic energy through seawater is so heavily attenuated that it is necessary to turn to acoustic energy to transmit information over any appreciable range of ocean. However, the absorption of acoustic energy also constitutes severe limitations.

Helium speech unscrambling is discussed in the chapter. The listener or receiver in the underwater communication system has many audiological problems which have been discussed in detail in Chapter III.

INTRODUCTION

Any system that uses man as an integral part of its design almost necessarily includes some form of communication. Our use of the term communication is very general in nature, and it is meant to indicate only the transmission of information from one location to another where it can be utilized. Several of the sensory modalities of both the sender and the receiver are often intimately involved in this transmission process, and therefore can be considered part of the communication system. Verplanck (1949) describes communications systems as being either direct or mediated. "Direct systems are those in which the sender is in direct contact with the receiver through the physical medium of communication and transmits the message by voice, by gesture, or other previously agreed upon code. In supplemented direct systems, the sender or the receiver, or both, may make use of special aids to communicate through the medium. For the sender, these may include signal lights, semaphore flags, megaphones, or similar devices for increasing the distances across which the symbols produced may be . . . transmitted."

Mediated communications systems are ones that do not require the sender to stimulate the receiver directly. They instead make use of more-or-less elaborate mechanical or electronic devices for the conversion of energies. These converted forms of energy are transmitted to the location requiring the information, where they are converted back to their original form for the ultimate stimulation of the receiver.

Verplanck also describes two general classes of messages. The first he calls persistent communications, or "those which are not necessarily addressed to a specific receiver, which neither require nor expect immediate action." An example of such a message in diving is the code-alpha flag flown by international diving vessels when they have divers in the water. The second general class is termed transient communications, or "those which either require immediate and precise response on the part of the receiver, or the contents of which are urgently needed by the receiver as the basis for immediate decisions on course of action." An example of a transient communication is a diver's rope-pulling signal indicating a need for more slack in his line. Persistent communications have tended to be largely visual, while transient communications have tended to be auditory, although just about any one of the human sensory modalities can be used for either type of message.

Because of the hazardous and unusual nature of the undersea environment and the fact that even relatively minor equipment malfunctions can prove fatal to a diver, most of the attention in underwater communications has been directed toward transient communication systems. Verplanck (1949) has listed the seven properties that are desirable in a transient communication system:

Speed. "Messages must be transmitted to the receiver without delay, and must stimulate the receiver in such a way that he in turn does not delay in responding."

Precision. "The system should permit no misunderstanding of the message. Transmission of the message should be in a precise and unequivocal manner."

Identification and acknowledgment. "The system should provide for clear identification of the sender, and of the intended receiver."

Simplicity. "Simplicity should lie not only in the design and construction of the instruments employed, but also in the method used."

Attention. "The system should demand the attention of the receiver. Since transient communications are almost always aperiodic, the sender must be able to prepare or set the receiver for the message to be transmitted."

Dependability. "A dependable system is one that is ready for efficient use at any time. Lack of dependability is one of the factors that has led to the general dissatisfaction with direct visual communication in the diving environment."

Freedom from interruption. "The ideal communication system for transient messages should be easily limited to use for its specific purpose. It should not lend itself to casual, unnecessary communication; this is best achieved if the system is designed in such a way that trivial communication is unlikely."

As more and more complex underwater systems are developed that require coordinated operator performance, the need for interoperator transient communication will increase. The environmental conditions in which interoperator communicaton is required are:

System Description	Sender's and Receiver Environment
Surface ↔ bell or habitat	Surface ↔ dry ambient
Surface ↔ diver	Surface ↔ wet ambient
Bell or habitat ↔ diver	Dry ambient ↔ wet ambient
Diver ↔ diver	Wet ambient ↔ wet ambient
Habitat or bell ↔ habitat or bell	Dry ambient ↔ dry ambient
Surface ↔ submarine	Surface ↔ 1 ATA dry
Submarine ↔ bell or habitat	1 ATA dry ↔ dry ambient
Submarine ↔ diver	1 ATA dry ↔ wet ambient
Submarine ↔ submarine	1 ATA dry ↔ 1 ATA dry

In addition to the interoperator communication channels described above, attention must also be given to the very critical link between a diver and his equipment. In the hazardous undersea environment, the diver's life may very well depend upon receiving correct, timely information from his environmental sensors and life-support equipment.

In the design or improvement of a communications system, a complete classification, census, and content analysis of all messages, their origins, and their intended destinations should be included. Such an analysis should reveal clear-cut distinctions between necessary and unnecessary communication in content and direction of messages.

The analysis should indicate the stations between which messages must be transmitted, the minimal content of such messages, and the frequency with which these minimal messages are transmitted. From this information it should be possible to produce a communications system versatile enough to handle all situations and yet not so complex that it exceeds an individual's immediate memory span. The fewer the messages and the greater the simplicity of content, the easier, more precise, and rapid the receiver's response.

In most cases analysis of the operational requirements determines the sensory modality to be used and the optimal display configuration. This may not, however, be the case in all situations, and an undersea researcher should be aware of some of the options open to him. The discussion that follows is designed to review what has been and is being done in developing undersea communication for divers.

VISUAL COMMUNICATION

Environmental Factors

Visual communication systems are dependent upon an unobstructed optical pathway between the sender and the receiver. The optical transmission of water sets an unavoidable limit on the ranges over which visual methods can be used. Because the optical characteristics of seawater vary so radically, the effectiveness of distant visual communication is very irregular.

Physiological Factors

Verplanck (1949) has described the human physiological functions that limit visual communication. They are:

1. Photopic and scotopic visibility.
2. Visual acuity.
3. Level of adaptation.
4. Intensity discrimination.
5. Hue discrimination.
6. Flicker discrimination.
7. Visual fields.

The sensitivity of all seven of these visual functions can be altered up or down by the conditions in the undersea environment. Special attention should be given to the information on vision in Chapter II. The functional integrity of the visual system pretty much governs the type of visual display used.

Display Factors

Verplanck also listed 10 dimensions of the visual signal that man is capable of detecting. Any one, or any combination, of the following dimensions can be used to communicate information in the undersea environment.

The variations in visual stimuli that may serve as the basis of communication are:

1. Brightness.
2. Brightness contrast.
3. Color.
4. Temporal patterning.
5. Size.
6. Shape.
7. Position.
8. Movement.
9. Numerosity.
10. Spatial patterning.

Disadvantages

Using these 10 dimensions, it is possible to create an almost infinite number of visual signals to communicate information. However, the number and variety of messages that can be transmitted without complex and bulky systems, or without extensive training, are limited. Verplanck (1949) reported: "A completely flexible visual communications system that does not utilize the printed word would require such a tremendously complex series of visual symbols, each with its own meaning, that only with extreme difficulty could the sender and receiver learn them" (p. 251). Divers have used printed words to communicate among themselves and with topside personnel for many years; however, this form of communication is limited, awkward, and slow and is usually employed only as a last resort.

Advantages

Visual communication is not all bad, however, and there are in fact some definite advantages to be gained with visual displays. Verplanck listed the following six advantages of visual communication:

1. It is easily rendered resistant to interference from various types of competition such as masking by noise.

2. The visual signals employed may be made to persist through a period of time great enough so that the immediate memory span of the receiver is not exceeded, as often happens in hearing.

3. A wide variety of information may be simultaneously transmitted.

4. Several individuals may simultaneously receive the message.

5. Rapid, accurate methods of acknowledgment are made possible.

6. Visual communication designed for specific purposes is not apt to be subject to circuit jamming.

Visual Systems in Use

Where the range of observation is limited to rather short distances and the environmental attenuation is negligible, as in the interior of a bell, submarine, or habitat, the use of visual communications is not only possible, but often the most advantageous. Present undersea systems use visually communicated information in several forms. The current systems can be classified as either fixed or flexible, and as either interoperator or operator-machine systems. Fixed systems are those designed to communicate one type of information, while flexible systems are used for many different types of information.

The following is a classification of available communication systems.

Fixed visual communication
    Interoperator
        Flags and buoys
        Flares and smoke
    Operator-machine
        Gages
Flexible visual communication
    Interoperator
        Television
        Electrowriters
        Hand signals
    Operator-machine
        Television

Dyes, flares, and smoke are obviously a rather inflexible communication system. By color-coding the signal, the receiver can determine the presence and gross status of the sender. No precise control of a receiver can be exerted through such a simple system, however.

The use of flags on surface-support craft to signal the presence of working divers has long been a standard international policy. However, even the most frequently used flag signals were not standardized until recently. For many years the "figure-4 flag" (Figure 6-1) was used by the U.S. Navy as its standard.

In 1971 the U.S. Navy adopted the international flag signal "code-alpha" (Figure 6-2). Military ships throughout the world fly both the code and the alpha flags. Merchant ships fly only the alpha flag.

A third flag signal used to signal the presence of divers is one that is not found among international flags. However, it seems to be universally recognized and is used by most of the sport diver associations of the world. This third flag is known simply as the "diving flag" (Figure 6-3).

With the exception of television, all the information an operator receives concerning the status of his undersea system comes via fixed visual sensing devices. Because of the shortcomings associated with this type of communication system, it is essenial that undersea operators monitor their displays constantly.

Flexible visual communication systems have the advantage of being able to handle many different kinds of information; however, they still require attention and constant monitoring on the part of the receiver. Verplanck (1949) points out that television systems are ideal for the transmission of visual information of any type over great distances. He also points out, though, that the size and complexity of television systems are a real disadvantage. Undersea engineers who have tried to maintain closed-circuit televisions in high pressure helium–oxygen environments can attest to the difficulties associated with these complex systems. The helium in the synthetic gas mixture used by manned deep diving systems penetrates just about everything and has devastating effects on television monitors.

For interoperator communication, television is a useful method when supplemented with an auditory signal. The receiver is stimulated both aurally and visually by the sender, and is effectively placed in direct contact with him.

Perhaps one of the most basic but still one of the most useful forms of undersea communications is the hand signal. But again, the sender must have the receiver's attention before he can communicate his information. Diachenko (1972) describes a device, the scuba horn, that can be used for getting a buddy diver's attention. It is a simple vibratory reed (metal or plastic) mounted inside a

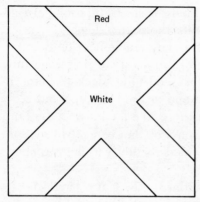

Figure 6-1. Figure 4 flag.

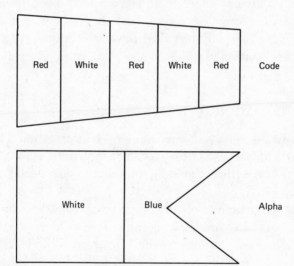

Figure 6-2. Code-alpha flags.

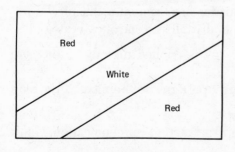

Figure 6-3. Diving flag.

blowpipe. The blowpipe is a small "noise maker" type of horn attached to a curved clip which permits the entire device to be inserted through the mouthpiece of a standard single-hose scuba regulator and seated in the upper portion of the regulator breathing tube section. To sound the horn, the diver need only block the mouthpiece opening under and around the end of the blowpipe and blow in a sort of "tongue-out" splitting position. The loudness of the horn is, of course, directly related to the mass of the reed set in motion; however, loud sounding can be obtained readily without strenuous blowing.

Figures 6-4 to 6-23 show the standard U.S. Navy hand signals used by scuba divers. These hand signals have been used since the 1940s, but to our knowledge they have never been evaluated as to their adequacy. The only test they have been exposed to is the test of time. Their continued use is to some extent an indication of their utility.

TACTILE COMMUNICATION

Man has always received environmental information (heat, cold, pain, etc.) through his skin senses. Yet, not until very recently has he attempted to utilize the skin for systematic interoperator communication.

The skin is sensitive to chemical, thermal, electrical, and mechanical energy, and any one of or combination of these could be used as a communication stimulus. Several different approaches have been tried in the past, but the two that seem to hold the greatest promise are electrical and mechanical stimulation. Readers interested in electrical cutaneous communication should read the report by McCray (1970). Most of the research thus far has been on mechanical stimulation. The studies available generally fall into one of two categories:

1. Those in which speech energy is applied directly to the skin (Gault, 1925).

2. Those in which coded energy patterns are applied to the skin (Geldard, 1960).

In one of the very early attempts at tactual communication, Gault

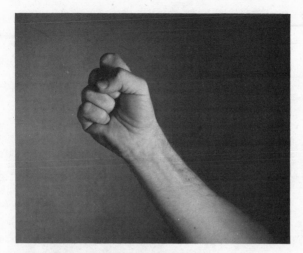

Figure 6-4. "Hold everything."

Figure 6-5. "I am having trouble with my ear."

Figure 6-6. "I am having trouble with my air."

(1925) amplified human speech and applied it to a subject's fingers. After a sequence of 28 half-hour training periods, the subject learned to recognize, with about 75% accuracy, 10 different short sentences. After 30 hr of practice, single words, presented without context, could be recognized about 50% of the time. Geldard (1961) points out, however, that these poor levels of performance deteriorated even further when the talker changed his rate of presentation or when another person presented the verbal material.

Although the eardrum seems to be an evolutionary descendant of cruder ectodermal tissue, the supportive neural networks are grossly different. Speech intelligence and hearing sensitivity are centered in the low-kilocycle frequency range. As the skin is most sensitive in the lower-frequency region of 50 to 500 cps, only the fundamental and first few harmonics can be felt. Even these are likely to be near

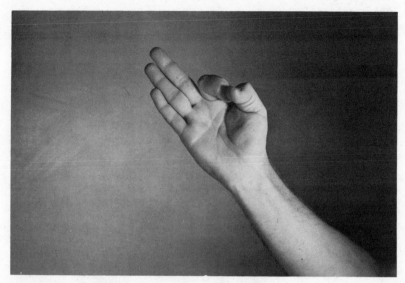

Figure 6-7.   "All right."

the higher, less sensitive end of the skin response range. Rather than attempting to force a receptor system to perform in an unnatural way by trying to adjust it to the world's hardware, it would be better to determine how the world and things in it could be modified to obtain the most from the senses. Geldard (1961) suggested that it is better to ask: "What discriminations are possible for the skin?," and "What is the stuff out of which a cutaneous language has to be built if it is to be optimally utilizable by the skin?"

As indicated above, the sensitivity of the skin to sound is quite high in the range 50 to 500 cps. At these frequencies, the displacement amplitude threshold is about 10^{-5} cm. At frequencies of 10 and 1000 cps, the threshold is about 10^{-3} cm amplitude. Newman (1960) noted that while the displacement required at these marginal frequencies is not large, to obtain displacement to bring extreme frequencies above threshold may result in exceeding the pain threshold at other frequencies.

In the area of mechanical stimulation, there are but a few stimulus dimensions of the first order available. They are location, dura-

Figure 6-8. "Let's go up."

tion, intensity, and frequency. In addition to those four first-order stimulus dimensions, Geldard (1961) also talks about the possibility of using derived stimulus dimensions. Two of the dimensions he suggests are intensity variations as a function of time and waveform. Neither of these derived dimensions has been researched very extensively, and the work that has been done seems to indicate that their usefulness will be marginal.

A tactile communication system that can be used in an operational setting has been developed by Geldard and Howell at the University of Virginia. The system, which is based upon the international Morse code, has been learned by experimental subjects in a laboratory.

Figure 6-9. "Pick me up."

With extensive training, subjects were able to receive a test sentence at the rate of 35 words per minute and achieve 90% accuracy in its reception. Just as in Morse code, the letters were transmitted 0.005 sec. apart, and words were separated by a 0.1-sec. interval. At this rate the average five-letter word takes less than $\frac{1}{10}$ sec to transmit.

The work of Geldard and Howell has been very influential because it is based upon two already well-established communication systems, the English language and the code developed by Morse. If they had tried to develop an entirely new system of flexible message sets, they may not have been as successful. The difficulty in estab-

Figure 6-10.   "Pick me up now."

lishing differentiations and discrimination increases as new responses
are added to the message set. The time required for training is an
exponential function of the number of different discriminations and
differentiations that must be made.

Coding of letters and numerals is really quite a pedestrian way of
getting meanings into tactile patterns, and when communication
speed is essential, other alternatives should be explored. Diachenko
(1971) examined the possibility of adapting the present limited set
of signals used by divers to a vibrotactile communication system.
By restricting the size of the message set and using already familiar

Figure 6-11. Sign for 0.

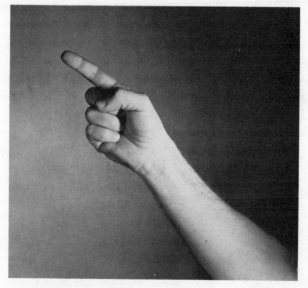

Figure 6-12. Sign for 1.

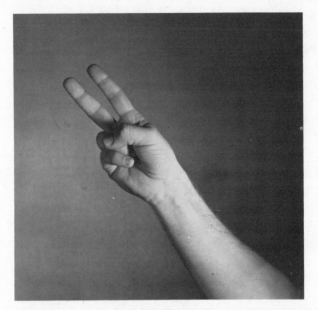

Figure 6-13. Sign for 2.

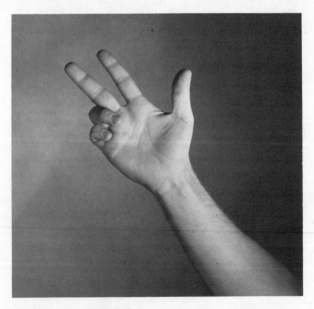

Figure 6-14. Sign for 3.

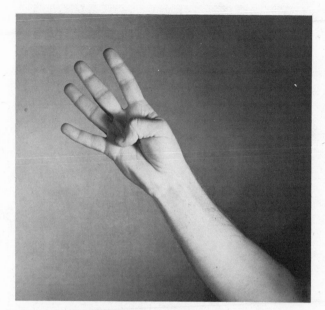

Figure 6-15.   Sign for 4.

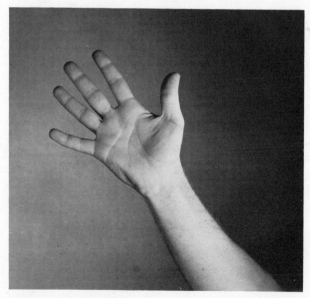

Figure 6-16.   Sign for 5.

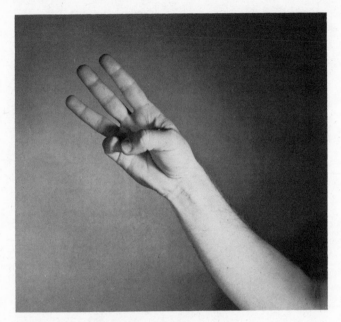

Figure 6-17.   Sign for 6.

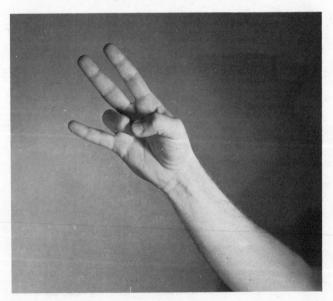

Figure 6-18.   Sign for 7.

Figure 6-19. Sign for 8.

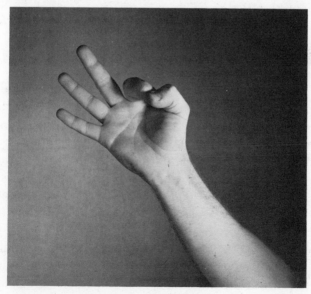

Figure 6-20. Sign for 9.

Figure 6-21. "How deep?"

signals, very little training is required to establish a usable communication system.

Diachenko used six U.S. Navy explosive ordnance disposal technicians, five of whom were experienced Navy divers. The tactual code devised for the study used a "fixed intensity and duration varied temporally between two locations—left and right lower abdomen." The number of stimulation patterns used provided a total of 16 discrete code combinations which could accommodate the 15 basic lifeline signals between tender and diver as well as almost all diver-to-diver visual hand signals. Diachenko selected the lower abdomen as the site for the vibrators for several reasons, the most important of which is diver movement. Because a working diver is rarely motionless, avoidance of signal error due to motion, and minimizing of physical encumberance, become important considera-

tions. Diachenko concluded from his study that the left-right stimulation patterns are satisfactory for a basic diver cutaneous code. It
is important to note, however, that Diachenko's study was conducted in a dry surface environment and that no one has tried to
use a cutaneous code under actual diving conditions.

Before leaving the subject of tactual communication, some mention should be made of Newman's (1960) use of phonemes in this
type of communication system. The use of phonemes offers greater
potential flexibility and speed than the use of words. Phonemes
could also be developed into a form of cutaneous shorthand. The
only real drawback to the use of phonemes seems to be the time
required for learning them.

VERBAL COMMUNICATION

General Information

It is generally accepted that one of the significant advantages over
other species that man has in dealing with his environment, is the
ability to communicate. It therefore seems obvious that providing
divers with the ability to communicate will improve their ability to
deal with their underwater environment. According to Thompson and
Thompson (1970), not only would a diving team be more efficient
in its performance of tasks if provided with speech communications
equipment, but also the manner of task performance in terms of
cooperation would be qualitatively different too.

As part of the Tektite II undersea research program, Thompson
and Thompson made off-line observations at several depths to
identify any changes in performance or behavior patterns that could
be attributed to the use of communications. The original hypothesis
was that divers in a saturated mode of operation demonstrate improved performance when equipped with communication devices.
However, the data were not sufficient to support this. The major
reason for the lack of data was the infrequent use of the communication devices by the diving crews.

Tapes of conversations in the habitat early in the mission reflected
some enthusiasm for the communications gear, particularly by the
first pair of divers. This enthusiasm tapered off by the end of the first

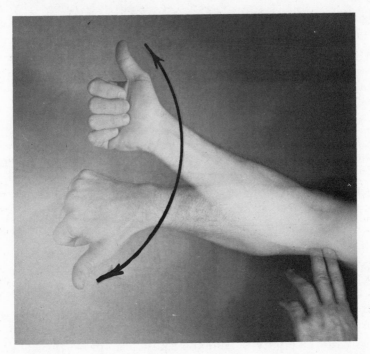

Figure 6-22.   "What direction?"

5-day period, and a negative reaction set in. This reaction was carried to the second diver pair during their 5-day session, and they exercised their option not to use the communication equipment. When the first pair resumed use of the communication equipment, they reinforced their opinion and the equipment was not used again during the mission.

Thompson and Thompson report that this lack of enthusiasm for the communication equipment was due to the following reasons.

"1. The performance of the equipment was below that anticipated by the diving crew. This led to the assignment of the experiment to a lower priority in their schedule of work."

"2. A major ingredient in the progressive reduction of diver interest was lack of experience with the equipment, which could have been alleviated somewhat with a more extensive training schedule."

Figure 6-23. "What time?"

"3. The equipment configuration appeared to cause some operational problems to the diving crew. The cables which interconnect the body mounted components had a tendency to snag on projections either in the habitat entry and exit ways or on sections of the reef when close-in work was performed. In addition, the time required to don the communication gear added to the time spent in assembling scientific equipment and preparing to dive, prolonged the predive activity beyond original expectations."

"4. The heavy work schedule already planned for the missions did not allow the divers any time to increase their skill with the communicators. As a consequence, performance deterioration or equipment failure posed a rescheduling problem which most of the crew did not feel disposed to solve."

"5. There was an understandable reluctance on the part of the crew to use unfamiliar equipment. When considering the background of the mission involving saturated diving in which none of the crew had previous experience, there was a tendency to be more cautious about the use of new equipment. Of the total members in both crews, only two had encountered communication equipment of this kind and configuration, and with all the other unfamiliar aspects of their environment, it is likely that this gear was relegated to a lower priority than would otherwise be the case under more familiar circumstances. An extended training regimen would alleviate this problem" (pp. 29 and 30).

The divers reported, however, that communication would have improved their work 85% of the time. They also estimated that 15% of the time the improvement would have made a "significant difference in performance."

At the conclusion of the mission, discussions were held with the crew to elicit their opinions and reactions to the use of the equipment. The crew reports were generally similar and were summarized as follows.

1. In none of the several attempts to use the equipment was a normal conversation possible. On at least two occasions, the equipment did not work at all.

2. The equipment itself was not comfortable, and loose connecting wires sometimes snagged on protuberances (Thompson and Thompson, 1970).

Speech as a Communication System

It is not too surprising, regardless of the above problems, that speech is still the preferred method of transmitting information from one individual to another. Sergeant (1969) states: "Although man does not achieve his physiological limit of information output during speech, the amount of information per second contained in normal conversation is quite high. In addition, people are accustomed to speaking. Since speech is natural and efficient, it is desirable to make use of voice communications as a means of transferring information between two people whenever possible" (p. 214).

Also, Verplanck (1949) notes that in general, owing to our well-established speech habits, verbal communication systems require far less training of both the sender and receiver than do other types of systems. To be as versatile as speech, other forms of communication become very complex and require relatively long training periods.

The rapidity of auditory communication, and the simplicity of the apparatus required, also ensure that audition will remain the normal and most important method of transient communication. Nevertheless, it may be added that visual communication may prove to be a useful supplement to the voice, particularly in the hyperbaric helium-oxygen environment.

A speech communication system, as described by McCormick (1964), consists of essentially four elements:

1. The message to be transmitted.
2. The individual transmitting the message.
3. The transmitting system (the air, a telephone, a radio, etc.).
4. The receiver.

McCormick (1964) also lists the four primary characteristics of speech which in turn give rise to corresponding sensations:

Speech Characteristics	Corresponding Sensation
Intensity (usually decibels)	Loudness
Frequency (usually Hz)	Pitch
Harmonic composition	Quality
Time characteristics	Time perception

Problems in Verbal Underwater Communication

Oral communication in underwater situations is difficult and often unsatisfactory for a variety of reasons. Speech in the underwater environment can suffer because of any one distortion or combination of distortions. These distortions may be a result of:

1. Electronic equipment.
2. High ambient pressures.
3. Exotic gases (especially as in a helium-rich atmosphere).
4. Reverberations within a chamber or headpiece.
5. Individual talker or listener differences.

6. Poor choice of words with respect to intelligibility (Sergeant, 1966a, 1969).

Bond and Myatt (1969) cite similar sources of distortion, but included also poorly designed oral cavities (the addition of restricted oral cavities to the normal vocal tract).

The media in which sounds are formed and transmitted plays an important part in vocal communications. Morrow (1970) notes that the velocity of sound in helium is approximately two and one-half times that in ordinary sea-level air. The formula for the velocity of sound in a gas,

$$c = \left(\frac{\gamma P}{\rho}\right)^{1/2}$$

where τ = ratio of specific heats of a gas
P = equilibrium or ambient pressure
ρ = equilibrium density of a gas,

gives a fair approximation of the formant shifts observed in helium speech (Sergeant, 1969). Actual observations give values less than those predicted. Part of the lack of agreement between predicted and observed values might be explained in terms of adaptations by the talker based on his auditory feedback system.

Sergeant (1969) also goes on to explain that, when an acoustic signal is transmitted directly through the water for any distance, echoes from the surface, bottom, or objects in the water can degrade the signal before it is received. The greater the distance, the larger these disturbances become. In addition to reverberation in the water, reverberation occurs within the cavities of diving helmets and in larger enclosures such as underwater habitats and/or hyperbaric chambers.

The problem of noise is another difficulty to be confronted. Noise might come from the environment of the talker and/or listener or from electrical and/or electromagnetic interference within the system itself (Morgan, Cook, Chapanis & Lund, 1963).

Examples of the noises produced by the diver or by the environment are:
Diver-produced:

Movement of clothing and breathing gear.
Breathing noises.
Rubbing movement of the microphone and earphone.
Hissing of gas.

Environmentally produced:
Biological sounds from porpoises, whales, snapping shrimp, and
other animals.
Local shipping.
Sonar transmissions.
Geological factors such as waves, surf, and falling rain.

The effects of noise on speech communication can be combated by
the use of ear-protection devices and microphone noise shields,
noise-canceling microphones, signal control and processing, and special headsets.

In many situations in which accurate communication is necessary,
masking noise is so high in intensity that an individual is not able to
discriminate the message from the background noise. An ambient
noise of 110 dB and higher has been measured in military and commercial diving helmets. This noise, 25 dB higher than health standards recommend, may be a contributing cause to the hearing loss
found in diving personnel. High-velocity input air and exhaust
bubble oscillation are considered contributing noise factors. Attempts to reduce input air noise produced significant results in the
octave bands between 500 Hz and 1000 Hz. The noise reduction obtained increased the signal-to-noise ratio in the helmet and enhanced the diver's communication capability (Beagles, 1969.)

Limitations of Voice Communication

Problems in auditory communication associated with the listener are
usually less severe than those associated with the speaker.

Sergeant (1966b) has pointed out that, if a voice signal can be
precisely produced, amplified, and projected into the water it can
usually be heard and understood at great distances. It is the production, amplification, and projection of the signal that is the major
problem in underwater voice communication.

If speech could be effectively transduced from a diver's speech
mechanism into several of the systems now available, it could be

transmitted through the water with a high degree of intelligibility (Hollien, Coleman, Thompson & Hunter 1968). Specifically, the diver must be aided in overcoming factors restricting the production of intelligible speech such as those enumerated below.

1. Acoustic effect of a nosecup and of inlet and exhaust hoses.
2. Bubble and inlet noise.
3. Constraint of facial movement.
4. Any pulsating of the mask on the face as a result of intermittent release of bubbles.

Three general ways were proposed by the Panel on Psychology and Physiology (1949) to improve the quality of the human and vocal elements in communication.

1. Operators manning the more important communication posts can be selected for their ability to speak intelligibly, and interpret messages that have been masked by noise.
2. All operators can be trained to speak more intelligibly.
3. All important messages can be standardized so that, without departing too far from common usage, they are short, simple, easy to say, and easy to understand.

The panel went on to explain that routine tests of hearing acuity, standard criteria of "good" speech, and conventional methods for rating and training public speakers are not valid for the peculiar conditions of military communication in noise, even though they may be very valuable for the concerns of everyday life. The criterion here is not effectiveness, pleasantness, nor any aesthetic quality. The crucial factor, is whether the message can be both heard and understood.

Testing Diver Communication for Greater Efficiency

In 1967, Hollien and Thompson described a system developed to provide a rigorously controlled milieu within which the testing of hearing and speaking functions under water can be accomplished. Provisions were made for:

1. The presentation and receiving of acoustic stimuli.

2. The transmission of visual material for use either as multiple-choice hearing test response items or as test material for studies of speech production.

3. The transmission of multiple-choice responses by the subject to a digital (IBM) surface control unit.

The Diver Communication Research System (DICORS) has been designed for testing diver communication in shallow water. It consists of an open framework of plastic tubing which is acoustically transparent to audible frequencies used to support a diver and appropriate equipment. The essential elements of DICORS include an underwater television monitor and camera, calibrated hydrophones, response switches, and sound projectors. A head positioner and weight belt ensure proper diver positioning; the use of a monitoring television camera, emergency switch, and reserve air supply ensure that a diver is protected from excessive hazards. DICORS allows studies in speech production, hearing evaluation, and instrumentation assessment to be carried out under controlled experimental conditions (Hollien & Tolhurst, 1969). Several of the underwater communication studies reported in this chapter were carried out using the DICORS system (Hollien et al., 1968, 1969, 1970).

As described by Morgan, Cook, Chapanis, and Lund (1963), most of the work done on intelligibility has been through the use of one of three tests:

1. Nonsense syllable tests.
2. Monosyllable word tests.
3. Sentence tests.

These are partly illustrated in Tables 6-1 to 6-6.

In monosyllable word tests items are usually drawn from a set of 20 lists of 50 words each in which the frequency of occurrence of the various fundamental speech sounds is proportional to their frequency of occurrence in everyday speech. These lists are called Harvard PB (phonetically balanced) word lists.

The articulation index (AI) is worth noting here. Morgan et al. (1963) describe the AI formulation as being based on the fact that, to obtain high intelligibility, one must deliver a considerable fraction of the total speech bandwidth to the listener's ear, and that the sig-

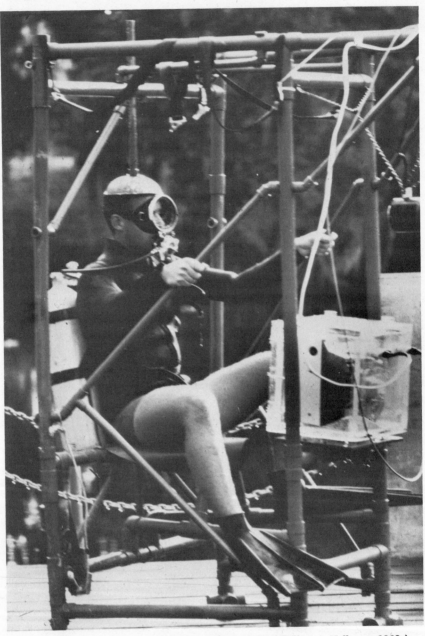

Figure 6-24.   Diver communication research system. (Hollien & Tolhurst, 1969.)

Table 6-1   Nonsense Syllable List No. 1
(Morgan, Cook, Chapanis and Lund, 1963)

1. monz	26. dahf	51. zohm	76. duhm
2. nihf	27. fohf	52. gohn	77. map
3. nan	28. fook	53. pahz	78. zaf
4. ʒeef*	29. kohth	54. thoop	79. puhf
5. dayth	30. thehʒ	55. dad	80. gahk
6. thayd	31. muhd	65. koof	81. pohd
7. gayf	32. kawd	57. pooth	82. nohg
8. thawf	33. zihg	58. fuhp	83. ʒuhg
9. dohp	34. kuhk	59. gehg	84. dihʒ
10. fayg	35. ʒihd	60. nood	85. pawg
11. meek	36. zehd	61. fehm	86. nawz
12. thuhn	37. ʒayp	62. dehz	87. mawʒ
13. geed	38. theez	63. mihth	88. fɑhd
14. kihp	39. fihn	64. faz	89. dawk
15. zahp	40. mehf	65. kaʒ	90. fawth
16. kayz	41. keem	66. nahʒ	91. gihz
17. pam	42. ʒehth	67. mahm	92. gawp
18. payʒ	43. nehk	68. kehn	93. neep
19. naym	44. ʒawm	69. goom	94. guhʒ
20. mayn	45. feeʒ	70. doon	95. zayk
21. deeg	46. peen	71. pihk	96. zeeth
22. ʒahn	47. thag	72. ʒak	97. zuhz
23. thahth	48. kahg	73. moog	98. gath
24. zawn	49. thihm	74. zooʒ	99. pehp
25. thahk	50. ʒohʒ	75. ʒooz	100. nuhth

* ʒ IPA Symbol for the zh sound.

nal-to-noise ratio at the listener's ear must be reasonably high. If the speech peaks are 30 dB or more above the noise throughout the frequency band from 200 to 6100 Hz, the listener will make essentially no errors (AI = 1.00). There are two AI methods, the 20-band method and the weighted-octave band method.

Following are certain intelligibility criteria:

AI	Description
0.7 to 1.0	Satisfactory to excellent.
0.3 to 0.7	Slightly difficult to satisfactory—up to 98%

of the sentences are heard correctly.

0.0 to 0.3   Impossible to difficult—special vocabularies and radio-telephone voice procedures are required.

Kohl and Searle (1957) describe articulation scores obtained at four depths in a deep-sea hard hat. Each run consisted of a different PB word list and was read by the diver/announcer to seven listeners. The average values were:

50 ft (15m)—36.8% correct   100 ft (30m)—23.4% correct
150 ft (46m)—17.6% correct   190 ft (58m)—17.5% correct

For deep-sea helmet diver/listener runs, the announcer was outside

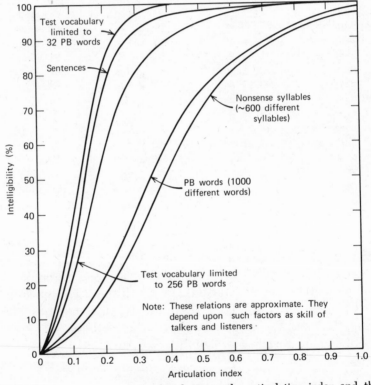

Figure 6-25. Approximate relationship between the articulation index and the intelligibility of various types of speech test materials. (Morgan, Cook, Chapanis & Lund, 1963.)

the pressure tank and the diver was the listener. The results were:

50 ft (15m)—61% correct   100 ft (30m)—55% correct
150 ft (46m)—52% correct   190 ft (58m)—40% correct

The articulation tests used were patterned after those developed for testing aviation voice communication systems.

The results indicate what most professional divers have known for years, that it is extremely difficult to communicate with top side personnel. The high noise levels in the diving helmet due to the circulating breathing gases make it almost impossible to send or receive

Table 6-2   Nonsense Syllable List No. 2
(Morgan, Cook, Chapanis and Lund, 1963)

1. neen	26. nehp	51. theeg	76. fawf
2. nahz	27. mood	52. thuhm	77. puhk
3. maym	28. ʒoog	53. fohk	78. fayd
4. kaz	29. poof	54. zohʒ	79. muhth
5. dehg	30. nihk	55. duhʒ	80. aeef
6. man	31. kook	56. dath	81. fehʒ
7. geeth	32. zahn	57. mahʒ	82. thawk
8. gawm	33. mawz	58. mihf	83. kahd
9. thad	34. gehd	59. ʒahm	84. meep
10. nohd	35. kehm	60. ʒayn	85. nayʒ
11. fag	36. ʒihth	61. thayth	86. gohm
12. dayf	37. mehk	62. mohg	87. payz
13. dawp	38. gihg	63. zuhg	88. zooz
14. dihz	39. fihm	64. gaf	89. kihn
15. thehz	40. guhz	65. ʒap	90. doom
16. thahf	41. nawg	66. ʒuhd	91. peem
17. kahf	42. gooʒ	67. gahp	92. kawth
18. zihd	43. fuhn	68. fahth	93. gayk
19. pawd	44. ʒohz	69. pehn	94. zawm
20. ʒeek*	45. dohn	70. pahg	95. ʒehf
21. dahk	46. ʒawʒ	71. foop	96. deed
22. feez	47. nuhg	72. zehth	97. nooth
23. thihʒ	48. kayg	73. pohth	98. nam
24. keeʒ	49. thoon	74. thohp	99. kuhp
25. zayp	50. pihp	75. paʒ	100. zak

* ʒ IPA Symbol for the zh sound

Table 6-3   PB Word List No. 1
(Morgan, Cook, Chapanis and Lund, 1963)

1. smile	14. box	27. are	40. fuss
2. strife	15. deed	28. cleanse	41. folk
3. pest	16. feast	29. clove	42. bar
4. end	17. hunt	30. crash	43. dike
5. heap	18. grove	31. hive	44. such
6. toe	19. bad	32. bask	45. wheat
7. hid	20. mange	33. plush	46. nook
8. creed	21. rub	34. rag	47. pan
9. rat	22. slip	35. ford	48. death
10. no	23. use (yews)	36. rise	49. pants
11. there	24. is	37. dish	50. cane
12. then	25. not	38. fraud	
13. fern	26. pile	39. ride	

Table 6-4   PB Word List No. 2
(Morgan, Cook, Chapanis and Lund, 1963)

1. gill	14. dab	27. mute	40. start
2. suck	15. earl	28. rib	41. bounce
3. perk	16. bean	29. awe	42. bud
4. fate	17. nut	30. trash	43. frog
5. five	18. ways	31. corpse	44. quart
6. need	19. wish	32. bait	45. rap
7. pick	20. pit	33. jab	46. charge
8. log	21. cloud	34. hit	47. sludge
9. nab	22. scythe	35. hock	48. tang
10. else	23. blush	36. niece	49. them
11. gloss	24. shoe	37. tan	50. vamp
12. hire	25. snuff	38. vast	
13. bought	26. moose	39. our	

clear verbal messages. A common practice among divers is to close the breathing gas supply valve when either sending or receiving information. Most open-circuit diving helmets and dry suits contain enough gas to allow the gas supply to be interrupted for several minutes.

Probably the single most important factor that would aid diotic

Table 6-5   Test Sentence List No. 1
(Morgan, Cook, Chapanis and Lund, 1963)

Question	Answer
1. What do you saw wood with?	Saw
2. What letter comes after B?	C
3. What is the color of coal?	Black
4. Which is smaller, a dog or a horse?	Dog
5. What is the opposite of white?	Black
6. What comes between 2 and 4?	3
7. How many weeks are there in a month?	4
8. What do you hear with?	Ears
9. Does a cat eat bricks or mice?	Mice
10. What do you use to unlock a door?	Key
11. What letter comes before D?	C
12. Do elephants have a hump or a trunk?	Trunk
13. What is the opposite of wet?	Dry
14. What number comes before 12?	11
15. What day comes before Wednesday?	Tuesday
16. How many pennies are there in a dime?	10
17. Does a horse eat oats or chickens?	Oats
18. What do you spread butter with?	Knife
19. What number comes before 2?	1
20. What color is ketchup?	Red
21. What is the opposite of young?	Old
22. What month comes after March?	April
23. Does an eagle have wings or arms?	Wings
24. What number comes after 20?	21
25. How many wheels does a bicycle have?	2

listening under almost every condition of noise interference is an increase in the bandwidth of the system (Tolhurst, 1971). Both laboratory and field experiments have shown that Shannon's theorem, reciprocally equating bandwidth and time, appears to be valid. That is, to transmit a fixed amount of information, as bandwidth is restricted, the time must be extended. Or, conversely, information transfer can take place in a shorter period of time if bandwidth is increased. As early as 1946, it was found that as bandwidth is restricted it is possible to compensate by increasing the intensity of speech. It was also reported that, in an experimental comparison of a military communication system versus a wide-band system, a 15-

Table 6-6   Test Sentence List No. 2
(Morgan, Cook, Chapanis and Lund, 1963)

Question	Answer
1. What letter comes after C?	D
2. What is the opposite of narrow?	Broad, wide
3. Which is higher, a hill or a mountain?	Mountain
4. What is the opposite of tall?	Short
5. What day comes after Tuesday?	Wednesday
6. How many months are there in a year?	12
7. What number comes after 5?	6
8. Does a man wear a hat or a table?	Hat
9. What do you chop wood with?	Axe
10. What letter comes before E?	D
11. What is the color of butter?	Yellow
12. What is the opposite of dry?	Wet
13. What day comes after Thursday?	Friday
14. What country is Moscow in?	Russia
15. What letter comes after B?	C
16. How many toes are there on each foot?	5
17. What do you tell the date by?	Calendar
18. What number comes before 3?	2
19. What is the opposite of love?	Hate
20. What color is the cloth on a pool table?	Green
21. What month comes after June?	July
22. How much is 1 and 8?	9
23. Does an owl lay books or an egg?	Egg
24. What number comes before 20?	19
25. Do palm trees grow in Alaska?	No

to 25-dB intensity increase in the military system was required to achieve articulation scores equal to those of the wide-band system. Licklider and Miller (1951) found that good speech reception scores required at least a 6-dB signal-to-noise ratio; but if the speech is distorted (band-limited), higher signal-to-noise values are needed to obtain adequate speech reception.

Effects of Breathing Systems upon Diver Verbal Communication

As discussed earlier, physical factors such as depth, gas mixture,

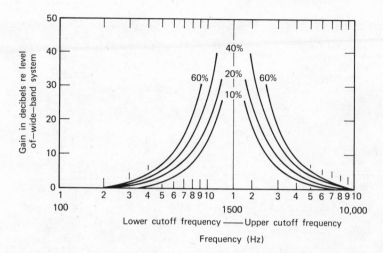

Figure 6-26. Equal articulation contours for bandpass systems in noise. (Egan and Wiener, 1946.)

mask design, and so on, degrade elements of the communication process via threshold shifts, formant frequency shifts, signal-to-noise ratio shifts, and so forth. The net consequence of these degradations, namely, loss of intelligibility, is seen as reduced verbal communication capability. This reduction may appear in a variety of modes including increases in transmission errors, reduction in transmission rates and, eventually, increases in task accomplishment times. In short, system performance may be degraded wherever time-dependent, integrated diver activity is required (Thompson & Streimer, 1971).

In an experiment, dealing with the effects of the breathing apparatus on communications (Table 6-7) Thompson and Streimer positioned two divers on opposite sides of a task board containing a 14 × 14 grid (Figure 6-27). The divers were required to send each other messages in accordance with instructions each diver received at the test site. In response to a command issued by the unseen diver on the other side of the task board, the receiving diver was required to select a stipulated tab from a specific peripheral grid location. The selection of the tab, its placement in a square on the board, and its orientation within the square matrix were all made in accordance with the instructions transmitted by the unseen diver.

Figure 6-27.   Divers working on task board. (Thompson & Streimer, 1971.)

Table 6-7   List of Dives Completed during Program
(Thompson and Streimer, 1971)[a]

Day	Dive No.	Breathing Equipment	Gas Mixture
1	1	Closed cycle	Air
	2	Open cycle	Air
	3	Closed cycle	Helium–oxygen
	4	Closed cycle	Argon–oxygen
2	5	Open cycle	Air
	6	Closed cycle	Argon–oxygen
	7	Closed cycle	Air
	8	Closed cycle	Helium-oxygen
3	9	Closed cycle	Helium-oxygen
	10	Closed cycle	Air
	11	Open cycle	Air
	12	Closed cycle	Argon-oxygen
4	13	Closed cycle	Air
	14	Closed cycle	Helium--oxygen
	15	Open cycle	Air
	16	Closed cycle	Helium–oxygen
5	17	Open cycle	Air
	18	Closed cycle	Air
	19	Closed cycle	Helium–oxygen
	20	Open cycle	Air
6	21	Closed cycle	Air
	22	Open cycle	Air
	23	Closed cycle	Helium

[a] Mean depth, 33 ft (10 m), mean water temperature, 78°F., visibility, 50 ft (15 m).

The transmitted instructions contained information pertaining to the location of the tab, the location of the placement grid, and the orientation of the tab with respect to which side was to be face up and which edge was to be at the 12 o'clock position.

The second diver acknowledged the transmission by repeating aloud his understanding of the message he received or, at his option, called for a repeat of the message from the first diver. The receiver could ask for up to three repeats of the message. The second diver was not given confirmation as to the correctness of his responses to the transmitted messages.

Over half of the messages transmitted suffered a complete loss in intelligibility when helium–oxygen was the breathing gas, while 25% of the message content was destroyed during transmissions in which air was the breathing gas.

When compared with results from 75 college students in a dry surface environment on the same task, it was observed that the underwater environment produced a performance degradation which slowed transmission of messages to a rate one-third of that on the surface.

The distribution of errors over selected sound pairs or groups was different for the helium/oxygen mixtures as compared to the nitrogen/oxygen mixture.

Later, it was noted by Thompson and Streimer that speakers developed an operational transmission pattern in open-circuit systems which consisted of accelerated delivery of the message and coincident breathing by both divers. This resulted in sporadic bursts of communication alternating with loud expulsion and inhalation sounds. The ability to coordinate breathing was facilitated by the nature of the instruction message, which allowed the listener to control his breathing so that respiratory sounds did not occur during the receiving of messages. This was possible because the message length and format were fixed.

It may be anticipated that in an operational situation involving the transmission of messages of varying lengths, the ability of divers to control their breathing pattern coincident with the message units may not be possible, causing a reduction in message units transmitted per unit time in open-circuit systems.

Underwater Sound Transmission

As noted by Doherty, Hollien, and Thompson (1967), refraction is also a major problem in underwater sound transmission. Pressure, salinity, temperature, and temperature gradients affect the velocity profile and thus may cause refraction. In shallow water the effect of these variables on acoustic transmission properties is minimized. In fact, the rate of attenuation due to divergence in shallow water is equal to that in air (i.e., inversely proportional to the square of the distance) only over short ranges. For longer distances divergence is no longer spherical but is limited to horizontal spreading, and the rate of attenuation decreases to a proportion that is related simply to the inverse of the distance.

In a field test by Doherty et al. (1967) using a water depth of 32 m (105 ft), three sound projector depths of 1, 16, and 30 m (3, 52, and 98 ft), and six horizontal ranges of 1, 16, 31, 100, 320, and 525 m (3, 52, 102, 328, 1050, and 1722 ft), only two consistent patterns were found. First, when the projector was near the surface, destructive interference was most effective at low frequencies; second, responses showed less variation when the transducers were at mid-depth or below. The sound pressure level reduction was frequency-dependent, but not to a degree that interfered with direct audio transmission of speech signals through the water.

The Sender

Speech Production

When a person speaks, air moves from the lungs, past the vocal cords in the throat, into the mouth and nose, and out into the environment. If the vocal cords are tensed, they are set into vibration by this stream of air. Vibration of the vocal cords in turn modulates the air stream so that it becomes a rapid sequence of puffs or pulses, the primary source of vocal sounds. A secondary source of vocal sound power is the turbulence produced as the air stream passes through narrow constrictions in the vocal passages (Morgan, Cook, Chapanis & Lund 1963).

As described by Cherry (1966), the vocal production system is constituted of a myriad of turbulent motions, each having a minute amount of energy; this system would set up an acoustic spectrum of uniform energy at all frequencies (at least over the audible range) were it not for the selective resonance characteristics of the vocal tract. These resonance characteristics differ for each vowel sound, and the particular frequency regions they reinforce most strongly are called formants. A formant, as defined by Chaplin (1968), is the timbre, or quality, which makes one vowel sound different from another.

Cherry (1966) goes on to say that formants continually shift about in frequency as the tongue moves, and the relative size of the front and back cavities varies. But there is no simple mathematical relation between formant and the dimensions of the cavities. The successive sounds of speech exert a considerable influence upon one another.

The problem of talking under water is more difficult than the problem of listening under water for the following reasons:

1. Because speech is generated by exhaling air, bubbles are emitted when a person talks, and the noise accompanying them tends to mask his speech.

2. If a diver has to hold his mounthpiece between his teeth, he cannot move his jaw or close his lips freely when he speaks. Consequently, his pronunciation of consonants is generally poor, and he cannot use the sounds "b" (as in bat) and "p" (as in pat) at all (Morgan, Cook, Chapanis & Lund, 1963).

In light of the problems of underwater speech, Morgan et al. made certain recommendations, but which are *only* for open-circuit scuba situations:

1. "The diver should be instructed to say only one word or phrase at a time and to wait before saying the next word until the bubble associated with the previous word escapes and the bubble noise dies away."

2. "Restrict the vocabulary for underwater communication to a few words, keep the messages simple, and devise a special code that uses only vowel sounds."

3. "If possible, provide the diver with a full face mask containing a microphone connected to an amplifier and transducer (underwater loudspeaker)."

Similar recommendations for improving underwater communication were made by McCormick (1964) also. He suggested:

1. The use of speech that will most likely get through, such as phonetic alphabets.

2. The selection and training of good talkers.

3. The selection of good listeners.

As cited previously, the intake of breathing mixtures produces noise which masks feedback from the diver's voice, affecting self-monitoring mechanisms. Reverberation within the helmet also interferes with production of clear speech (Sergeant, 1966a).

It must also be noted that face masks and helmets restrict free movement of the articulatory mechanism. Hansen (1952) found that physical restriction of jaw movement alone has an insignificant effect upon speech intelligibility. However, further studies should investigate compression of the facial muscles and the resonance characteristics of the cavities in the mask.

Speech in man, as previously discussed, is generated by an airstream traveling from the lungs through the vocal tract. This vocal tract acts as a continuous acoustic tube having several resonant chambers. The oral muzzle used in scuba for communication adds another resonator to the oral tract as closely coupled to the larynx as the mouth. Hence Coleman and Krasik (1971) add that the acoustic pulse initiated at the vocal folds in the larynx is further modified by an additional resonator, subsequently shifting the characteristics of speech. It would then be expected that certain patterns of phoneme articulation and air pressures associated with them would also vary when the oral muzzle in scuba is used in communication.

Coleman and Krasik (1971) reported that an average 20% decrease in intelligibility resulted from wearing an oral mask (muzzle).

Speech output from an oral muzzle is dependent upon the interrelation of the mask and the microphone used as a transducing device. The combination should be designed to produce a flat frequency response over the speech range. However, most muzzles produce a resonance at certain frequencies thus making a flat frequency response impossible.

The results of Coleman and Krasik's investigation demonstrate a systematic trend for intelligibility scores to decrease with increases in muzzle release pressure. The average decrease in intelligibility was approximately 2.3% per increase of 1 cm of water pressure.

In general the results of Coleman and Krasik (1971) indicates that:

1. "There is a systematic decrease in speech intelligibility with increases in oral muzzle release pressures."

2. "The major effect on speech in their study was due to the wearing of an oral muzzle and face mask."

3. "Plosive consonants appeared to be confused most often with changes in oral muzzle pressure, with a moderate trend for lingua-

velar and lingua-alveolar consonants to be shifted forward; (plosive consonants such as p, h, g, and k require a momentary build-up of a small burst of breath. These pressure build-ups are caused by momentary closure of the lips or throat cavity)."

4. "Final consonants appeared to be more affected by differential changes in muzzle release pressure than initial consonants."

5. "Nasal consonants were shifted perceptually from a nasal form of production to fricative and plosive form, while perceptually maintaining the same approximate place of articulation."

Hollien and Tolhurst (1969) describe work done at the University of Florida on the effects of the external cavity size of an underwater breathing apparatus on speech. They suggest that the data gathered in these studies could be used to provide predictions of the size and configurations of the cavities optimal for intelligible speech. It is anticipated that empirical research will be utilized to discover which of the existing muzzles most closely approaches the ideal.

Speech Distortion

The distortion of a diver's speech in an undersea high-pressure environment is due to two factors (Fant & Lindquist, 1968). One is the pressure, or rather density, factor which causes a nonlinear shift in low-frequency vocal resonances, subjectively perceived as "nasality." This effect originates from the participation of vocal cavity walls in vocal resonances. The other factor is the well-known linear transposition of vocal resonances in proportion to the velocity of sound for a particular gas mixture ("Donald Duck effect").

It may be stated that speech distortion is due to the sound velocity characteristics of the gas. Velocity depends upon gas density which in turn depends upon molecular weight, the percentages of the various gas constituents, and the pressure.

The velocity of sound in an ideal gas is

$$c = \sqrt{\frac{\gamma p}{\rho}}$$

where $\gamma = C_P/C_v$
p = pressure,
ρ = density,

C_P = specific heat at constant pressure,
C_v = specific heat at constant volume.

Calculating γ for a gas mixture involves dividing the weighted mean of C_P by the weighted mean of C_v.

$$\gamma = \frac{\Sigma (P_i M_i C_{pi})}{\Sigma (P_i M_i C_{vi})}$$

where P_i = volume per cent of gas i,
M_i = molecular weight of gas i.

The density is obtained from the expression

$$\rho = \frac{\Sigma (P_i M_i)}{\Sigma 22.41} P \frac{273.16}{T}$$

where P = pressure in atmospheres absolute,
T = absolute temperature in degrees Kelvin.

For any given gas mixture there exists an optimum diving depth for cancellation of the nonlinear shifts of low-frequency formants (Fant and Lindquist, 1968). The characteristic impedance of the air passages, increases with the density ρ, that is, with pressure. The bandwidth of vocal resonances, however, is not radically changed with increasing pressure. It is possible to find a depth and a pressure P where the closed tract resonance shift expression $\sqrt{\gamma P/\gamma_0}$ is the same as that of the overall transposition expression $\sqrt{\gamma \rho_0/\rho\gamma_0}$, thus avoiding nonlinear F_1 shifts.

A tape recorder adjusted for optimal input level at $P = 1$ ATA may be severely overloaded at $P > 10$ ATA. The gain in voice level might also be a point to consider in speaker training, since the voice effort might be reduced accordingly.

Fant and Lindquist (1968) also note that there is a tendency for subjects to use a higher voice fundamental frequency at higher pressures. In an analysis of two speakers' recordings, they noted that the slowing down in speaking tempo was about the same for both speakers at two different depths, 38% for subject C at 200 ft (60 m) and 38% for subject J. At 450 ft (140 m) the results were 30% for C and 38% for J. Incidentally, the correlation is excellent with the partial pressure of oxygen which under both conditions was 42% higher than at 1 ATA, or air. This may suggest that the amount of oxygen affects the speaking tempo.

Effects of Raised Air Pressure on Speech

Increased operating depth results in increased ambient pressure. This changes the characteristics of the resonant cavities and the density of the breathing gas.

In 1955, White reported an investigation conducted for the purpose of determining the extent of changes in the human voice caused by increased atmospheric pressure in the range 1 to 7 ATA. Results indicated that under the conditions of the experiment the articulation score exhibited a loss of 24.7% when PB monosyllable word lists were used in a signal-to-noise ratio of 30 dB. It was concluded that, since increased atmospheric pressure did not significantly affect the intelligibility of human speech in air when studies were made under controlled conditions, improvement in communication for divers and underwater swimmers must be sought by improving communication equipment.

Subsequent studies of the effects of high ambient air pressure on speech output actually showed that there was a loss in intelligibility of about 4% for each atmosphere of pressure. The mean score for a depth of 190 ft (58 m) was 68.8% (Kenny, 1971).

Fant and Sonesson (1964) describe a "nasal" quality in voices when air was breathed at pressures equivalent to about 100 ft (30m) of seawater. They also reported a differential alteration in the sound pressure of such speech. At high ambient air pressure there is a decrease in the sound pressure level of fricatives and stops relative to the average level of voiced sounds.

They go on to explain pressure effects on speech in terms of changes in the walls of the vocal cavity and systematic factors of impedance loading of the vocal tract. These variations appear to be caused mainly by the increased density accompanying higher ambient pressure.

Frontal and sagittal X-ray pictures showed the velum to be in normal condition at 6 ATA. These negative results exclude the velopharyngeal opening as the main cause of the observed spectrum distortion, which strongly indicates the presence of some kind of shunting mechanism in vocal transmission. A theoretical analysis has supplied evidence that the shunting mechanism is associated with the vibration of the walls of the vocal cavities and the soft parts of the throat.

Formants

Formants are concentrations of energy in a speech signal around specific frequencies located above the fundamental frequency. They shift upward in frequency in a nonlinear fashion with increases in pressure. According to Bond and Myatt (1969), "the first formant is affected more than the second formant. It is also observed that the intensity level of voiced sounds increased with increasing ambient pressure but that typical noise sounds, such as fricatives, and the burst part of unvoiced stops display a drop in intensity relative to voiced sounds."

In 1967, Fant and Sonesson reported on investigations of a similar nature. From a spectrographic analysis it was found that the fundamental frequency (F_0) remained at its original level when the air pressure in the chamber was increased. The first and second formants, however, tended to increase in frequency, and the F_1 shift was with few exceptions greater in magnitude than the shifts in F_2. It is also of interest to note that the distinction between the F_1 of the vowels e and i tended to be eliminated at the higher pressure (6 ATA), which in turn impaired the auditory distinction between these two vowels.

The distortion of vowels at high pressure is the result of a rise in both F_1 and F_2, but generally more in F_1, bringing this formant rather close to F_2. The rise accounts for the nasal quality of certain vowels.

From a spectrographic analysis it was concluded that a shunting mechanism in the vocal transmission was the probable cause of the particular distortion and nasal quality. The analysis suggested that the distortion was caused by a shunting mechanism operating directly through the soft walls of the supraglottal cavities. This effect is attributable to the increased density, and causes the soft walls of the vocal tract to vibrate when the air pressure is increased.

By means of the resonance formula of Helmholtz, the lowest

resonance frequency of the vocal tract can be estimated, and Fant and Sonesson's calculations of this limiting value for the first formant (F_{1w}) assuming complete closure of the vocal tract resulted in

$$F_{1w} = P \times 150 \ \text{Hz}$$

where P = air pressure.

This means that the first formant in the human vocal tract can never go below 150 Hz ($P = 1$ ATA). In these experiments, P was increased to 6 ATA; thus $F_{1w} = 370$ Hz, which is in good agreement with the results. Below this frequency no resonance is possible in the vocal cavity when the air pressure is 6 ATA.

The upward shift in resonant frequency means that communication systems designed for use in this environment must include broad-band microphones. This is especially true if the voice signals are to be electronically processed in any way.

Effects of Helium on Speech

The fundamental periodicity of vocal fold vibration, which de-

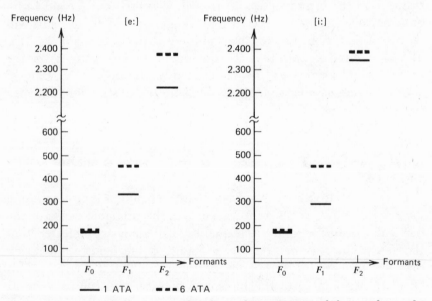

Figure 6-28.   Graphical representation of speech spectrogram of the vowels e and i obtained in the decompression chamber at normal pressure (1 ATA) and at increased air pressure (6 ATA). (Fant & Sonesson, 1967.)

termines the pitch of the voice, is basically the same for air and for helium atmospheres. According to Sergeant (1969), the primary change the listener hears in helium speech is the upward shift in the frequency of the formants.

Formants are the major determinants of vowel perception, as explained previously, and therefore the details of formant shifts are important to a precise understanding of the perception of helium speech.

Sergeant (1969) goes on to explain that discrimination between speech sounds depends upon frequency information combined with temporal variations and transitions between vowels and consonants. The shift in formant frequency is such that the ratios between the two formants are generally the same for specific vowels, whether spoken in an air or helium atmosphere. The timing aspects of speech sounds other than vowels, such as plosives, are also similar under the two conditions. However, a major change can be expected for the slopes of frequency transitions between vowels and consonants.

Sex Effect. A recent study was conducted by Coleman and Krasik (1971) to determine the existence of sex differences in helium speech. They concluded that the sex of the speaker did not appear to be a significant factor in their study. However, in view of the limited number of speakers, two female and three male, additional investigation of the effect of speaker sex on underwater intelligibility is needed.

Time Effect. Nixon, Mabson, Trimboli, Endicott, and Welch (1968) and Nixon, Mabson, Trimboli, and Welch (1969) reported that the effects of a helium atmosphere on the rate of speaking were negligible. Subjects were instructed to read a sample test sentence in a normal speaking voice. They were not aware that the time consumed in speaking the sentence was the main effect of interest. Recorded sentences were analyzed by a Grason-Stadler Speech Time Analyzer and the various speech rates determined for each subject.

Nixon et al. also reported on changes over time on a long duration study. They indicate that the decrease in formant ratios observed prior to the third day of the experiment continued at a lesser rate throughout the helium exposure. This decrease, or return to pre-helium speech, is interpreted as talker adaptation. Although a plateau was not reached during this exposure, talker adaptation is limited by the physical characteristics of the environment so that a return to normal speech will not occur.

Speech Distortion. In 1971, Stewart analyzed distortions of speech in a helium breathing mixture through the aid of a model of an ear. Several existing techniques for helium speech correction were reviewed. He concluded that no scheme yet proposed is likely to be satisfactory in an actual noisy environment, suggesting that much more research is essential.

A helium-rich mixture distorts the resonance characteristics of the vocal cavities, producing the "Donald Duck effect" mentioned earlier. Mean second formant frequencies, as investigated by Nixon and Somner (1968), were 1.35 times higher in 56% helium and 1.62 times higher in 80% helium than in room air. These ratios are slightly less than those calculated for the velocity of sound in helium atmospheres to that in room air.

Although, according to Sergeant (1969), the sound is strange, speech produced at normal atmospheric pressure by someone breathing an 80/20% helium–oxygen mixture is 95 to 100% intelligible under favorable listening conditions. At greater depths intelligibility drops for both air and helium–oxygen, although the drop seems to be more severe for helium. These conclusions were also drawn by Hollien, Thompson, and Cannon (1971).

Figure 6-29, as presented by Nixon and Somner (1968), illustrates the effects of helium concentration on speech as discussed above. Note, however, that the data were obtained at the surface.

Helium Speech in Hyperbaric Environments

Tape recordings made in the helium–oxygen atmosphere of the U.S. Navy Sea Lab II have been analyzed by spectrographic techniques (Mac Lean, 1966). The divers exhibited the customary "Donald Duck" speech. The Sea Lab II experiment permitted speech analysis of divers living in such an atmosphere for several days. A study of the recorded data has led to the following, already partly discussed observations:

1. Formant shifts are responsible for the unusual quality of the helium–oxygen speech.

2. Formant shifts are nonlinear, the first formant shift being greater than the higher ones.

3. Energy associated with fricative sounds has also been observed to shift upward.

4. Pitch or fundamental frequency changes are usually not significant.

5. After several days in a preponderantly helium atmosphere, changes occurred in speech quality that made it sound more natural.

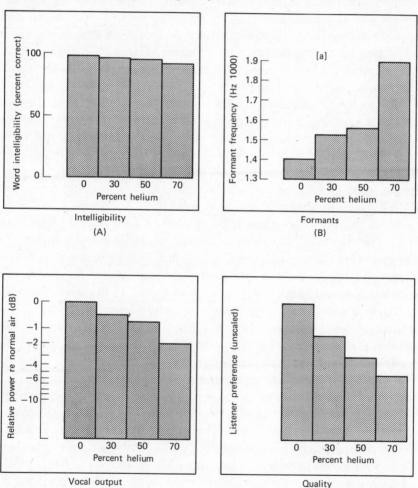

Figure 6-29. Effects of Helium concentration on speech: (A) intelligibility, (B) formants, (C) vocal power output, (D) quality. (Nixon and Somner, 1968.)

Normally, the slightly compliant vocal tract wall causes only a small increase in the frequency of F_1. The effect of the wall is greatest at the lowest frequency and diminishes with increasing formant frequency. However, in a pressurized helium atmosphere, the tract wall becomes more compliant. This causes the F_1 frequency to increase even more markedly than higher-order formants.

Sergeant (1963, 1963a, 1967) added that this upward shift in formant frequency is produced by changes in the resonating characteristics of the human resonators for speech (i.e., oral, nasal, and pharyngeal cavities). Assuming that frequency content of speech is an important perceptual cue in phonemic recognition, it is logical that changes in frequency can interfere selectively with the intelligibility aspects of certain phonemes.

Holywell and Harvey (1964) found intelligibility of helium speech to be improved simply by slowing down the playback of magnetic-tape recordings, thereby reducing the frequency spectrum to a more normal position. This might be an argument in support of the contention that frequency is a perceptual standard in phonemic intelligibility; of course, the time constants are also tampered with by slowing down the original speech.

Spectography was utilized, by Brubaker and Wurst (1968), to study the distorting effects of a pressurized helium environment on the speech of three experienced divers at five submersion depths. As expected, they noted that vocal fundamental, vowel formants, and consonant-vowel amplitude ratios are elevated. Implications for one-half speed processing were presented, and the results were interpreted as consistent with the hypothesis that, in addition to the helium and pressure effects, increased vocal effort contributes to speech distortion in such environments.

Alteration in the pitch of speech produced by breathing mixture suggests the possibility of increased intelligibility of such speech by selective frequency filtering (Sergeant 1966a). In his study, Sergeant evaluated speech, spoken after breathing an 80%/20% helium-oxygen mixture, which was combined with broad-band noise and then passed through a selection of bandpass filters. Results indicated that while intelligibility did not suffer appreciably when frequencies of 300 Hz and below were eliminated, the loss of frequencies below

600 cps caused marked deterioration. Even with the severe filtering restrictions of a 600 to 1200 Hz bandpass and a 1-dB speech-to-noise ratio, 38% intelligibility was achieved. Apparently, the intelligibility of speech in a helium mixture, as in air, is quite distortion-resistant. The estimated frequency at which high- and low-pass filtering would have equal effects on intelligibility was lower than 1000 Hz, in contrast to approximately 1600 Hz for speech in air. No conditions of filtering increased intelligibility over the no-filter condition.

Interaction of Gas Mixture and Depth. Altogether, four different breathing mixtures were studied by Gerstman, Gamertsfelder, and Goldberger (1967) from which was established that, as the percentage concentration of helium increases, so does the formant multiplication. The relation is not simple: 1.1 at 18%, 1.3 at 50%, and 1.65 at 84%. Gerstman et al. also observed the effects of breathing mixture and depth as separate effects on helium speech. Spectrographic analysis confirmed previous reports of nonlinear formant frequency shifts and changes in relative formant amplitudes, but failed to reveal improvements with time in talker intelligibility, especially at the lowest depths. A mathematical model, incorporating both the effects of helium concentration and of depth, was found to account successfully for the observed changes in formant frequencies.

Effects of Noise. In 1968, Willott and Sergeant made acoustic and intelligibility analyses of speech from five talkers, breathing air or a mixture of helium and oxygen, when their speech was or was not masked by 95-dB noise. Mean intelligibility scores, as detemined from responses by 26 listeners, were significantly improved by about 10 percentage points for both air and helium conditions when noise interfered with a talker's ability to hear his own speech. The average long-term power spectra of speech in air and speech in the helium mix did not differ to an appreciable degree as had been expected. However, sound spectrograms for helium speech and speech in air revealed differences between talking in noise versus talking in quiet.

Further research was performed on the intelligibility of helium speech as a function of speech-to-noise ratio by Sergeant and McKay in 1963. They constructed three experiments designed to compare the intelligibility of helium speech and normal speech when both were masked by loud noise. Recordings were made of five talkers reading intelligibility word lists. Several panels of listeners heard these recordings masked by different levels of background noise. In the first experiment a fatigue effect seemed at first to be present for helium speech, suggesting that short-term auditory fatigue may occur with helium. However, the second of the three experiments, designed to observe the effect on intelligibility of time during the listening session that material was heard, refuted the notion of short-term fatigue effects. The third experiment incorporated results of the first two experiments to evaluate the effect of introducing varied levels of noise upon the intelligibility of helium speech and normal speech when the order of presentation of gas mix was minimized. Helium speech and speech in air were equally intelligible both in the presence of loud noise and in the presence of low-level noise. However, helium speech was approximately 10 percentage points less intelligible than speech in air when the level of noise was close to the level of speech.

Nixon, Mabson, Trimboli, Endicott, and Welch (1968), at the conclusion of a study conducted at 1 ATA, also reported that helium speech appears to be somewhat more susceptible to masking noise than ordinary speech. Helium speech, they continue, showed a greater reduction in word intelligibility when masked than speech under non-helium conditions.

Word intelligibility in noise (from the same 1 ATA study) was significantly less in both 56% and 80% helium mixtures than in room air, while only speech in 80% helium was less intelligible than in room air without masking noise.

The Message

An area not to be overlooked in our discussion of verbal communication is the message itself. In fact, Morgan, Cook, Chapanis, and Lund (1963) suggested that the actual performance of a speech communication system depends to a great extent upon such factors as the size of the message set or the vocabulary employed, the degree of standardization of messages, and the familiarity of personnel using the system with the messages and the equipment. Heavy information loads and poorly trained personnel, they add, are as hard on system performance as are noise and distortion. Similar observations in the undersea environment have been made by Thompson and Streimer (1971).

The important language factors associated with the message can be considered under the following headings:

1. Information content of individual words.
2. Sentence or phrase structure.
3. Size of the message set.
4. Situation constraints.
5. Interaction of the characteristics of certain speech sounds.

Other things being equal, the more frequently a word occurs in everyday usage, the more readily it is correctly identified when transmitted over a speech communication system.

In 1957, Howes mentioned that there is a drop in threshold of about 4.5 dB per logarithmic unit of word frequency. This ratio is independent of the length of the word, although the thresholds for words of a given frequency of occurrence are lower for long words. Also, see Beil (1962).

The length of the word also influences its intelligibility; that is, the longer the word, the easier it is identified.

Both frequency and length, then, are strong factors. They can change by 10 to 15 dB the signal-to-noise ratio required for a given level of intelligibility (Morgan, Cook, Chapanis & Lund 1963).

An effect somewhat similar to that of word length arises as words are formed into phrases and sentences. The grammar and syntax of the phrase or sentence dictates to some extent what words must go with other words.

The whole message carries information about the speaker's mood. The parts of the message are variously emphasized by melodic pattern (pitch change), intensity changes, or by pauses preceding or following an important word. The same sequence of words, therefore, can have many different meanings, depending upon how the words are spoken (Tolhurst, 1971).

Speech intelligibility is greatly dependent, too, upon the size of the overall message set; the smaller the set, the easier it is for the listener and talker to communicate. Morgan and associates recommend that to take advantage of limited message-set size, both the talker and listener must study the set and know it thoroughly so that when the talker uses short stereotyped phrases, what the talker sends conforms to the listener's expectations (Mc Cormick, 1964).

In addition, it is very important to remember that the performance of many communication systems is influenced by the "extra" information contained in *a priori* knowledge of various aspects of the prevailing situation. In other words, the more the persons in the communication circuit know about what is supposed to happen at various points of an operation, the easier communication is.

It is proposed by Morgan et al. (1963) that one should place emphasis first on designing a communication system so that it will provide adequate intelligibility without the need of a special language or voice procedure. A special language or voice procedure should be used only as a supplement to the best possible equipment design.

But, of course, those factors germane to the language itself must be analyzed. Hence below are five general rules for building up standard words and phrases:

1. Provide a context for critical words by embedding them in phrases or sentences.

2. Use familiar words rather than unfamiliar ones.

3. Use as small a total vocabulary as possible.

4. To obtain words that are easily disinguished, select polysyllables.

5. Avoid words containing sounds that are easily confused.

Naturally, fundamental to the process of communication is the use of language. Special vocabularies, circuit discipline, and communicative behavior are areas requiring expansion within research related specifically to operations under water (Sergeant, 1966a).

In 1969, Murry discussed the possibility of a special lexicon. "One of the goals of analyzing phonemic errors," he stated, "is to obtain the preliminary data needed for the development of a set of phonemes which can be used to develop a lexicon for the diver's use similar to the type that has been developed in air tower communications."

Phonemes found to have high intelligibility under many conditions at various depths and to various communicators would be the core of such a lexicon.

Murry collected data concerning phonemic errors. The data indicated that the majority of confusion occurs among unvoiced sounds produced within the same manner of articulation category. This trend also occurs with unvoiced and voiced fricatives. The majority of fricative substitutions are made with fricatives produced with the same voicing component but not necessarily at the same place of articulation. With regard to the place of articulation, the types of substitutions are approximately random.

Figure 6-30 (Morgan, Cook, Chapanis & Lund, 1963) shows a "tree of confusions" characteristic of a wide-band communication system limited only by random background noise at the signal-to-noise ratios indicated at the left-hand side of the illustration.

Sergeant conducted a study in 1967 to produce a master phonemic matrix for speech in common underwater situations, using a mixture of 80% helium and 20% oxygen. The results are presented in Table 6-8 in the form of a stimulus/response matrix, with the entries converted to percent response to particular phonemes.

Column headings are the stimuli, and row headings are the responses. The diagonal connecting the upper-left and lower-right corners contains the percent of correct responses for each phoneme tested. These values are the specific phonemic intelligibility scores. The average score of 59% for the values in the diagonal is the overall consonant intelligibility for helium speech.

The /l/ and /m/ phonemes were most often correctly recognized, while the sound /s/ was the most often missed. The /m/ was the second most correct sound. Note, however, that for the /m/ and all the other sounds except /l/, the incorrect responses seldom fell outside the general classification of the sound. These classifications in Tables 6-8 are boxed in. One can easily see that there were very few responses outside these squares of phonemic classification.

The specific phonemic intelligibility of a sound is defined as the percentage of times that a correct response is made out of the total number of times the sound is actually the stimulus. These results suggest that priority in the selection of words for diver communications should be given to the specific phonemes that maintain their stability with increases in pressures.

Murry and Sergeant (1970) have taken data from several investigations of speech intelligibility under various diving conditions and

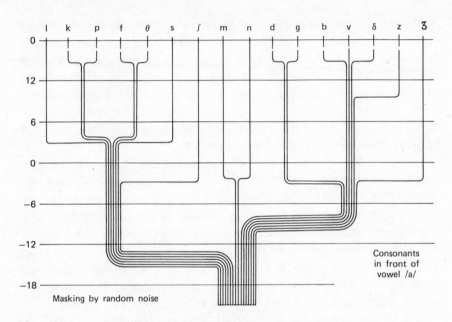

Figure 6-30.   Tree of confusion. (Morgan, Cook, Chaparis & Lund, 1963).

attempted to compare the phonemic confusion. The data from the four studies evaluated are shown in Table 6-9. Murry and Sergeant ranked each of the sounds for each gas mixture–pressure condition according to the proportion of the time that it was correctly perceived. Murry and Sergeant (1970) report that "from the table it can be seen that [m] is easily recognized in air and in helium–oxygen mixtures under standard atmospheric pressure. However, when pressure increases, such as is the case at a depth of 200 feet, the [m] sound becomes one of the least intelligible sounds." (p. 3).

Table 6-10 is a intercorrelation matrix for the various conditions investigated. The low correlations among the various conditions suggest that one can not predict the specific phonemic intelligibility from one gas/pressure condition to another.

Murry and Sergeant conclude that their survey of available data indicates that minor changes in the phonemic structure of messages may provide increased intelligibility. They also conclude that having divers use a fixed format for information would also greatly improve communication. A fixed format would help prepare the listener for

Table 6-8 Stimulus-Response Matrix for 13 Consonants Spoken in a Mixture of 80% Helium and 20% Oxygen (Sergeant, 1967)[a]

	Voiceless fricatives		Voiceless plosives			Voiced plosives			Nasals		Semivowels		
	f	s	p	t	k	b	d	g	m	n	r	l	w
f	48	10	4	3	5	3	3	0	0	0	1	0	0
s	10	28	0	2	3	1	0	0	0	1	0	0	1
p	3	17	59	22	19	0	0	2	0	0	2	0	0
t	18	14	10	49	16	2	3	1	2	1	0	0	1
k	11	4	8	22	49	1	1	1	0	0	0	0	0
b	3	7	1	4	1	75	9	7	1	4	1	1	1
d	1	3	1	1	1	7	55	6	0	1	1	0	1
g	0	3	0	0	0	1	13	73	0	0	1	0	0
m	1	1	0	0	0	0	0	2	78	18	0	0	0
n	0	0	0	0	0	0	0	1	11	61	2	0	1
r	0	0	1	1	0	0	2	1	1	2	55	7	26
l	1	2	2	4	0	2	3	2	5	4	27	90	14
w	0	1	0	0	0	0	0	0	0	3	7	0	48
y	0	0	0	1	0	0	3	0	0	1	0	0	0
Omit	2	6	2	1	1	6	1	4	0	4	0	2	1

[a] Entries have been converted to percent response to a particular phoneme.

the material that is coming. They suggest the format include:

1. Caller's tag or name.
2. Receiver's tag or name.
3. Position information.
4. Present condition.
5. Specific message.

Once a set message format is adopted, its phonemic organization could be evaluated for further improvement.

Transmission Equipment

Generally, a communication link consists of three main subsystems, a input transducer which converts the diver's speech into an electrical equivalent, a transmission system which delivers the signal to the receiver/transducer system, and a receiver/transducer which converts the signal to a form suitable for perception (Kenny, 1971).

When a diver's head is in the gas environment of a diving helmet,

Table 6-9 Specific Phonemic Intelligibility and Its Rank Order for Each of Four Environmental Conditions (Murry and Sergeant, 1970)[a]

| | Air | | | | | | Helium–Oxygen | | | | |
| | 0 feet | | | 250 feet | | | 0 feet | | | 200 feet | |
R	Stimulus	Percent	R	Stimulus	Percent	R	Stimulus	Percent	R	Stimulus	Percent
1	ʃ[b]	97	1	ð	98	1	l	90	1	h[b]	87
2	m[b]	97	2	w	96	2	m	78	2	r[b]	87
3	n	95	3	tʃ	95	3	b	75	3	ʒ	81
4	ʒ	92	4	ʃ	94	4	g	73	4	j	80
5	θ	86	5	r	91	5	n	61	5	s[b]	79
6	t	79	6	−[b]	89	6	p	59	6	n[b]	79
7	d[b]	76	7	v[b]	89	7.5	r	55	7	z	78
8	f[b]	76	8	θ	88	7.5	d	55	8	t[b]	75
9	b[b]	75	9	s	83	9.5	k	49	9	k[b]	75
10	v[b]	75	10	g[b]	82	9.5	t	49	10	l	71
11	s[b]	75	11	d[b]	82	11.5	f	48	11	p[b]	68
12.5	g	60	12	l	79	11.5	w	48	12	b[b]	68
12.5	z	60	13	f	78	13	s	28	13	dʒ	66
14	k	52	14	z	71				14	d	61
15	ð	51	15	b	69				15	ʃ	60
16	p	50	16	p	66				16	m	57
			17	t	63				17	v	56
			18	n	57				18	f	54
			19	m	54				19	ð	50
			20	k	44				20	tʃ	47
									21	g	43
									22	θ	42
									23	w	32

[a] Specific phonemic intelligibility is the percent correct for each phoneme based on the number of presentations of the particular phoneme. The higher percentages indicate the more easily recognized sounds.

[b] The rank order for this sound was determined prior to rounding off to the nearest percent correct shown.

Table 6-10   Correlation Matrix of Specific Phonemic Intelligibility
(percent correct) for Different Environmental Conditions
(Murry and Sergeant, 1970)[a]

	Air		Helium–Oxygen	
	0 feet	250 feet	0 feet	200 feet
Air				
0 feet		$-.07\ (N = 15)$	$+.23\ (N = 10)$	$-.08\ (N = 15)$
250 feet			$-.32\ (N = 13)$	$-.32\ (N = 20)$
Helium-Oxygen				
0 feet				$-.08\ (N = 13)$
200 feet				

[a] The coefficients are rank-order correlations.

the normal sound-sensing system of the ear is operative; hearing is simply a function of a favorable signal-to-noise ratio. The best performance is obtained by mechanically reducing gas flow noises and placing a moderate-level signal close to the ear with earphones, rather than a high-level signal several inches from the ear.

Anderson (1970) points out that the transmission of electromagnetic energy through seawater is so heavily attenuated that it is necessary to turn to acoustic energy to transmit information over any appreciable range of ocean. In the sea the absorption of acoustic energy is several orders of magnitude less than that of electromagnetic waves. Still, this absorption constitutes a limitation on the upper and lower boundaries of the ocean, and the multipaths caused by them distort the communication path and further reduce the usable bandwidth.

The transmission of acoustic energy through the ocean is subject to absorption that is strongly frequency-dependent. This frequency dependence is the dominant factor determining the usable bandwidth of an acoustic channel for any particular range in the ocean.

This energy attenuation is discussed further by Doherty, Hollien, and Thompson (1967). According to them, little energy is lost at each of the boundaries for water. At the interface between the water and the air, for example, the magnitude of the differences in acoustic impedance prevents the transmission of sound energy from the water to the air; that is, virtually all the energy is reflected. At the lower boundary somewhat larger percentages of the energy present in rays impinging upon the bottom are transmitted to the sand or rock. However, since the velocity of sound in the water is less than that at the bottom, at incident angles equal to or greater than some critical angle, the energy is totally internally reflected. This phenomenon of sound energy being "trapped" in the water (as in a waveguide or reverberation chamber) effectively increases the transmission range of sound in this medium. It must be noted, though, that these principles apply only to a smooth air/water surface such as that associated with very calm weather or an inland lake.

Equipment Evaluation

Hollien, Coleman, and Rothman (1970) spearheaded an evaluation of diver communication systems by a diver-to-diver technique.

1. The evaluation technique developed provides what are probably optimum scores for a unit, and it differentiates satisfactorily among different systems.

2. No particular approach (hard-line, acoustic, modulated) to diver communication dominates the others with respect to close-range intelligibility.

These investigators concluded that none of the major diver communication systems currently available provides acceptable levels of speech intelligibility. Similar evaluations and findings of this same nature are also described by Hollien, Coleman, Thompson, and Hunter (1970). Again, the most significant conclusion was that all the evaluated communicators transmitted speech with somewhat low intelligibility.

A brief description of the systems evaluated follows, as provided by Hollien et al.

1. *"Hard-line" systems.* "A hard-line unit employs a closed system, comparable to a telephone, including (a) a microphone, (b) a cable over which the signal is transmitted, and (c) a receiver. These systems require a physical connection between the talker and the listener."

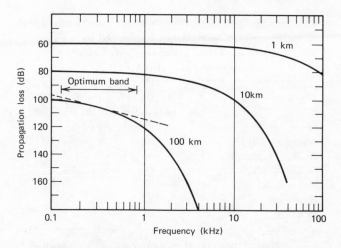

Figure 6-31.   Acoustic propagation loss versus frequency for several ranges, assuming inverse-square-law spreading and frequency-dependent absorption only. (Doherty, Hollien & Thompson, 1967.)

2. *"Acoustic" systems.* "An acoustic system characteristically transmits speech directly into the water by means of a projector (underwater loudspeaker); the signal produced can be received by divers without any special auditory processing equipment. Two different units were evaluated; both were units that transmit voice signals at normal speech frequencies into the water via specially built audio systems."

3. *"Modulated" systems.* "Amplitude modulation employs a carrier frequency varied by a superimposed speech signal. Systems of this type usually consist of a microphone, power module, amplifier, modulator, and underwater transducer. Speech produced in this manner can be understood only by another diver having an appropriate receiver and demodulator."

In 1958, Ide presented information on improved experimental equipment for communication and homing by underwater sound. Two submersible supersonic receivers, for use with noise-making devices were used successfully for taking bearings when strapped to the chest of a fully submerged swimmer. Tests in the Potomac River demonstrated that the electronic signaling and homing equipment permitted voice communication of good quality to ranges of 2300 m

Table 6-11 Intelligibility Scores for Seven Diver
Communication Systems Evaluated by a Diver-
to-Diver Technique (Hollien, Coleman,
Thompson and Hunter, 1970)[a,b]

Communication System	Number of Listeners	Percent Intelligibility
Aquasonics 811	34	72.4
Bendix Watercom	35	64.1
Aquasonics 420	36	62.9
Aquaphone	36	58.1
Raytheon Yack-Yack	36	57.4
PQC-2	34	54.3

[a] Evaluation of the PQC-1a was attempted also; unfortunately the available units could not be kept operational. The little data obtained for the PQC-1a suggested an intelligibility level substantially below those of the other units.
[b] Five experienced talkers were utilized; each wore the communicator in conjunction with a double hose regulator and a BioEngionics (Nautilus) muzzle. Speech materials were the Clarke 50-word, multiple-choice lists; the project was conducted in 30 ft of fresh water at Bugg Springs, Florida.

(2500 yd), and homing with 5° bearing accuracy to a maximum range of 3700 m (4000 yd).

A similar device has been described by Burnett (1961). This device, however, is an integral portion of a full diving suit. The head portion of the suit contains a built-in earphone while the microphone is built into the neck portion. The components can, however, be used separate from the suit.

Woods (1963) described a communication device similar in operation to a "walkie-talkie" set used on land. It is fully transistorized and works with a 12-V battery pack intended to take the place of an aqualung diver's weight pouch. An 80 kHz signal, modulated by the diver's speech, is projected into the sea by a transducer. The ultrasonic wave spreads out in all directions at the speed of sound (1½ km/sec in seawater) to arrive, considerably reduced in strength, at another diver's transducer which changes it back to an electrical signal for detection and amplification to the original level. The

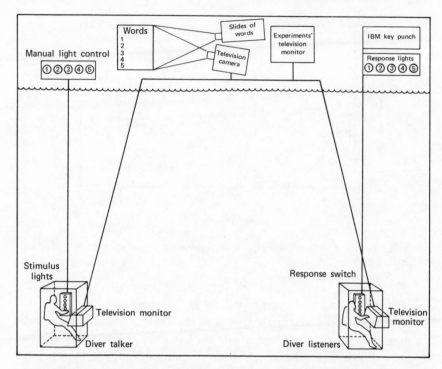

Figure 6-32. Presentation and response apparatus for diver-to-diver evaluation of underwater communication systems. Both the talker and listeners (in pairs) were situated in DICORS (Hollien and Thompson, 1967) 30 ft apart in 30 ft of fresh water. The five multiple choice words were displayed by a slide projector and transmitted via a television camera to television monitors observable by (1) the experimenters, (2) the talker, and (3) the listeners. The talker was instructed to speak the appropriate stimulus word by a set of five manually controlled stimulus lights; the listeners recorded their responses by activating switches coupled to a IBM key punch and sets of response lights. (Hollien, Coleman, Thompson & Hunter, 1970.)

speech is then presented at a bone-conduction headpiece on the diver. The audio amplifier and headphone are used for both listening and speaking by switching between "transmit" and "receive." With this apparatus, divers can communicate with each other or with persons in a vessel on the surface of the sea. Full voice communication is attained over a distance of 30 m; tests have shown that with more power the distance can be as much as 100 m.

Finally, an efficient underwater communication device has been developed called Scuba Com (Mc Kenney, 1969). The diver simply

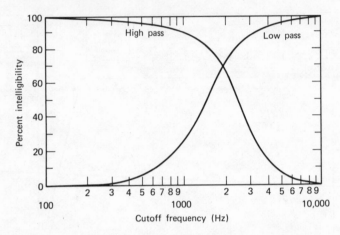

Figure 6-33. Effect on intelligibility of elimination of frequencies by use of filters. (McCormick, 1964.)

blows into the unit and then talks into it. The voice sound waves are transferred into the water by direct passage through a silicone rubber diaphragm, and by direct radiation from the resonating chamber or plastic body. The silicone rubber compound is highly transparent to sound. The voice can be heard over 100 ft away. Comments must be brief, since long sentences tend to become scrambled at the end. The ease with which this device can be effectively used varies with the individual; voice pitch is apparently an important factor.

Microphones

An important element of the transmission equipment is the microphone. Morrow (1970) notes that past research has shown that the question of microphone type and mask cavity size are not independent. The choice of a microphone has been greatly influenced by cavity characteristics.

Morrow (1970) reported an experiment with a new ceramic (piezo-electric) gradient microphone for use in diving masks from sea level to very deep depths. He demonstrated that speech intelligibility is insensitive to mask cavity size and shape, in both air and helium, when a microphone of this type is used. The specific conclusions were:

1. A ceramic gradient microphone with response to 10,000 Hz was demonstrated to be the best microphone for a diving mask to be used at depths down to 187 m (600 ft). Extrapolation of the data suggests the same will be true to 300 m (1000 ft) or more.

2. With the gradient microphone, consonant differentiation is approximately independent of cavity volume from 63 in.^{3} (100 cm^3) down to 7 in.^{3} (11 cm^3) or less, except that a volume of 3.3 in.^{3} (5 cm^3) was found to lower the voice level a talker can produce.

3. The gradient microphone tends to reject bubble and inlet gas noise.

Helium Speech Unscrambling

As discussed previously, helium speech greatly shifts the frequency of formants. Hence, unless one employs a microphone with a wideband pass (i.e., >10,000 Hz), the shift in formants will not be picked up. If a signal is not picked up, it certainly cannot be unscrambled.

The following methods have been suggested by Sergeant (1966b) for increasing the intelligibility of helium speech by reducing the formant frequencies of the speech spectrum.

1. Slowing down original speed of transmission.
2. Incorporating sideband techniques.
3. Utilizing computers.
4. Splicing a magnetically taped speech sample, either physically or electronically.
5. Utilizing a speech pattern playback machine.

Sergeant goes on to explain that, in a chamber containing 94% helium at a simulated depth of 400 ft (120 m), a slow playback of one-half speed produced an increase in intelligibility of the talker from 78 to 97%.

The major difficulty in simply slowing down speech is that one loses time and the fundamental frequency of the voice is also lowered. Nevertheless, for routine messages when time is not a major consideration, this technique is quite appealing.

A report by Fairbanks, Everett, and Jaeger (1954) describes a rotating pick-up head for use on a tape recorder, which enables a tape to be electronically spliced nearly in real-time. There exist two commercially produced machines that operate on this principle. Although preliminary data indicate that the improvement using this technique is not as great as that obtained by the simpler slowing-down technique, there is a decided advantage to this method. The process is in real-time except for an insignificant delay caused by separation of the recording and pickup heads.

The absence of breathing exhaust noises also resulted in marked improvement in speech intelligibility. Playback of taped conversations between divers using closed-cycle breathing equipment could be understood for better than 80% of the content. However, a similar playback from open-cycle breathing equipment was less than 50% understandable (Thompson & Thompson, 1970).

Previous analysis of helium speech has shown that the peculiar characteristics of this speech are due primarily to changes in formant frequencies of the speaker. Changes in the fundamental pitch frequency of the speaker are small and usually can be neglected. Computation of the resonant frequencies of the vocal tract, as a function of the gas mixture occupying the tract, gives a reasonable estimate of the changes that can be expected in the formant frequencies. A modified channel vocoder was designed to approximate the normal values of the talker's formant frequencies while preserving the fundamental pitch frequency. This "formant-restoring vocoder" (FRV) separates the spectral energy of helium speech into several narrow bands and then amplitude-modulates the lower-frequency pitch harmonics derived from the helium speech. Helium speech for Sea Lab II was processed by an FRV simulated on a digital computer. Results of several simulations indicated that considerable improvement in naturalness and intelligibility of helium speech can be achieved (Golden, 1966; Sergeant, 1966).

Three systems for unscrambling helium speech produced at simulated depths of 800 (140 m) and 1000 ft (300 m) were evaluated by Russotti and Duffy (1969). Recordings of a modified rhyme test read by an experienced male diver in a pressurized helium atmosphere were processed through three commercial frequency-shifting devices. The intelligibility of words passed through these systems was compared to scores obtained when the same helium recording was presented directly without alteration and when presented at one-half playback speed to groups of listeners. Half-speed playback (58.5% intelligibility) was significantly superior to all other conditions.

In 1964, Holywell and Harvey reported on another unscrambler for helium speech. This one uses the single-sideband technique that has been used by the U.S. Navy for speech in helium-rich atmospheres. However, serious distortions typically are introduced by single-sideband equipment, and the linear frequency shift suggests that completely normal speech might never be attained by this technique.

Gill (1971) has developed an electronic unscrambler for combating the distortion effect of helium on human speech. So far, this particular device appears to be the best one on the market. It was successfully used in the British 1500-ft (450-m) dive made at the Royal Navy Physiological Laboratory in Portsmouth, England. It has also been tested with great success at the U.S. Navy Experimental Diving Unit down to depths of 1000 ft (305 m).

The Receiver

As described by Hollien and Tolhurst (1969) and cited previously, the results of studies conducted at the University of Florida have demonstrated the following points about the human receiver in the underwater communication system.

1. Ambient pressure alone has little or no effect on underwater hearing acuity.

2. Immersion of the head in water creates a substantial hearing loss.

3. Underwater hearing is probably accomplished by bone conduction.

However, if the speech signal is intense enough to be heard, there appears to be little disruption of normal speech discrimination. This subject is dealt with in Chapter III.

SUMMARY

Direct and mediated communication systems are defined in the chapter and both forms are used under water. Visual communication systems are dependent upon an unobstructed optical pathway between the sender and the receiver, a condition that very seldom can be realized. However, there are some visual communication systems in use, the hand signal is one of great importance. Also, a tactile communication system can be used at least in some situations under water.

One of the significant advantages man has over other species in dealing with his environment is the ability to communicate verbally. Not only would a diving team be more efficient in its performance of tasks if provided with speech communication equipment, but also the manner of task performance in terms of cooperation would be qualitatively different.

Oral communication in underwater situations is difficult and often unsatisfactory for a variety of reasons which are discussed in the chapter. In many situations in which accurate communication is necessary, the masking noise is so high in intensity that the individual is not able to discriminate the message from the background noise. In addition, auditory systems depend greatly for their efficiency upon the intelligence and training of the receiver.

The problem of talking under water is difficult and depends very much upon training. The talker has to use few words in short messages and must avoid certain consonants because his pronunciation of consonants is generally poor. The diver's speech is distorted by the physical properties of the breathing gas mixtures. Thus helium has a very bad influence on the intelligibility of the diver's speech. Certain helium speech unscrambling apparatuses have been constructed with varying success. Transmission equipment problems are difficult because of the physical properties of seawater. Audition under water is discussed in details in Chapter III. There are many physical, physiological, and psychological problems connected with the ability to be a good listener. Some of these problems are further discussed in this chapter (Chapter VI).

VII
HUMAN PERFORMANCE
UNDERWATER

Diver Activity — The diver as a system component — Inert gas toxicity — The nitrogen theory — The carbon dioxide theory — Other theories — Gas mixtures other than air as a breathing media — Oxygen — Noble gases as oxygen diluents — Performance testing in hyperbaric environments — Performance testing equipment — Surface studies with toxic gases — Studies under hyperbaric conditions — Studies underwater — Summary.

Because of the diversity of tasks anticipated in future underwater systems, it is difficult to think of a specific human skill that will not be required. Future aquanauts will have to perform essentially the same type of work presently performed in the surface environment. Observations during diving operations and experimental studies have shown that performance deteriorates as a function of pressure when air is the breathing media. The various theories explaining this phenomena are discussed in this chapter, and alternative gas mixtures are explored.

Testing human performance in the hyperbaric environment presents some rather unique problems. Several of the measurement devices that have been used are evaluated and their use in various studies described. The environmental constraints associated with high pressure and immersion are outlined.

THE WORKING DIVER

A diver must be a person capable of a vast array of skills. Today he is expected to act as a general laborer, as well as a fine mechanic, a draftsman, and a construction engineer. Sometimes he has to perform as an artist while making underwater drawings of the damage on sunken ships or of the sea bottom. Above all, he is always expected to be watchful and observant in order to report accurately to the staff on the surface. As technological advances extend the operating duration and depth of tethered and free-swimming divers, the number and complexity of tasks to be performed underwater increase rapidly. Propst (1965) states that future skill requirements are expected to include operation and maintenance of sophisticated electronic equipment, advanced life-support systems, and autonomous underwater power sources. When one adds to these considerations the diverse demands for normal living within a habitat, which cut across the spectrum of social and psychological parameters, and the dynamic control skills required in the use of underwater vehicles and tools, it becomes clear that there is very little in the way of performance that will not be required of future aquanauts.

General Areas of Diver Activity

Although future diver activities are virtually without limit, it is apparent that present activities will continue in their current form for some time and may be expected to proliferate along dimensions already well in evidence. Reilly and Cameron (1968), have enumerated some general types of activities in which divers are presently engaged:

1. "*Salvage operations.*   These include raising sunken ships, repairing damaged ships, refloating grounded ships, and clearing harbors. Knowledge and use of simple and complex pneumatic tools, cutting and welding techniques, and explosives may be required."

2. "*Rescue operations.*   These involve activities concerned with freeing trapped men from undersea craft, structures, and equipment of all types."

3. "*Search and recovery missions.*   These include: locating and recovering undersea objects (practice torpedos, anchors, etc.); verifying contacts made by drags, sonar gear, and electromagnetic detection systems; and devising and implementing techniques for raising objects."

4. "*Inspection and repair activities*   These involve: conducting ship-bottom surveys for suspected damage, leakage, sea suction problems; checking sonar equipment; and searching for underwater ordnance. A diver may be required to clear fouled propellers,

straighten bent blades, replace zincs, or repair damaged sonar equipment."

5. "*Construction and maintenance tasks.* These include building and maintaining tunnels, bridges, wharves, piers, pipelines, and so on."

6. "*Tactical diving missions.* These include bottom reconnaissance, location and demolition of underwater obstacles, primary approach to enemy beaches, direct attack on ships, inactivation of underwater ordnance, destruction of bridges, and providing defense against individual attacks on shipping."

7. "*Science support activities.* These include underwater exploration and charting, environmental research, geophysical testing, and aquaculture."

Although these activities are quite general and diverse, Reilly and Cameron (1968) have found it possible to delineate certain categories of human performance which are common to the majority of these operational settings. These are:

Visual surveillance
Navigation
Information retrieval
Information processing
Decision making
Work production

Obviously, these classes of performance do not function independently in the operational world or in the laboratory. Each type of performance is in fact one facet of a dynamic process involving interactions between the man, his vehicle (or equipment), and the environment.

The Diver as A System Component

The selection and design of underwater work systems is dependent on the ability of the designer to estimate quantitatively the performance of the proposed systems. The diver is clearly one element of a system which at any point in time has well-defined objectives. Therefore, in studying various aspects of diver performance, it is appropriate to view such activities within the context of an entire system. Further, a system-analytic approach lends structure and organization to the problem by delineating the various man-machine environment interfaces and loops within the total situation.

Reilly and Cameron (1968) have described a typical man-machine environment system (Figure 7-1). Various energy sources acting upon the human operator may be traced from initial stimulation of receptor mechanisms through the perceptual and cognitive stages and terminate in the form of physiological and motor responses. See also Teichner and Olson (1971).

Major feedback loops are shown to illustrate interactions among human, vehicle, and environment. The term vehicle refers to surface and/or submersible craft as well as to equipment requiring adjustment of controls to achieve a desired output function or change in status.

Thus, since man is the center of all these work systems, or at least plays a vital role as a system component, it is necessary to analyze, evaluate empirically, and quantify the capabilities of the human operator to perform applied undersea work tasks not only as a diver, but also in his role as the operator of a manipulator-equipped, small submersible. The impairment in human performance during the course of a dive has been related (Imbert, Chouteau & Alinat, 1968) to three types of factors: (1) environmental influences, (2) constraints of equipment and safety requirements, (3) depth narcosis or inert gas narcosis.

It is difficult to separate the psychological and physiological domains of a problem when measuring performance underwater, especially when we are talking about "stress." For instance, such variables as heart frequency and respiration can easily increase markedly during periods of stress; however, the performance can be rather unaffected in experienced subjects and highly affected in unexperienced subjects with equal physiological responses (Selye, 1971; Levi, 1972). Another difficulty is the measurement of cognitive performance (decision making, information retrieval, information processing, etc.), which very often is affected earlier than physiological changes show. Although there are quite special stress-inducing factors underwater (biological life under the surface, increased ambient pressure, special breathing gases, etc.), stress-inducing factors in general do not differ from those in other dan-

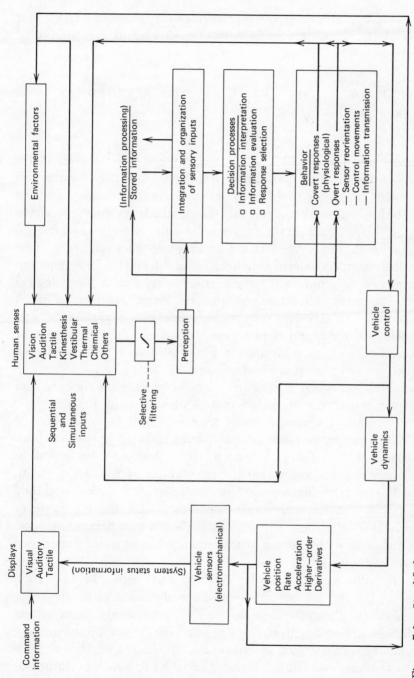

Figure 7-1. Simplified representation of man-machine-environment interaction. (Reilly & Cameron, 1968.)

281

gerous and troublesome situations. However, one can expect that many of the stress factors in normal environments are intensified underwater.

HYPERBARIC ENVIRONMENT FACTORS RELATED TO DIVER PERFORMANCE

Background

Teichner and Olson (1971) have recently presented a preliminary theory on the effects of task and environmental factors on human performance. They state that functionally oriented human performance models do not use task analysis, and that available system models have utilized "black boxes" in their approach for intervening physiological mechanisms. They suggest that this approach does not seem to be practical when considering environmental effects, because most environmental data obtained have been concerned with physiological effects rather than effects on performance. These investigators found it necessary to develop relationships between performance and physiological data, and then to use them to predict the effects of the environment on performance for conditions in which physiological, but not performance, data are available.

Some physiological effects are common to all environments, and Teichner and Olson suggested that the first step in analyzing the effects of any environment on performance must be an analysis of the compensatory physiological responses induced by the environment, and of the sensory phenomena that accompany the responses. These workers also noted that the adaptability of the receiver with regard to the environment must be given careful attention, and they emphasize that an individual's experience with the environment must be evaluated since the activating effect varies depending upon how habituated the person is and upon what previous experience he has had with it.

An important point made by Teichner and Olson (1971) is that, even though not all environments have the same critical physiological effects, they may have similar activation effects. These effects might be correlated with changes in heart rate, oxygen consumption, arterial oxygen saturation and blood flow. If this is true, then according to Teichner and Olson, these are variables to which performance should be related and with which central nervous system variables should be related.

Inert Gas Toxicity

A definition of the term inert gas narcosis comprehensive enough to satisfy science is at present impossible. Loosely, it could be defined as the changed behavior of an individual exposed to increased atmospheric pressure either in a dry chamber or under the surface of the sea. Something happens to alter the individual's characteristic response pattern; that is, he displays atypical behavior and degraded performance. This is summarized in Table 7-1.

Undoubtedly, the increased pressure and the nature of the breathing medium assume significant roles in the creation of these uncharacteristic responses. Other physical and psychological factors (cold, darkness isolation, etc.) may also play a part. Disturbed pulmonary, cardiovascular, brain, and neural function, along with other physiological disturbances, have been documented as consequences of this general circumstance. Several investigators have found alterations in mood and affectivity, alterations of consciousness, perceptual and psychosensorial phenomena, motor disturbances, and performance decrement (Hill & Greenwood, 1906; Damant, 1930; Behnke, Thompson & Motley 1935; Schilling & Willgrube, 1937; Adolfson, 1965, 1967).

When air is breathed, the first signs are already observable visually and by introspection at an ambient pressure of 4 ATA (equivalent to a water depth of 30 m), and motor and mental changes then increase successively with the ambient pressure. Divers are still conscious at 13 ATA (120 m), although most of them are probably very close to the border of consciousness at this pressure level.

In 1835, Junod reported that when compressed air is breathed "the functions of the brain are activated, imagination is lively, thoughts have a peculiar charm and, in some persons, symptoms of intoxication are present." Twenty-six years later, in 1861, Green observed that breathing compressed air while diving produced "a feeling of sleepiness." At 5.8 ATA he also noted hallucinations and impairment in judgment. Green suggested that the signs and symptoms were of sufficient severity to merit an immediate return to atmospheric pres-

Table 7-1   Behaviorial Changes due to Inert Gas Narcosis

Stimuli	Organism	Response[a]
Pressure *and* gas mixture	Disturbed pulmonary function	Alterations in mood and affectivity
Physical factors	Disturbed cardiovascular function	Alterations in consciousness
Psychological factors	Other physiological disturbances	Perceptual and psychosensorial phenomena
	Biochemical changes?	Motor disturbances
	Pressure effects per se?	Performance decrement
	Disturbed brain and nerve function	Other behavioral changes

[a] Responses detailed:

Alterations in Mood and Affectivity	Alteration of Consciousness	Perceptual and Psychosensorial Phenomena	Motor Disturbances	Performance Decrement
Hypomanic exaltation	Autistic (contemplative)	Disorganization of the perception of time	Clumsiness	In general
Aggressiveness	Unaware of the situation	Echolalia or echophrasia	General deterioration of fine-skilled movements	
Irritability	Cannot be reached by commands	Reverberation or "after-hearing"	Deterioration in handwriting	
Insolent		Micropsia	Tendency to write figures toward the right side of the paper	
Fussy	Does not answer when spoken to	Changes in figure-background contrast		
Laughing		Diplopia		
Happiness in general	Complete amnesia	Levitation	Stiffness or slight paralysis of the facial muscles	
	Impaired memory	Fixation of ideas	Catatoniclike stupor	
	Concentration difficulties	Deteriorated auditory perception	Motionless	
	Uncertainty		Saliva dribbling	
	Attention difficulties		Extraordinary sweating	
	Impaired judgment		Coordination disturbances	
	Association difficulties		Tremor	
			Increased body sway	
			Nausea and vomiting	

sure. Later, Bert (1878) reported on the narcotic conditions of divers at great depths, and in 1903 Hill and McLeod observed in caisson workers similar signs and symptoms at 5.5 ATA, as did Green. Since then, several investigators, a few of whom are cited below, have described various symptoms of depth narcosis (Case & Haldane, 1941; Kiessling & Maag, 1960; Bennett, 1963, 1963a, 1966; Adolfson, 1967; 1968; Baddeley, 1966, 1966a).

Damant (1930) attributed the symptoms of depth narcosis to the high partial pressure of oxygen in pure air when inhaled at increased pressure. He noted that divers at 10 ATA were abnormal mentally and suffered a loss of memory. At that time the British Navy appointed a committee to study the problems of deep diving and submarine escape (Hill, Davis, Selby, Pridham & Malone, 1933). Bennett and Elliot (1969) report that among the studies of this committee was a phenomenon, entitled "semi-loss of consciousness," which referred to lapse of consciousness in a diver in 17 of 58 dives from 7.6 to 11 ATA. Normal hand signals were acknowledged but not acted upon, and amnesia for events during the dive was common upon return to the surface. Consciousness, however, returned rapidly during decompression. Various efforts were made to eradicate the condition, including flushing the helmet with air to remove retained carbon dioxide, lowering of lights, and psychological screening of the men, but they met with little or no success.

The Nitrogen Theory

Behnke, Thomson, and Motley (1935) were the first to attribute narcosis to the raised partial pressure of the physiologically inert gas nitrogen in the air. They observed "euphoria, retardment of the higher mental processes and impaired neuromuscular co-ordination" at 3 ATA, and noticed that at 4 ATA the subjects were definitively aware of a feeling of stimulation and well-being—a distinct euphoria. They found an objective reduction in mental activity involving errors in arithmetic and recording data. Responses to visual, auditory, olfactory, and tactual stimuli were delayed, and there was a tendency toward idea fixation. Behnke et al. concluded that the narcotic action of inert gases is related to the solubility of the gas in the lipid substances of the central nervous system. These findings were verified by Kiessling and Maag (1960), who also found prolonged disjunctive reaction time and a deteriorated motor performance at 4 ATA.

Case and Haldane confirmed the results obtained by Behnke et al. They were unable, however, to demonstrate any symptoms until 8.6 ATA was attained. At that pressure a slight reduction in manual dexterity and a somewhat larger reduction in the ability to solve arithmetical problems were observed. At 10 ATA the deterioration increased a little. When helium or hydrogen was substituted for nitrogen in the air, no signs of intoxication appeared. However, when the air was comprised of about 4% carbon dioxide, there was at 10 ATA a marked deterioration in manual dexterity. Case and Haldane thus demonstrated that small concentrations of carbon dioxide in the air at increased pressure had strong effects on psychomotor performance, effects not obtained by carbon dioxide in air at normal pressure.

Bennett and Glass (1957, 1961) and Bennett and Cross (1960) carried out electroencephalographic (EEG) studies, the results of which seem to support the notion that nitrogen is an important factor in the production of depth narcosis. They observed that the normal blocking of the occipital alpha rhythm that occurred in normal subjects when they solved arithmetical problems at normal air pressure (1 ATA) did not arise when the subjects were exposed to increased air pressure. However, when helium was substituted for nitrogen in the air inhaled, the original blocking appeared once again. The time from the start of compression until abolition of blocking occurred was found to vary inversely with the ambient pressure. When the reciprocal of the square root of the time to abolition (T) was plotted against the pressure (P), a linear relationship was found; that is, $P\sqrt{T}$ was a constant for any one individual but varied from subject to subject. Carbon dioxide, however, had no such effect.

However, Ingvar and Adolfson (1964) were not able to confirm the findings of Bennett and Glass when investigating 10 experienced divers by means of EEG studies on performance of arithmetical tests at 1, 3, 7, and 10 ATA while air was breathed. The time at each pressure level was 10 minutes, and the experiments were counterbalanced so that five subjects started at 3 ATA and five at 10 ATA. Only slight symptoms of inert gas narcosis were visually observed, but the ability to solve arithmetical problems at 10 ATA was reduced by about 80%. Normal blocking occurred as well at normal air pressure (1 ATA), as at all the pressure levels tested. It was suggested, then, that the findings of Bennett and Glass may not be a general phenomenon and that further investigations were necessary, a suggestion with which Bennett seems to agree in a recent study on auditory evoked potentials (Bennett, Ackles & Cripps, 1969).

The Carbon Dioxide Theory

The dominating role of nitrogen in the production of hyperbaric air narcosis, nonetheless, has not been considered fully demonstrated, and there is still doubt among some investigators. Thus Bean (1950), Seusing, and Drube (1960) and Buhlmann (1961, 1963, 1963a) were of the opinion that an increase in carbon dioxide tension in the body tissues is the main cause of the intoxication. Bean suggested that increased gas density can lead to (1) reduced carbon dioxide diffusion, and (2) deteriorated mixing between inspired and alveolar gases, with a consequent reduction in carbon dioxide elimination and elevation of carbon dioxide tension in the tissues. These changes in alveolar carbon dioxide tension and resulting changes in carbon dioxide tension of the blood and tissues are, according to Bean, a very important causative factor in the subjective and neurovascular disturbances appearing at rapid compression. Although Bean did not exclude the possibility of nitrogen as a narcotic agent, he did not consider it necessary to explain these reactions as being hypothetical nitrogen intoxication.

Buhlmann was also of the opinion that depth narcosis is due to raised carbon dioxide tension in the tissues. Increased airway resistance means increased work in breathing. At a pressure of 16 ATA, it is difficult to maintain even a small respiratory gas flow. If the ventilation is inadequate, there will be retention of carbon dioxide. Consequently, the carbon dioxide tension in the alveoli and in the arterial blood will rise, and respiratory acidosis will result. If the carbon dioxide retention reaches a high level, signs of intoxication and carbon dioxide narcosis will occur. Of special interest is a report by Buhlmann concerning a practical experiment made in 1959 in which a diver descended to a depth of 120 m (13 ATA) in the Lake of Zurich while breathing a mixture of 90% nitrogen and 10% oxygen. The diver did not manifest any signs of intoxication, or any other disturbances.

Carbon dioxide retention in divers was clearly demonstrated by Lord, Bond, and Schaefer (1966), who carried out experiments in a dry chamber. Three subjects were exposed for 12 days to 7 ATA breathing a gas mixture of 92% helium, 3.5% oxygen, and 4.5% nitrogen. Maximum breathing capacity decreased 38% on the first day of compression and remained at that level for the rest of the exposure period. Tidal volume increased significantly, and alveolar carbon dioxide was markedly elevated. Pulmonary as well as urinary carbon dioxide excretion was significantly increased throughout the exposure, indicating a marked build-up of carbon dioxide (Schaefer, Bond, Mazzone, Carey & Dougherty, 1968).

What is actually the role of carbon dioxide in inert gas narcosis? The divergent opinions as to the cause or causes of inert gas narcosis may be explained, at least in part, by the fact that the extent of narcosis at a given raised ambient pressure is dependent upon the interrelationship between the alveolar partial pressures of nitrogen, oxygen, and carbon dioxide. Thus, Frankenhaeuser, Graff-Lonnevig, and Hesser (1960, 1963) found that the degree of performance impairment at a constant high level of nitrogen pressure increased with the increase in oxygen pressure. Case and Haldane (1942) observed, as mentioned earlier, that whereas the addition of 4 to 6% carbon dioxide to the inspired air at atmospheric pressure had little or no effect on manual and arithmetical skill, at 10 ATA the same surface-equivalent level of inspired carbon dioxide caused a marked deterioration in performance. At somewhat higher carbon dioxide pressures, most of the subjects became unconscious within 5 min. It was concluded that the *combined* effects of high partial pressures of nitrogen and carbon dioxide were much more severe than those of either alone.

In a series of experiments performed by Hesser, Adolfson, and Fagraeus (1971), an attempt was made to assess the role of carbon dioxide in nitrogen narcosis by relating performance to changes in alveolar nitrogen and carbon dioxide tensions. At a constant partial pressure of oxygen, either both of the inspired nitrogen and carbon dioxide pressures were varied simultaneously, or one or the other was varied singly. The nitrogen and carbon dioxide components of compressed air narcosis were separated by comparing a variety of carbon dioxide partial pressures in air at 6 ATA. The partial pressure of oxygen was 1.3 ATA and equivalent in all cases. The parameters examined in 10 human subjects were alveolar carbon dioxide tension and performance on the Moede perceptual motor test and the Stroop color decision test.

The results indicated that (1) the carbon dioxide component is negligible at alveolar carbon dioxide tensions below 40 mm Hg (which is the normal carbon dioxide tension in the alveoli), and (2) high alveolar nitrogen and carbon dioxide pressures were simply additive in their effects on performance. In contrast, when related to inspired gas tensions, the changes in performance induced by raising nitrogen and carbon dioxide pressures simultaneously were greater than the arithmetic sum of the changes induced by either gas alone.

Hesser et al. have pointed out that, in studies concerning psychophysiological effects of carbon dioxide, the measured variables should be examined in relation to the carbon dioxide occurring at the site of action of carbon dioxide. Therefore, since carbon dioxide narcosis is apparently due to an effect on the brain, performance changes should be related to the cerebral rather than to the inspired carbon dioxide tension. Since there are no simple methods available for measuring cerebral P_{CO_2} in human subjects, these workers used the changes observed in alveolar (or end-tidal) P_{CO_2} as an index of the concomitant changes in cerebral P_{CO_2}. This was made on the assumption that the difference existing between alveolar and arterial P_{CO_2} on the one hand, and between arterial and cerebral P_{CO_2} on the other, remain approximately constant when the inspired carbon dioxide tension is increased at a constant oxygen pressure. The importance of relating changes in performance to alveolar rather than to the inspired carbon dioxide tension, especially in a hyperbaric environment, is emphasized by the fact that, with equal inspired carbon dioxide tensions, alveolar P_{CO_2} rose to higher levels in the air experiments at 6 ATA than in the oxygen experiments at 1.3 ATA.

Other Theories

In a quantitative study of mental and neuromuscular responses to increased air pressure, Schilling and Willgrube (1937) discussed the different theories concerned with the causes of hyperbaric intoxication. They strongly critized the nitrogen theory of Behnke et al. and were of the opinion that depth narcosis is possibly due to the combined effects of increased oxygen pressure, increased nitrogen pressure, and psychological factors.

To differentiate and evaluate possible factors responsible for compressed air narcosis, Frankenhaeuser, Graff-Lonnevig, and Hesser (1963) studied changes in psychomotor performance induced by exposure to different nitrogen–oxygen gas mixtures at raised ambient pressures. The impairment in performance became more pronounced upon the addition of oxygen to the inspired air, indicating that oxygen excess demonstrates a potentiating effect on the narcotic action of nitrogen at high pressure. It was also concluded that oxygen excess acts indirectly by interfering with the elimination of carbon dioxide from the tissues, and that compressed air narcosis is not due to interference with oxidation in the tissues by nitrogen excess.

Many of the mechanisms involved in anesthesia (a phenomena which itself remains the subject of speculation) seem to be directly related to the mechanisms of inert gas narcosis (Bennett & Elliot, 1969). Thus, in studying inert gas narcosis, many electrophysiological investigations have been conducted. Marshall and Fenn (1950), for instance, found that after 260 min of exposure to nitrogen at 17 ATA and argon at 10 ATA *in vitro* frog reflex preparations, were reversibly blocked whereas helium had no effect at 82 ATA (2700 ft or 823 m). Carpenter demonstrated that, to affect a block in conduction in isolated peripheral nerves, pressures as high as 310 to 340 ATA with argon were required. However, he was also able to show that considerably lower pressures protected mice from electroshock convulsions (Carpenter, 1953, 1955).

In vivo investigations by Bennett (1963a, 1965) of transmission in spinal synapses and peripheral nerve of 36 lightly anesthetized rats suggested that, as with anesthesia, inert gases act on the anterior horn cell of the synapses. The response of the rats to a minimal electric shock was used in 92 experiments to measure the extent of narcosis produced by 180 psi (12 ATA) argon and nitrogen before and after Frenquel (α-benzhydrol hydrochloride) administration. Frenquel was found to be effective in controlling inert gas narcosis in rats. Also, three men were tested by means of arithmetic and letter cancelation at 10 ATA, and it was found that a 900-mg dose of

Frenquel was effective. Subjective sensations of narcosis were still evident, however.

Bennett concluded that inert gas narcosis is not due to carbon dioxide excess alone. But he did confirm the findings of Case and Haldane (1941) that carbon dioxide and nitrogen have a marked synergistic action, and concurred with the observations of Frankenhaeuser et al. (1963) that oxygen has a potentiating effect on inert gas narcosis. According to Bennett, increased oxygen pressure rather than increased density is primarily responsible for the retention of carbon dioxide in hyperbaric environments. Whether or not inert gas narcosis occurs therefore depends upon the summated effects of three factors:

1. Nature and partial pressure of the inert gas.
2. Oxygen partial pressure.
3. Density of the breathing mixture.

Gases and Gas Mixtures Other Than Air as Breathing Media

Pure Oxygen

It is very hazardous to use pure oxygen as a breathing medium in diving to depths in excess of 10 to 20 m (33 to 66 ft) of seawater. Depending upon pressure and the duration of exposure, pure oxygen may result in such adverse physiological effects as convulsions (the "Paul Bert effect"), pulmonary damage (the "Lorrain Smith effect"), visual disturbances, and additional deleterious effects with positive accelerations. Furthermore, a pure oxygen atmosphere has the operational drawback of being a fire hazard (Behnke, Johnson, Poppen & Motley, 1934; Behnke, Forbes & Motley, 1935; Herderer & Andre, 1940; Bean 1945, 1963, 1964; Edstrom & Rockert, 1962).

Frankenhauser, Graff-Lonnevig, and Hesser (1960) compared psychomotor performance (single and choice reaction times and mirror drawing) of 10 subjects during exposure to oxygen at 3 ATA with performance under normal air breathing conditions at 1 ATA. No statistically significant differences in psychomotor performance under the two conditions could be demonstrated. Nor did performance show any tendency to deteriorate with time within the 30-min periods employed. These workers inferred that during this period no major disturbances occur in those areas of the cerebral cortex that control psychomotor performance.

Noble Gases as Oxygen Diluents

The harmful nature of a pure oxygen atmosphere requires the introduction of one or more metabolically inert gases in order to mitigate its noxious effects. Apart from nitrogen (the natural inert gas in air), those inert gases that may be employed as oxygen diluents are: helium, neon, argon, krypton, and xenon. According to Bennett (1965), neon is less narcotic than nitrogen, argon about twice as narcotic as nitrogen, and xenon the most narcotic of all inert gases.

Hydrogen is generally not considered suitable for synthetic breathing mixtures because of its explosive potential when used together with oxygen. However, oxygen–hydrogen mixtures, prepared in such a way as to be outside the explosive concentration limits, have been used in diving with no signs of intoxication (Case & Haldane, 1941; Zetterstrom, 1948; Bjurstedt & Severin, 1948; Fife, Eder, Holland & Fischer, 1971).

The most commonly used diluent gas for deep diving is helium. Helium–oxygen gas mixtures have been used in dives as deep as 2000 ft. Performance measures gathered on helium–oxygen dives have failed to show the degradation associated with other diluent gases. Biersner and Cameron (1970) of the U.S. Navy Experimental Diving Unit gathered data on four performance tests during a deep helium–oxygen dive at Duke University. The tests were administered during a shallow training dive, and at depths of 900, 1000, 500, and 50 ft (274, 305, 152, and 15 m). The four measurements included tests of learning and memory, spatial orientation, and psychological stress (the Stroop color confusion test). A tracking task was used to evaluate motor performance. Preliminary results indicate that motor performance, as well as learning and memory, did not vary consistently under any test condition, thereby confirming the assumption that helium does not become narcotic at depths down to 1000 ft (305 m). Noticeable changes were found, however, in psychological stress and spatial orientation. These changes were most apparent during the descent and began to diminish after 2 days on the bottom. Increases in psychological stress were moderate, but are considered normal under the stressful conditions associated with hyperbaric chamber studies at these very great depths (Biersner and Cameron 1970). These results suggest that simulation dives may play an important role in stress adaptation and diver selection.

PERFORMANCE TESTING IN HYPERBARIC ENVIRONMENTS

Background

Most of the human performance research that has been done to date has been carried out in chamber simulation facilities similar to the one at the U.S. Navy Experimental Diving Unit (Figure 7-2). There has been some work in the open sea, but it is the exception rather than the rule. The enormous practical difficulties of obtaining surface-support craft, trained divers, and a suitable geographic site are major barriers to this type of research. Relatively simple straightforward experimental procedures such as gathering and recording data become major problems during underwater performance studies. Because of these many hindrances, most researchers have chosen to gather their data during chamber simulation dives. The physiological changes associated with pressure and various gas mixtures can be reproduced in a chamber, but the psychological stresses of diving in the open sea are missing. Care must therefore be taken in generalizing from the results of pressure-chamber studies to open-sea conditions. The importance of psychological stress is difficult to quantify, although it has been demonstrated by Baddeley (1966) and Weltman and Egstrom (1966).

Human performance testing in just about any environment is done for one of two reasons: (a) to evaluate the integrity of the central nervous system, or (b) to assess an individual's ability to perform a given type of task. The majority of the studies performed in hyperbaric environments have focused on the first objective. Several different performance tests have been used. For every active researcher in the diving field, there are at least two or three different tests. The use of so many measures has made it extremely difficult for investigators to compare their results. This situation is not unique to diving, however, and the need for uniformity among tests extends to just about every human performance research program.

The most commonly used technique for comparing performance test results is to express the results in percent decrement. This procedure is inadequate for two reasons; first, it is dependent on the measurement scale used, which in most cases has only interval properties rather than the ratio properties needed; and second, the vari-

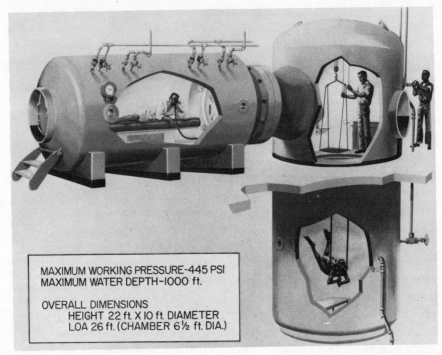

MAXIMUM WORKING PRESSURE-445 PSI
MAXIMUM WATER DEPTH-1000 ft.

OVERALL DIMENSIONS
    HEIGHT 22 ft. X 10 ft. DIAMETER
    LOA 26 ft. (CHAMBER 6 ½ ft. DIA.)

Figure 7-2. Hyperbaric research chamber at the U.S. Navy Experimental Diving Unit.

ance associated with performance usually changes with the level of stress, thus altering the needed statistical assumption of independence (Stevens, 1960).

Fowler (1970) has suggested using information bits as a unit of common measure. Every performance task requires the handling of some type of information. Attneave (1959) has derived a procedure for converting some performance tasks into information bits, which would eliminate the differences between the various measurement scales. Although this idea is technically sound, the problem of converting all the various performance tasks used into information bit scores is overwhelming if not impossible.

A third alternative for comparing the results of various tests is the use of Z scores (standard scores). By converting all test results to standardized Z scores, we could eliminate the measurement scale problem. These resulting Z scores can be compared using a critical ratio which compensates for any shifts in variance. This statistical technique has been used for years in the psychological testing field, but has not been used in underwater research as yet.

Testing Equipment

The tests being used in underwater performance research are rather crude by today's technological standards. The three tests shown in Figures 7-3 through 7-5 are examples of the type of measures still being employed in many laboratories. The digit-symbol test shown in Figure 7-3 is an enlarged version of the paper and pencil test. It has been enclosed in plastic, and the diver subjects use a grease pencil to mark their responses. The test is designed to measure associative memory. A test subject marks below each number the corresponding symbol, and his score is the number of correct responses made. Figure 7-4 shows a modified Purdue pegboard. The board is made of plastic so it can be used underwater. The test requires the diver to assemble a set of pins, collars, and washers in a prescribed order on the pegboard. The score consists of the number of parts assembled correctly in 30 sec. The gross motor test shown in Figure 7-5 is the Bennett hand tool dexterity test. The test involves removing of nuts, washers, and bolts from one side of a steel frame and reassembling them on the other side of the frame, using a standard set of wrenches and a screwdriver. This test has also been modified for use underwater. Normally, the test frame is made of wood. Practical testing problems such as bolts rusting, grease pencils breaking, and divers cheating make these testing devices rather difficult to use effectively.

In 1966 the U.S. Navy Experimental Diving Unit initiated a program with Biotechnology, Inc. to design equipment to measure a broad spectrum of basic performance dimensions. Measures were selected on the basis of their relative independence and their relevance to present and anticipated diver activities. The resulting measurement system is characterized by (1) substantial flexibility in the selection and administration of tests, (2) relative ease in setting up tests and obtaining performance data, (3) safe and reliable operation in wet and dry chambers at an ambient pressure of up to 30.6 ATA (450 psi) (Reilly and Cameron, 1968).

Substantial time and effort were given to identification of the

Figure 7-3. Digit-symbol associative memory test.

measures selected for inclusion in the test battery and in modifying
them to meet engineering constraints imposed by the testing environment, methodological factors concerned with retaining test
validity while altering test format, and restrictions associated with
the firm requirements for an integrated package as opposed to a
conglomeration of test equipment.

The testing system has been named SINDBAD, an acronym
standing for System for the Investigation of Diver Behavior At
Depth. A broad spectrum of abilities may be assessed, ranging
from simple visual reaction time to complex manual tracking in two
axes with higher-order system dynamics. There are perceptual tasks
of varying difficulty, and tests of mental functions such as induction,
mental arithmetic, and associative memory. Table 7-2 summarizes
the 26 tests involved.

Figure 7-6 shows the testing system in use at the U.S. Navy Experimental Diving Unit. Tests are programmed and administered by
the experimenter at a master control console. The diver views test
stimuli on an underwater rear projection screen (the projector itself
being outside the chamber), an oscilloscope, and an optical digital

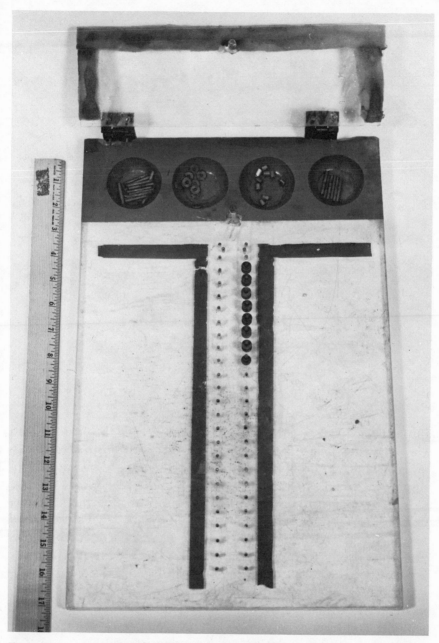

Figure 7-4. Purdue Pegboard fine motor dexterity test.

Figure 7-5. Bennett hand tool dexterity test.

display. The latter two displays are located outside the chamber and viewed by the diver through a porthole. Specially constructed swing-away mounts are designed to permit rapid and easy substitution of display by a single operator.

In performing various tests, the diver uses the alphanumeric keyboard and dual-tracking controls shown in Figure 7-7. The keyboard is completely sealed and filled with an inert, nonconductive fluid. The diver uses a permanent magnet probe to actuate magnetically sensitive reed switches within the keyboard compartments. The keyboard is used in cognitive tests such as induction and mental arithmetic, tests involving mental manipulation of geometric figures and patterns, and for a variety of perceptual-motor tests including manual dexterity, finger dexterity, and wrist-finger speed.

In tests of manual tracking ability, the diver views the oscillo-

Table 7-2 Basic Abilities/Behavior Measured by the Developed System (Reilly and Cameron, 1968)

Ability	Description of Behavior
Cognitive	
Memory span	Recall sequences of digits presented visually
Associative memory	Recall second element of previously learned paired associates when presented with first element of each pair
Perceptual speed	Make rapid comparisons of items of visual information
Number facility	Mentally solve addition, subtraction, multiplication, and division problems
Induction	Discover rule governing classification of items into subgroups
Flexibility of set	Detect change and make adaptive response to changes in pattern of binary stimulus sequence
Flexibility of closure	Identify specific figures within complex visual surround
Length estimation	Discriminate difference in distance of two stimulus points from a given reference point in the presence of visual distractors
Perceptual-Motor	
Arm-hand steadiness	Hold arm and hand steady while fully extended
Wrist-finger speed	Make rapid repetitive tapping movements
Finger dexterity	Manipulate small objects with fingers
Manual dexterity	Manipulate large objects with hand
Multilimb coordination	Use hands and/or feed simultaneously (tracking)
Speed of arm movement	Make discrete, rapid arm movement
Visual reaction time	Respond as rapidly as possible to discrete visual signal
Perceptual-Motor	
Time interval estimation	Estimate prescribed intervals of time
Time sharing	Divide attention among two visual displays to detect occurrence of critical event(s)
Response orientation	Make directional control responses to nondirectional stimuli
Spatial scanning	Visually trace components of a complex visual field
Visualization	Recognize relationships between two-dimensional and three-dimensional representations of stimulus figures
Spatial orientation	Discriminate relation of figures in one axis as opposed to a different axis.
Perceptual	
Visual monitoring	Attend to continuously changing visual display to maintain cognizance of system status

Table 7-2 - Continued

Ability	Description of Behavior
Vigilance	Attend to information source for prolonged period to detect occurrence of infrequent event(s)
System equalization	
Position control	Two axis tracking—zero-order dynamics
Rate control	Two axis tracking—first-order dynamics
Acceleration control	Two axis tracking—second-order dynamics

Figure 7-6. SINBAD Performance System installed in hyperbaric research chamber. (Reilly & Cameron, 1968.)

Figure 7-7. Subject console and tracking sticks for SINBAD test system. (Reilly & Cameron, 1968.)

scope and uses one or both tracking controls. A wide range of tracking tasks can be selected on the experimenter console. Combinations of control/display directionality, system dynamics, forcing functions (tracking courses), and pursuit or compensatory modes are available simply by setting a few switches.

Finally, the diver has a photocell stylus which is used to obtain a measure of arm-hand tremor and also speed of arm movement, both in conjunction with the underwater rear projection screen.

Figure 7-8 shows the experimenter console with its data readouts and task selection controls. All the timing, programming, and scoring logic employ solid-state integrated circuits.

In tests requiring a large number of binary responses, that is, a series of "yes" or "no" answers, the correct answers are located in binary code along the top edge of each test slide. (The code is not visible to the subject.) A mirror reflects the coded portion of the slide into an array of photocells (Figure 7-9) whose outputs are

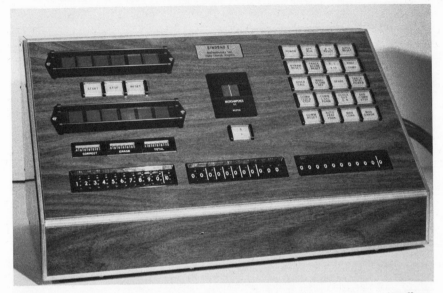

Figure 7-8.   Experimenter Console for test selection and programming. (Reilly & Cameron, 1968.)

compared serially with the subject's responses as they occur. Correct, incorrect, and total responses are accumulated and displayed at the experimenter's console. Although this system is designed with all performance scores displayed visually to the experimenter, an interface unit has been constructed whereby signals can be fed directly into an IBM card punch. This allows for off-line processing and statistical analysis of the performance scores.

There are at least three major areas where comprehensive performance profiles obtained by the present tests may be used to advantage.

One area is in the development of diver selection criteria. Work in this area would proceed on the assumption that a significant relationship exists between certain constellations of basic components of behavior (primary abilities) and performance of complex tasks in the operational environment.

A second domain where information concerning the human operator is necessary is that of design and evaluation of systems and equipment. A well-organized, methodically developed body of

Figure 7-9.   Slide Projector with pickup mirror in front of lens and photocell array above. (Reilly & Cameron, 1968.)

knowledge concerning human mental and psychomotor performance capabilities in the undersea environment should be of considerable value to engineers required to develop systems that maintain and extend these capabilities.

The third area includes planning military and commercial diver missions. Decisions as to what may reasonably be expected of divers who are required to travel various distances and perform specified tasks under relatively extreme environmental conditions would clearly be aided by the availability of fundamental data.

Surface Studies with Toxic Gases

Inert gas narcosis has been the subject of many investigations over the years. However, relatively little attention has been directed toward specifying which basic performance factors are susceptible to narcosis, or toward determining whether learning or memory is most readily impaired. Results of several studies indicate that practice and experience may result in improved performance under narcosis (Schilling and Willgrube, 1937; Kiessling & Maag, 1962), while another study has shown that long-term memory may be less impaired than short-term memory (Steinberg & Summerfield, 1957).

Biersner (1972) initiated a study to investigate some of the specific performance effects of inert gas narcosis when subjects remained on the surface. He used a gas mixture of 30% nitrous oxide and oxygen to simulate the anesthetic properties of air at a depth of 210 ft of seawater. The performance factors studied included motor coordination, orientation, learning, long- and short-term memory, and visual recall.

Motor performance in the Biersner study was measured with the Bennett hand tool dexterity test (BHTDT) (Figure 7-5) and the Purdue pegboard (PPB) (Figure 7-4).

Table 7-3 shows the results for performance on the BHTDT and the PPB. No statistically significant differences were revealed between performance on air versus performance on nitrous oxide, indicating that neither gross nor fine motor performance was impaired at this level of narcosis. Performance on the two motor tasks was highly variable, however, and represented rather rough measures at best.

Biersner also administered a series of cognitive tests during this study. The Wechsler Memory Scale (WMS) used consisted of six subtests which test for knowledge of personal and current information, orientation to time and place, mental control, recall of logical material, digit span (forward and backward), reproduction of simple geometric figures from memory, and associative learning. Results of the WMS are presented in Table 7-4. Orientation time and place,

Table 7-3   Psychomotor Performance (Biersner, 1972)

Test	Air		Nitrous Oxide		
	Mean	S.D.	Mean	S.D.	t
Bennett hand tool	346.48	43.66	342.38	30.72	0.69
Purdue pegboard	38.24	5.39	38.33	3.87	−0.10

Table 7-4   Performance on the Wechsler Memory Scale (Biersner, 1972)

Test	Air Mean	Air S.D.	Nitrous Oxide Mean	Nitrous Oxide S.D.	t
Orientation	10.57	0.74	10.09	1.11	1.50
Mental control	7.04	1.73	6.04	1.78	1.84
Digit span					
Forward	7.09	1.05	6.57	1.30	1.86
Backward	5.04	1.51	4.61	1.39	1.91
Visual Memory	11.80	2.30	12.00	1.92	0.34
Short-term memory	14.90	3.12	8.28	2.07	9.92*
Associative learning					
Simple	5.51	0.75	4.39	1.16	4.37*
Complex	2.13	1.24	1.21	1.06	3.47*

*$p < .01$.

mental control, digit span, and visual recall remained essentially normal under 30% nitrous oxide, while short-term memory for logical material and associative learning were significantly impaired ($p < .01$).

Figure 7-10 shows that substantial improvements in performance occurred, however, in the associative learning task over three trials with nitrous oxide. These data suggest that some learning is possible even with moderate narcosis.

Although Biersner's study was sound in design, it still remains for someone to demonstrate that breathing nitrous oxide on the surface is the same as breathing air at some depth. If this could be shown to be true, it would make research on the narcosis problem much easier.

Performance under Hyperbaric Conditions

From the various hyperbaric performance studies that have been conducted, it appears that human performance is affected by four different types of variables; or at least it is convenient to think in terms of four variable groupings. These four groupings are shown in Figure 7-11. Some of the specific variables that may well affect performance are listed under their appropriate group headings. Most of the research that has been done to date deals with environmental

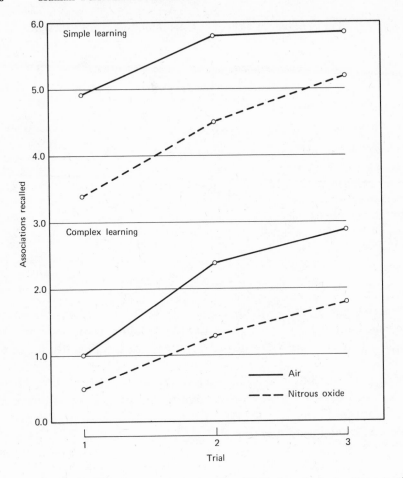

Figure 7-10. Performance comparisons on the WMS for air and nitrous oxide (Biersner, 1972.)

factors. There has been some work on human factors, but little or no effort has been expended on equipment or procedural factors.

The procedures used in underwater work have evolved through trial and error rather than through any systematic research or engineering effort. Equipment studies such as evaluations of underwater breathing apparatus have concentrated on physiological rather than performance criteria. This has been done on the supposition that if the diver is physiologically intact he will be able to perform his assigned task. This does not always hold true. If the equipment is cumbersome, hard to handle, or unreliable (or if the diver just thinks it is unreliable), the diver will have to time-share between his equipment and his task, and his performance will suffer.

Performance Underwater

Field studies of diver performance during the Sea Lab II project were undertaken by three teams of 10 men each, who lived in and operated from an underwater habitat situated on the ocean floor at 62 m (205 ft) (Bowen, Anderson & Promisel, 1966).

The purposes of the human performance studies were (1) to examine the effects of the environment and the condition of diving on the performance of divers, (2) to study the work capability of divers operating from a submerged habitat, and (3) to extract preliminary conclusions on tool and equipment design and the design of task processes with the aim of eventually establishing human engineering specifications for equipment and tasks.

Performance under Sea Lab conditions was compared to performance on dry land and to performance in shallow water 4.5 m (15 ft). The experiment consisted of a strength test, an assembly test, a two-hand coordination test, a group assembly test, and a visual test of the detection and recognition ranges of targets of different forms and colors. These tests are described below.

The strength test involved two torque wrenches mounted on the shark cage of the Sea Lab II structure. The handle of one wrench was horizontal; the other was vertical. The lift test, carried out using the horizontal handle, consisted of bracing one's feet on a platform and lifting upward on the handle, which was positioned about 30 in. above the platform. The pull test was carried out with the vertical handle. It consisted of grasping the handle with the left hand at about shoulder height and grasping a grip with the right hand. By having the position of the right-hand grip adjustable, each man could achieve a full armstretch position. In both tests the subjects were told to exert maximum force. The forces achieved were recorded by a deflection arm which moved a recording marker along a scale. The foot-pounds applied were then read directly from the recording marker. The results appear in Table 7-6 which gives the mean measurements and standard deviations on the strength test of

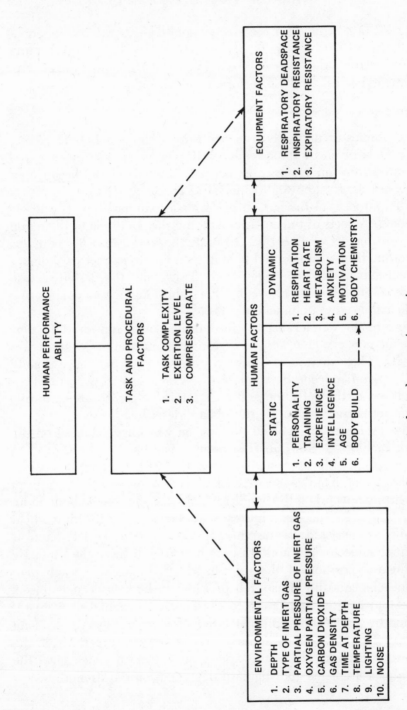

Figure 7-11. Factors affecting human performance in the undersea environment.

Table 7-5   Strength Test (Bowen, Anderson and Promisel, 1966)[a]

	Stretch			Lift		
Conditions	No. of Subjects	Mean	S.D.	No. of Subjects	Mean	S.D.
Dry land	14 (11)	238 (238)	27.4	14 (12)	614 (628)	103.5
Sea Lab	22 (11)	187 (200.1)	42.3	23 (11)	557 (600)	104.5
Percent difference		21% (16%)			9% (5%)	

[a] Data are given in foot-pounds. The number of subjects, means, and percent differences given in parentheses are for divers who took the test both on dry land and under Sea Lab conditions.

all data collected. The data were also inspected for any differences between taking the test at the beginning versus the end of the sortie; no differences were found. Also, the data showed no trends across the 15-day period of each team's stay.

The triangle test consisted of assembling three 1-ft lengths into a triangle by joining the ends of the lengths together with nuts, washers, and bolts. The subjects were required to assemble each corner by placing a washer on each side of the two lengths and a bolt through the four pieces, and securing it with a nut to finger-tightness.

Figure 7-12 illustrates results of the triangle test. It is interesting to note that the decrement in performance between shallow water and Sea Lab diving conditions for the triangle test was 23%. This compares closely with the 32% found by Baddeley (1966) for a comparable test performed under comparable conditions. This degree of agreement is encouraging for it tends to indicate that the performance capability of divers can be measured and predicted with some consistency.

The two-hand coordination test required the diver to move a peg along a track by means of turning two knobs which controlled the position of the peg in X, Y coordinates. The test required continuous visual monitoring of the position of the peg with respect to the track, and coordination of rotary movements between the two hands.

Unfortunately, the data gathered on this test from the trials run

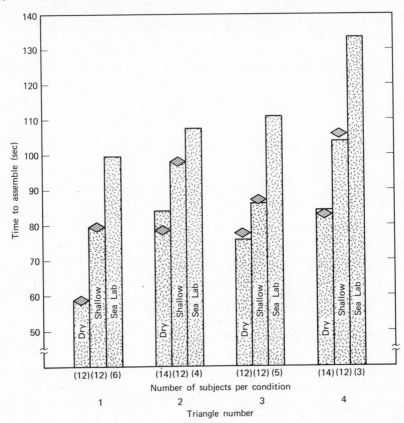

Figure 7-12. Triangle test—mean times to assemble triangles for dry land, shallow water, and sea lab conditions. Triangle no. 1, large Bolts, same corners; no. 2, small bolts, same corners; no. 3, large bolts, different corners; no. 4, small bolts, different corners. Number of subjects providing data for each mean are given in parentheses; the symbol indicates mean performance of the 11 subjects who performed the test for both dry land and shallow water conditions.(Bowen, Anderson & Promisel, 1966.)

under Sea Lab conditions are unreliable because the machine involved became corroded. See Figure 7-13, however, for overall results for dry land and shallow water conditions.

The group assembly test required four subjects to cooperate in assembling a structure from lengths of pipe and connectors. The subjects were shown the structure in a perspective drawing. Eighty-four separate pieces had to be used.

Only one trial of the group assembly test was conducted during

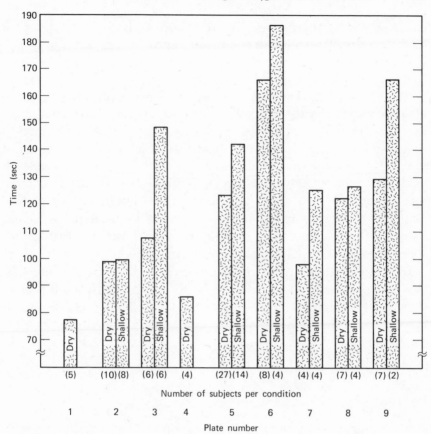

Figure 7-13. Two-hand coordination test—mean times of performance for dry land and shallow water conditions for each of the nine test plates (Bowen, Anderson & Promisel, 1966.)

the Sea Lab submersion. The time taken for assembly was 12 min. and 20 sec. The circumstances of the test were that, for about 1 hr before exiting from the Sea Lab, the four men concerned practiced building the structure and deciding precisely how to do it. Each man had also assembled the structure before on dry land or in shallow water. Under these circumstances the authors felt that it was appropriate to select for comparison the best times achieved under shallow water and dry land conditions; these were 8 min. 10 sec. and 6 min. even, respectively. The other time for shallow-water conditions was 22 min., and for dry land trials the times ranged from 6 min. to 40 min. to not completed. The difficulty was the divers had very little practice at the assembly task and only limited time to devote to the human performance test program during the actual at sea experiment. The Sea Lab team reported only one or two abortive moves during their assembly, and it seems fair to conclude that their degree of preparation was ideal for the task. The major difficulty facing the underwater teams was the lack of verbal communication. Other difficulties were low visibility and the lack of control over body motions which caused much bumping and movement among the divers clustering around the work item. Indeed, the Sea Lab team reported that their task would have taken much longer if they had not been working on a platform attached to the shark cage and thus had something to hang onto.

It is apparent from the comments collected during this project that more research effort needs to be directed toward work procedures and techniques. In the last 3 or 4 years, there has been increased research on diver tools. The information gained through this program will be helpful in establishing underwater work procedures for the future.

SUMMARY

A diver must be a person capable of a vast array of functions. Some general types of activities in which divers are at present engaged are scored in the chapter. In the future, as technological advances extend operating duration and depth, there will be very little in the way of performance that will not be required of a diver. The diver is clearly a very important system component, and must be looked upon in that role when underwater performance is tested.

Some physiological effects are common to all environments, and a first step in analyzing the effects on performance of any environment must be an analysis of the compensatory physiological responses induced by the environment, and of the sensory phenomena that accompany the responses. Also, the individual's experience with the environment must be evaluated. In diving it has been found that experienced divers are less affected by narcosis than novice divers.

When exposed to increased ambient atmospheric pressure, a diver displays atypical behavior and degraded performance. This is referred to as inert gas toxicity. The ethiology is obscure, and there are several theories about it among which the nitrogen theory and the carbon dioxide theory are the most common. These and other theories are discussed in the chapter.

Psychomotor tests are frequently used to accumulate basic information concerning man's ability to function in the hostile undersea environment. Most of these tests are constructed for use in a normal atmosphere. Some of them are useful in studies of underwater performance, but it is necessary for the psychologist working with these tests or constructing new instruments for diving performance measurement to be familiar with the environment and the general areas of diver activity.

Several basic performance factors are susceptible to inert gas intoxication, and different measurement systems have been constructed to measure them. One of the most promising programs, the SIND-BAD testing system, is characterized by substantial flexibility in the selection and administration of tests, relative ease in setting up tests and obtaining performance data, and safe and reliable operation in wet and dry chambers to considerable depths.

GLOSSARY

AUDIOMETRY.   The measurement, or testing, of the sense of hearing.

AUTONOMIC NERVOUS SYSTEM.   One of the principal divisions of the nervous system consisting of a large outflow of peripheral, efferent fibers which regulate visceral and glandular responses. The system consists of two divisions, the sympathetic and the parasympathetic.

AZIMUTH.   The distance in angular degrees in a clockwise direction from the north (in the Northern Hemisphere) or the south (in the Southern Hemisphere.)

BARIC.   Pertaining to the weight of the atmosphere.

BAROTRAUMA.   Physiological injury caused by pressure changes.

BENDS.   See Decompression sickness.

BIAURAL INTENSITY DIFFERENCE.   The intensity differences at each ear which account for directional hearing.

BIAURAL TIME DIFFERENCE.   The "sound shadow effect" that results from one ear being nearer the sound source than the other, enabling one to judge direction.

BINAURAL.   Referring to both ears.

BINOCULAR DISPARITY.   The slight difference between the two retinal images (due to the separation of the eyes) when viewing a solid object.

BULB.   A type of encapsulated nerve ending.

CAISSON.   Water-tight ambient pressure chamber used for underwater construction.

CAISSONS DISEASE.   See Decompression sickness.

CAPILLARY.   A minute blood-vessel connecting the smallest ramifications of the arteries with those of the veins.

CARBON DIOXIDE NARCOSIS.   The carbon dioxide theory of narcosis suggest that the reduced mental and motor functions observed at depth are the result of retained carbon dioxide rather than the partial pressure of the inert gas.

CENTER CLIPPING.   The elimination (in transmitted speech) of the central portion of the wave, with loss of intelligibility.

CERAMIC GRADIENT MICROPHONE.   The best microphone presently

available for use in a diver's mask, due to its bandwidth response and
pressure insensitivity.

CEREBRAL CORTEX.   The greatly invaginated outer layer of cerebral gray
matter and the center of many complex neural adjustments.

CITRIC ACID.   An acid contained in many fruits, especially in limes and
lemons.

COCHLEA.   The bony snail-like part of the ear which contains the organ of
hearing.

COCHLEAR MICROPHONICS.   See Cochlear potentials.

COCHLEAR POTENTIALS.   An electrical response generated in the cochlea of the inner ear by stimulation.

CODE-ALPHA FLAGS.   Signal flags flown by military ships throughout the
world when divers are in the water.

COGNITIVE PERFORMANCE.   The operation whereby man becomes aware
of objects of thought or perception, including understanding and reasoning.

COLLICUL.   Two pairs of small protuberances on the dorsal side of the midbrain, of which the uppermost are called superior and the lower inferior.
The superior colliculus mediates visual reflexes; the inferior mediates
auditory reflexes.

CONDUCTIVE IMPAIRMENT.   Impaired hearing caused by a defect in the
conducting mechanisms, that is, the eardrum or auditory ossicles.

CORNEA.   The anterior, transparent part of the sclerotic coat of the eye.

CONES.   Specialized receptor cells in innermost portion of the retina which
are capable of transforming the energy of light into nervous impulses.

CPS.   Cycles per second.

CREST.   The high point of a wave in any given cycle.

CRISTA.   The "swinging door" arrangement within the canals of the vestibular mechanism.

CRITICAL FLICKER-FUSION FREQUENCY (CFF).   The rate at which
a flickering stimulus fuses into a smooth, continuous stimulus.

CUTANOUS KINESTHESIS.   Sensitivity to changes and movements of the
skin relative to what it touches.

CYLINDER.   A type of nerve ending believed to mediate warmth.

DECIBEL.   A unit of measurement of the perceived differences in sound. The
standard sound exerts a pressure of 0.0002 dynes per cm^2 on the eardrum.
This is of approximately average threshold value for a tone of 1000 cps.
The decibel is a $10 \times \log_{10}$ of the ratio between this sound and a comparison sound.

DECOMPRESSON SICKNESS.   Caused by bubbles of gas coming out of
solution due to a reduction in pressure and their blocking the circulation
or injuring the body tissue.

DEPTH NARCOSIS. See Inert gas narcosis.

DICORS. *Di*ver *c*ommunication *r*esearch *s*ystem.

DIFFRACTION. The breaking up of a ray of light into the spectrum colors.

DIOPTER. A unit of measurement which is applied to the power of a lens to bring light rays to a focal point.

DIPLOPIA. Double vision; one object being seen by the eye or eyes as two.

DONALD DUCK EFFECT. The changes incurred in the speech of a person breathing a helium–oxygen atmosphere.

DYNE. A unit of measurement for the force necessary to accelerate 1 g of material 1 cm/sec.

ECHOLALIA. A meaningless repetition by a person, of words spoken to him by others.

EDEMA. Presence of abnormally large amounts of fluid in the intercellular tissue spaces of the body.

ELECTROENCEPHALOGRAM. A graphic record of the electrical currents developed by the cerebral cortex.

ELECTRONYSTAGMUS. A machine designed to measure nystagmus (rapid oscillation of the eyeballs).

EMMETROPES. Individuals possessing normal vision.

ENCAPSULATED NERVE ENDINGS. Nerve endings characterized by a covering as opposed to free nerve endings.

ENDOLYMPH. The straw-colored fluid within the semicircular canals and structures of the inner ear.

END-TIDAL. Method of CO_2 measurement whereby the level of carbon dioxide is sampled at the end of tidal expiration.

EPITHELIUM. Covering of the internal and external surfaces of the body, including the lining of vessels and other small cavities.

EPITYMPANIC RECESS. A recess on the cavity in the middle ear.

ESOPHORIA. A condition of muscular imbalance between the two eyes, resulting in one of the eyes deviating from its normal position.

EUSTACHIAN TUBE. A valved tube connecting the middle ear and the mouth, permitting equilibrium of atmospheric pressure between the outside and the middle ear.

EXTERNAL AUDITORY CANAL. The canal leading from the outer ear to the eardrum.

EXTEROCEPTORS. The sense organs of the skin which give information on changes in the immediate external environment.

FASCICULUS. A bundle of nerve fibers which make up a tract in the spinal cord.

FEEDBACK.   Information returned from a source and used in regulating behavior.

FENESTRATION.   The process of making an artificial opening into cochlea for the purpose of correcting conduction deafness.

FLEXIBILITY OF CLOSURE.   The ability to keep one or more definite configurations in mind so as to make an identification in spite of perceptual distractions.

FOVEA.   The small depression in the center of the retina which is the area of fixation and the center of clearest vision.

FREQUENCY.   The number of times a phenomenon occurs.

FRICATIVE.   A sound formed by forcing air through the narrow opening of the teeth and lips.

GANZFELD.   An unstructured, homogenous field of view.

GENERAL REASONING.   The ability to solve a broad range of problems, including those of a mathematical nature and of deduction.

GEOPHYSICS.   The physics of the earth, dealing with the study of inaccessible portions of the earth by instruments and apparatus such as the torsion balance, seismograph, and magnetometer.

GESTALT.   An integrated whole which is greater than the sum of its parts.

HAPTIC.   Pertaining to the cutaneous system of senses.

"HARD-LINE" SYSTEMS.   A communication system similar to a telephone which consists of a microphone, cable, and receiver.

HARVARD PB WORD LIST.   A set of 20 lists of 50 words, each of which is phonetically balanced (PB) with the frequency of the sounds in the word list being proportional to that of everyday speech.

HEMO.   A prefix making reference to the blood.

HEMOCONCENTRATION.   The concentration of blood.

HERTZ (Hz).   Cycles per second.

HETEROPHORIA.   See Esophoria.

HUE.   The dimension of visual sensation that is primarily related to the wavelength of the stimulus.

HYDROSTATIC PRESSURE.   The pressure caused by liquids in their equilibrium state.

HYDROSPHERE.   Pertaining to the water on the surface of the earth.

HYOSCINE.   Liquid alkaloid found in hyoscyamus. It is a powerful depressant of the cerebrum and the motor centers of the cord and is employed in insomnia, mania, and excessive sexual excitement.

HYPER.   A prefix meaning "over" and implying excess.

HYPERMETROPIC.   See Hyperopia.

HYPEROPIA.   A condition in which the rays of light entering the eye come to a focal point behind the retina because of shortness of the eyeball (commonly called farsightedness).

HYPERVENTILATION.   Decrease in carbon dioxide in the blood caused by rapid heavy breathing.

HYPOGLYCEMIA.   Deficiency of sugar in the blood.

IMMERSION HYPOTHERMIA.   Subnormal body temperature due to immersion in water.

INCANDESCENT ILLUMINATION.   Light produced by passing an electric current through a filament in a vacuum.

INDUCTION.   Reasoning from the specific to the general. It requires the finding of general concepts or principles that will fit sets of data.

INERT GAS NARCOSIS.   Degradation of performance caused by high partial pressures of krypton, argon nitrogen, or any other of the "noble gases."

INTENSITY.   The quantitative attribute of a sensation which is correlated with the magnitude of the stimulus.

INTEROCEPTORS.   The sensors associated with the visceral organs.

ISOMETRIC RELAXATION.   Relaxation of a muscle without shortening.

KINESTHESIS.   The muscle, tendon, and joint sense which helps to yield information about the position of the body in space.

LANDOLT RINGS.   Circles with gaps of varying sizes, which are used in the determination of visual acuity.

LORRAIN SMITH EFFECT.   The physiologist Lorrain Smith first observed the pulmonary toxic effects of high-pressure oxygen.

LUMINANCE.   Light energy which is transmitted, reflected, or emitted from a source.

MASKING.   The partial or complete obscuring of one sensory process by another.

MEATUS.   Two canals, external and internal, in the temporal bone of the skull; one is the pathway for sound waves to enter the ear, and the other carries the auditory and facial nerves with blood vessels.

MECHANORECEPTORS.   The receptors in the body that are sensitive to mechanical energy (for touch, pressure, and audition).

MERCURY ILLUMINATION.   Light made by passing an electric current through a mercury vapor bulb or tube.

MICROPSIA.   A defective state of vision in which objects appear very small.

MODALITY.   Two sensations are said to differ in modality when it is impossible to pass by graduations of quality from one to the other.

MODIFIED RHYME TEST. A test used to measure the intelligibility of speech.

MODULATED SYSTEMS. Amplitude modulation employs a carrier frequency varied by a superimposed speech signal. Systems of this type consist of a microphone, power module, amplifier, modulator, and underwater transducer.

MORSE CODE. A system of dots, dashes and spaces corresponding to an alphabet. Used mainly in telegraphy.

MUCOUS MEMBRANE. A membrane in the nose which is involved in the secretion of mucus.

MYOPIA. A condition in which light rays come to a focus in front of the retina because the eyeball is too short (commonly referred to as near-sightedness).

NEOPRENE. An oil-resistant synthetic rubber made by polymerizing chloroprene. Because of its insulation properties, it is used for diver wet suits.

NITROGEN NARCOSIS. An intoxication caused by breathing of high partial pressures of nitrogen at hyperbaric pressures. (See also inert gas narcosis)

NONSENSE SYLLABLE. A pronounceable combination of letters that does not make a meaningful word.

NYSTAGMUS. Involuntary, jerky movements of the eyes.

OCCIPITAL. Pertaining to the back part of the brain or the occipital lobe which contains the centers for vision.

OCULOMOTOR NUCLEUS. The nerve cells in the superior colliculus and third ventricle which give rise to the oculomotor nerve.

OPACITY. The condition of being impervious to light.

OPHTHAMALOGIST. A person who deals with the eye with respect to structure, function, and diseases.

OPTIC NERVE. The connecting pathway between the retinas of the eyes and the cranium.

OPTOKINETIC NYSTAGMUS. Rapid ocillation of the eyeballs.

ORAL CAVITY. The cavity that extends from the lips to the pharynx.

OSSICULAR CHAIN. The auditory chain of small bones in the middle ear, consisting of the malleus (hammer), the incus, (anvil), and the stapes (stirrup).

OTITIS. Inflammation of the ear.

OTOLITUS. Small calcium deposits in the endolymph of the inner ear which, when the head moves, activate neuronal endings to aid in maintaining equilibrium.

OTOLOGICAL. Pertaining to the ear with respect to its anatomy, physiology, functions and disorders.

PAUL BERT EFFECT.   The French physiologist Paul Bert first observed that oxygen at high pressure is toxic to the central nervous system.

PEAK CLIPPING.   The elimination of the high-amplitude portion of the speech wave (transmitted speech) with minimal loss of intelligibility.

PERCEPTUAL SPEED.   The ability to compare a perceived configuration with a remembered one under speeded conditions.

PERILYMPH.   The clear fluid that fills the perilymphatic space and is in direct communication with the cerebrospinal fluid through the cochlea aqueduct.

PERSISTENT COMMUNICATION.   Messages not addressed to a specific receiver/or which do not require some sort of immediate action.

PHILOERECTION.   Erection of the hair.

PHONEME.   A group of closely related speech sounds which are spelled with the same or equivalent letters and are commonly regarded as the same sound.

PHOENEMIC MATRIX.   A stimulus-response chart showing how well a specific sound (stimulus) is understood (response).

PHONETIC.   Pertaining to the systematic representation of speech sounds by means of symbols.

PHONATION RATIO.   The ratio of pause time to the time required to make speech sounds.

PHORIA.   The turning of the eyeballs in sighting an object.

PHOTON.   A measure of brightness defined as the retinal illumination which results when a surface brightness of one candle per square meter is seen through a pupillary area of 1 mm^2.

PHOTOPIC VISION.   Daylight vision; vision under conditions of relatively strong illumination, when the cones are functional (hence color vision).

PINNA.   The fleshy part of the external ear.

PINNIPED.   An animal that has finlike feet or flippers.

PLASMA.   The fluid part of the blood and the lymph.

PLOSIVE.   A speech sound produced by the complete stoppage and sudden release of breath.

POLARIZED LIGHT.   Light that has been broken up into its seven basic colors by passing through a prism or similar device.

PROPRIOCEPTORS.   The sense organs found in muscles, tendons, joints, and in the labyrinth, which provide information concerning the movement and position of the body in space.

PSYCHOMOTOR PERFORMANCE.   Motor acts that involve sensory-neural feedback loops to the brain.

PSYCHOMOTOR TESTS.   Tests which, while based upon other psychological processes (sensory, perceptual), call for a motor reaction such as pressing a key, holding a stylus as steady as possible, or manipulating controls.

QUININE SULFATE. A bitter, colorless salt.

REFLECTION. The throwing back of sound, light, heat, and so on, by a surface.

REFRACTION. To bend while passing from one medium to another; usually in reference to light.

RESONANCE. The vibration of any sounding body in response to an external sound.

RESPIRATORY ACIDOSIS. An accumulation of acid in the blood caused by a buildup of carbon dioxide.

RESPONSE ORIENTATION. Skill in making the correct movement in relation to the correct stimulus, especially under highly speeded conditions.

RETICULAR FORMATION. A network of cells, extending from the top of the spinal cord to the brain stem which controls sleep, alertness, attentiveness, and so on.

RETINA. The innermost layer of the eye, which contains the light-sensitive cells, namely, rods and cones.

REVERBERATION. A reechoing or, in the case of light, reflection.

RHINITIS. Inflammation of the nasal mucous membrane.

RODS. The elongated elements in the retina which function in scotopic (twilight) vision.

SACCULE. The smaller of the two sacklike swellings of the vestibule in the inner ear.

SAGGITAL. The line or plane passing through the long axis of the head.

SATURATION DIVE. A dive of such a duration that no more gas can be absorbed into the tissues of the body. The tissues and the free gas in the environment are in equilibrium.

SCLERA. The firm, fibrous, outer membrane of the eyeball, continuous with the sheath of the optic nerve behind and with the cornea in front.

SCOTOPIC VISION. Vision under conditions of dim illumination.

SEMICIRCULAR CANALS. Three semicircular tubes in the inner ear which are set at approximate right angles to each other in three planes and which contain the receptors sensitive to acceleration and deceleraion of the body.

SIDETONE. The voice of the talker as it reaches his own ears.

SIGNAL-TO-NOISE RATIO. A measurement comparing the signal with background noise.

SINUSITIS. Inflammation of a sinus located within the bones of the skull.

SIZE CONSTANCY. The tendency to perceive objects as the same size regardless of wide variations in the conditions of viewing.

SOMATIC SENSE.   Sensations arising in structures located in the wall of the body as opposed to the viscera.

SOMESTHESIA.   The body sense including tactile, kinesthetic, and internal sensitivity.

SPATIAL ORIENTATION.   A person's ability to remain unconfused by the various alignments of objects or patterns with respect to the person.

SPATIAL PATTERNING.   A stimulus pattern based upon position.

SPATIAL SCANNING.   Speed in exploring a wide or complicated field.

SPECTRUM.   The band of radiant energy which can be projected after being passed through a prism.

SPEED OF CLOSURE.   The ability to unify an apparently disparate perceptual field into a single percept.

SPINDLE.   Type of encapsulated nerve ending.

SPIROKINESIS.   The proposition that all animals have a fundamental circling mechanism.

SPL.   Sound-pressure level; the intensity of a sound usually expressed in decibels.

STATIC SENSE.   The sense with its receptors in the inner ear, upon which maintaining equilibrium depends.

STATOMETER.   An instrument for measuring standing steadness.

STENOSIS.   Constriction or narrowing, especially of a channel or aperture.

SUBLARYNGEAL TRACHEITIS.   Inflammation of the trachea below the larynx.

SUPERIOR COLLICULI.   The anterior pair of the corpora quadrigemina (rear portion of the midbrain), believed to function in optic reflexes.

SYLLABLE.   A word, or part of a word, which is pronounced with a single uninterrupted sound.

SYLLOGISTIC REASONING.   Ability to reason from stated premises to their necessary conclusions.

SYMPATHESTOMIZE.   To cut off part of the sympathetic nerve.

SYNAPSE.   The region where the processes of two neurons come into close contiguity, and the nervous impulse passes from one to the other.

SYNOVIAL FLUID.   The clear fluid secreted within synovial membranes. The membrane lines the cavity attached to a bone and through which a tendon glides.

SYSTOLE RELAXATION.   Relaxation with a contraction of the muscles.

TACTILE SENSE.   Refers to the sense of touch. The touch receptors can be divided into two groups; (1) complex, multicellular organs, capsules or corpuscles, incorporating nerve endings inside them; (2) free nerve endings—naked nerve terminals which may branch out or may wind around certain cells.

TASTE MODALITY.   The sense by which the flavor or savor of things is perceived when they are brought into contact with special organs of the mouth.

TELEORECEPTOR.   A distance receptor such as the eye or ear.

TEMPORAL PATTERNING.   A stimulus pattern based upon time.

TEMPOROMANDIBULAR JOINT.   Pertaining to the point where the lower jawbone (the mandible) joins the skull (the condyloid process).

TERMINALS.   Free or encapsulated nerve endings.

TIDAL VOLUME.   The depth of breathing; the volume of gas inspired or expired during each respiratory cycle.

THERMOCOUPLE.   A pair of dissimilar electrical conductors so joined that an electromotive force is developed by the thermoelectric effects when the junctions are at different temperatures.

TINNITUS.   A ringing in the ears caused by pathological conditions in the receptor mechanism.

TRANSDUCER.   A device that converts energy from one form to another.

TRANSIENT COMMUNICATIONS.   Messages that have a specific receiver or require immediate response.

TRANSMISSABILITY.   The ability to cause something to go from one place or person to another.

TRIGEMINAL NUCLEUS.   A mass of nerve cells in the pons and medulla from whence the fifth cranial nerve (trigeminal nerve) arises.

TROCHLEAR NUCLEUS.   A mass of nerve cells in the ventral portion of the gray matter which surrounds the aqueduct and gives rise to the fourth cranial nerve (trochlear nerve) which sends afferent impulses to the superior oblique muscles of the eye.

TROUGH.   The low point of a wave in any given cycle.

TYMPANIC MEMBRANE.   The membrane separating the external auditory canal from the middle ear.

TYNDALL EFFECT.   The effect (a cone of light) caused by shining a light through a colloidical suspension.

UNVOICED SOUND.   A speech sound that does not use the vocal chords.

UTRICLE.   The socklike structure of the inner ear containing the receptors which react to changes in head position.

VALSALVA MANEUVER.   The forcing of air into the middle ear cavity by means of forcible expiratory efforts made while the nose and mouth are tightly closed.

VASOCONSTRICTION.   The constriction of blood vessels.

VASODILATION.   Enlargement of the blood vessels.

VENTRICULAR EXTRASYSTOLES.   A premature contraction of the heart which is independent of the normal rhythm and whose impulse is supposed to arise in the auriculoventricular node.

VESTIBULAR KINESTHESIS.   Sensitivity to movement of the skull.

VESTIBULAR MECHANISM.   A system comprised of three semicircular canals located in the bony labyrinths of the head.

VESTIBULAR SYSTEM.   A general term used to describe the whole neural mechanism involved in receiving the sensory data from the static sense, and providing for the making of the necessary responses for the adjustment of the equilibrium of the organism with reference to gravity, or other forces affecting it.

VISCERAL.   Pertaining to the functioning of the organs that make up the viscera and which are enclosed in the abdominal and thoracic cavities.

VISCOSITY.   Property of a fluid or gas that resists change in the shape or arrangement of its elements during flow.

VISUAL KINESTHESIS.   Sensitivity to a change in one's field of view.

VISUALIZATION.   This involves the ability to comprehend imaginary movements in three-dimensional space or to manipulate objects in the imagination.

VOICED SOUND.   A sound produced by the use of the vocal chords.

WATER EFFECT.   A term coined by H. Bowen to describe the cause of reduced human performance upon immersion in water.

WATT.   A unit of power equal to 1 J/sec; the power of a current of 1 A flowing across a potential difference of 1 V.

REFERENCES

Adler, F. H. (1950). *Physiology of the Eye,* Henry Kimpton, London.

Adolfson, J. (1965). Deterioration of Mental and Motor Functions in Hyperbaric Air. *Scand. J. Psychol.* 6:26.

Adolfson, J. (1967). Human Performance and Behavior in Hyperbaric Environments. In *Acta Psychologica Gothoburgensia VI.,* J. Elmgren, Ed., Almqvist & Wiksell, Stockholm.

Adolfson, J. (1968). Psychotic Symptoms in Hyperbaric Air. *Med. Sport* 21(6): 231.

Adolfson, J. and E. Fluur (1965). Horselforandringar i Hyperbar Miljo. *Forsvarsmedicin* 4:167.

Adolfson, J. and E. Fluur (1967). Hearing Discrimination in Hyperbaric Air. *Aerosp. Med.* 38:174.

Adolfson, J. and A. Muren (1965). Air Breathing at 13 Atmospheres. Psychological and Physiological Observations. *Forsvarsmedicin* 1:31.

Adolfson, J., L. Goldberg, and T. Berghage (1972). Effects of Increased Ambient Air Pressures on Standing Steadiness in Man. *Aerosp. Med.* 43(5):520.

Adolfson, J., K. Bjerver, E. Fluur, and L. Goldberg (1970). Vestibular Reactions during Hyperbaric Conditions. *Forsvarsmedicin* 6:234.

Adolfson, J., K. Bjerver, E. Fluur, and L. Goldberg. Balance Disturbances in Divers at 10 ATA Ambient Air Pressure. In press.

Adolfson, J. and J. W. Miller (1971). Diving Scientists Explore the Sea Floor in Tektite II *Forsvarsmedicin,* 17:55.

Agarate, C. (1971). *Respiratory Heat Loss in Deep Diving.* Unpublished letter, COMEX, France.

Albano, G. (1970). *Principles and Observations on the Physiology of the Scuba Diver,* Office of U.S. Naval Research, Department of the Navy, Arlington, Va., ONR Rept. DR–150.

Albers, V. M. (1970). *The World of Sound,* A. S. Barnes, Cranbury, N.J.

Almour, R. (1942). Industrial Otology in Caisson Workers, *N.Y. State J. Med.* 42:779.

Alpern, M. (1962). *Types of Movement in the Eye,* Vol. 3, *Muscular Mechanisms,* H. Davson, Ed., Academic Press, New York.

Alpern, M. and C. D. Hendley (1952). Visual Functions as Indices of Physiological Changes in the Acid-Base Balance of the Blood. *Amer. J. Optom.* Monograph 139.

Alt, F. (1896). Uber apoplectiforme Labyrintherkrankungen bei Caissonarbeitern. *Mschr. Ohrenheilk.* 30:341.

Andersen, B. G. (1968). *Diver Performance Measurement: Underwater Navigation, Depth Maintenance, Weight Carrying Capabilities*, Human Factors Section, Electric Boat Division, General Dynamics, Groton, Conn., Ref. No. U-417-68-030.

Andersen, B. G., A. J. Pesh, and F. L. Allen, Sr. (1967). Open Ocean Diving Operations Using Scuba Divers and Deep Submersible Vehicles. In *Man-in-The Sea: Symposium Proceedings*, Metropolitan Chapter, Human Factors Society, New York, N.Y.

Anderson, S. and H. T. Christensen (1969). Underwater Sound Localization in Man. *J. Aud. Res.* 9:358.

Anderson, V. C. (1970). Acoustic Communication is Better than None. *IEEE Spectrum* 7(10):63–68.

Armstrong, H. G. and J. W. Heim (1937). The Effect of Flight on the Middle Ear. *J. Amer. Med. Ass.* 109:417.

Attneave, F. (1959). *Applications of Information Theory to Psychology*. Holt, Rinehart, and Winston, New York.

Baddeley, A. D. (1965). *The Relative Efficiency at Depths of Divers Breathing Air and Oxygen-Helium*. In J. N. Lythgoe and J. D. Woods, Ed., *Symposium of the Underwater Association of Malta*, Published by the Association, 13. Guildford, England.

Baddeley, A. D. (1966). Influence of Depth on the Manual Dexterity of Free Divers: A Comparison between Open Sea and Pressure Chamber Testing. *J. Appl. Psychol.* 50:81.

Baddeley, A. D. (1966a). Time Estimation at Reduced Body Temperature. *Amer. J. Psychol.* LXXIX, (3):475.

Baddeley, A. D., J. W. de Figheredo, J. W., Hawkswell-Curtis, and A. N. Williams (1969). Nitrogen Narcosis and Performance under Water. *Ergonomics* 11:157.

Bader, M. E. and J. Mead (1949). *Vascular Responses in Relation to Cold Tolerance*. U.S. Army, Office of the Quartermaster General, Lawrence, Mass., Quartermaster Climatic Research Laboratory, Environmental Protection Section, Rept. no. 157.

Bader, M. E., J. Mead, and M. E. Phillion (1950). Individual Differences in Vascular Responses and Their Relationship to Cold Tolerance. *J. Appl. Physiol.* 2:608.

Barnard, E. E. P. (1961). Visual Problems Underwater. *Proc. Roy. Soc. Med.* 54:755.

Bartley, S. H. (1969). *Principles of Perception*. 2nd ed., Harper & Row, New York.

Bartley, S. H. (1970). The Homeostatic and Comfort Perceptual Systems. *J. Physiol.* 75:157.

Bateman, J. B. (1951). Preoxygenation and Nitrogen Elimination. In *Decompression Sickness*, J. F. Fulton, Ed., W. B. Saunders, Philadelphia.

Bauer, B. B. and E. L. Torick (1966). Experimental Studies in Underwater Directional Communication. *J. Acoust. Soc. Amer.* 39:25.

Bazett, H. C. (1949). *Acclimatization to Cold.* Conference on Acclimatization, National Research Council Committee on Aviation Medicine, Washington, D.C.

Beagles, J. A. (1969). Problems of High Ambient Air Noise in the Diving Environment. *J. Occup. Med.* 11:228.

Beagles, J. A. and E. K. Coil (1966). *Divers Body Heat Loss.* U. S. Navy, Electronics Laboratory, Rept. no. 1408.

Bean, J. W. (1945). Effects of Oxygen at Increased Pressure. *Physiol. Rev.* 25:1.

Bean, J. W. (1950). Tensional Change of Alveolar Gas in Reactions to Rapid Compression and Decompression and Question of Nitrogen Narcosis. *Am. J. Physiol.* **161**:417.

Bean, J. W. (1963). Effects of Oxygen in Diving. *Proceedings of the Second Symposium on Underwater Physiology, National Academy of Sciences—National Research Council,* Publ. no. 1181, Washington, D.C.

Bean, J. W. (1964). General Effects of Oxygen at High Tension. In *Oxygen and the Animal Organism,* F. Dickens and E. Neil, Eds., Proceedings of a symposium of the International Union of Biochemistry and the International Union of Physiological Sciences, Macmillan, New York, pp. 455.

Beckman, E. L. (1959). *Escape from Ditched Aircraft,* Institute of Aviation Medicine, R.A.F., Farnborough, England.

Beckman, E. L. (1964). *A Review of Current Concepts and Practices Used to Control Body Heat Loss During Water Immersion,* U.S. Naval Medical Research Institute, Bethesda, Maryland.

Beckman, E. L., E. Reeves, and R. Goldman (1966). A Review of Current Concepts and Practices Applicable to the Control of Heat Loss in Air Crews Subjected to Water Immersion, *Aerosp. Med.* **37**:(4):348.

Behan, F. L., R. A. Behan, and H. W. Wendhausen (1972). Color Preception Underwater. *Hum. Factors* **14**(1):41.

Behnke, A. R., H. S. Forbes, and E. P. Motley (1935). Circulatory and Visual Effects of Oxygen at 3 Atmospheres Pressure. *Amer. J. Physiol* **114**:436.

Behnke, A. R., F. S. Johnson, J. R. Poppen, and E. P. Motley (1934). The Effect of Oxygen on Man at Pressures From 1 to 4 Atmospheres. *Amer. J. Physiol.* **110**:565.

Behnke, A. R., R. M. Thomson, and E. P. Motley (1935). The Psychologic Effects from Breathing Air at 4 Atmospheres Pressure. *Amer. J. Physiol.* **113**:554–558.

Beil, R. G. (1962). Frequency Analysis of Vowels Produced in a Helium-Rich Atmosphere, *J. Acoust. Soc. Amer.* **34**:347.

Bennett, P. B. (1963). The Cause and Prevention of Depth Intoxication. *J. Roy. Nav. Sci. Serv.* **18**:272.

Bennett, P. B. (1963a). Neuropharmacologic and Neurophysiologic Changes in Inert Gas Narcosis. In *Proceedings of the Second Symposium on Underwater Physiology, National Academy of Sciences—National Research Council,* Publ. 1181, Washington, D. C.

Bennett, P. B. (1965). Cortical CO_2 and O_2 at High Pressures of Argon, Nitrogen, Helium, and Oxygen. *J. Appl. Physiol.* **20**:1249.

Bennett, P. B. (1965a). The Action of Inert Gases in Hyperbaric Pressure. *Mondo Sommerso* **VII**:10.

Bennett, P. B. (1966). *The Aetiology of Compressed Air Intoxication and Inert Gas Narcosis,* Pergamon Press, London.

Bennett, P. B. and A. J. Brook (1969). Action of Selected Drugs on Decompression Sickness in Rats. *Aerosp. Med.* **40**:607.

Bennett, P. B. and A. V. C. Cross (1960), Alterations in the Fusion Frequency of Flicker Correlated with Electroencephalogram Changes of Increased Partial Pressures of Nitrogen. *J. Physiol.* **151**:28.

Bennett, P. B. and D. H. Elliot, Eds., (1969). *The Physiology and Medicine of Diving*, Williams & Wilkins, Co. Baltimore.

Bennett, P. B. and A. Glass (1957), High Partial Pressure of Nitrogen and Abolition of Blocking of the Occipital Alpha Rhythm. *J. Physiol.* 138:18.

Bennett, P. B. and A. Glass (1961). Electroencephalographic and Other Changes Induced by High Partial Pressures of Nitrogen. *Electroencephalog. Clin. Neurophysiol.* 13:91.

Bennett, P. B., K. N. Ackles, and V. J. Cripps (1969). Effects of Hyperbaric Nitrogen and Oxygen on Auditory Evoked Responses in Man. *Aerosp. Med.* 40:521.

Berghage, T. E. (1966). *Summary Statistics: U.S. Navy Diving Accidents*. U.S. Navy Experimental Diving Unit, Rept. no. 1–66, Washington Navy Yard, Washington, D.C.

Berghage, T. E. (1969). *Factors to Consider in the Selection of Respirable Gas Mixtures for Undersea Habitats*. Unpublished paper.

Bergman, W. R. (1970 Winter). Chino—A New Experience in Diving. *Faceplate*.

Bert, P. (1878). *La Pression Barometrique*. English translation by M. A. Hitchcock and F. A. Hitchcock (1943). College Book Company, Columbus, Ohio.

Bice, R. C. (1969). Apparent Movement in Vibrotactile Displays. *Percep. Mot. Skills* 29:575.

Bien, A. and P. J. McDonough (1970). *Naval Applications of Man-In-The-Sea Concepts*. Report to the Office of Naval Research, Contract N00014-68-A-0243-002, Stanford Research Institute, Menlo Park, Calif.

Biersner, R. J. and Cameron, B. J. (1970). Cognitive performance during a 1000 ft. helium dive. *Aerospace Med.* 41(8):918.

Biersner, R. J. (1972). Selective Performance Effects Of Nitrous Oxide. *Hum. Factors*, 14(2), 187.

Bijlsma, R. (1901), Duiker-doofheit. *Med. Weebbl.*, 8:273.

Bjerver, K. and P. A. Persson (1957). The Effect of Hypoxia on Standing Steadiness. *Arch. Int. Pharmacodyn.* CXII:247.

Bjurstedt, H. and G. Severin (1948). The Prevention of Decompression Sickness and Nitrogen Narcosis by the Use of Hydrogen as a Substitute for Nitrogen. *Mil. Surg.* 103:107.

Bliss, J. C., J. W. Hill and B. M. Wilber (1971). *Tactile Perception Studies Related to Teleoperator Systems*, Stanford Research Institute, Menlo Park, Calif., NASA-CR-1775.

Bodell, B. R. (1965). An Artificial Gill. *Amer. J. Med. Electron.* 4:170.

Bodell, B. R. (1967). Artificial Gill. U.S. Patent 3,333.583.

Bond, W. H. and J. M. Myatt (1969). *Investigation of Distortion of Diver's Speech Using Power Spectral Estimates Based on the Fast Fourier Transform*. U.S. Naval Postgraduate School, Monterey, Calif., M.S. Thesis.

Bowen, H. M. (1967). *Diver Performance and the Effects Of Cold*, Dunlap and Associates, Inc., Tech. Rep. BSD no. 67-441, ONR Contract no. N00014-67-C-0263. December.

Bowen, H. M. (1968). Diver Performance and the Effects of Cold. *Hum. Factors* 10(5):445.

Bowen, H. M. and R. D. Pepler (1967). *Studies of the Performance Capabilities of Divers: The Effects of Cold,* Office of U.S. Naval Research, Contract no. N0014-67-C-0263, Washington, D.C.

Bowen, H. M., B. Anderson and D. Promisel (1966). *Studies of Diver's performance during the Sea Lab II Project,* ONR Contract Rept. no. ONR 4930, March.

Brandt, J. F. and H. Hollien (1967). Underwater Hearing Thresholds in Man. *J. Acoust. Soc. Amer.* 42:966.

Brandt, J. F. and T. Hollien (1968). Underwater Speech Reception Thresholds and Discrimination. *J. Aud. Res.* 8:71.

Brandt, J. F. and H. Hollien (1969). Underwater Hearing Thresholds in Man as a Function of Water Depth. *J. Acoust. Soc. Amer.* 46:893.

Briggs, R. O. and G. L. Hatchett (1965). Techniques for Improving Underwater Visibility with Video Equipment. *Ocean Sci. Engi.* 2:1284.

Brown, D. E. S. and D. A. Marsland (1936). The Viscosity of Amoeba at High Hydrostatic Pressure. *J. Cell. Comp. Physiol.,* 8:159.

Brown, J. L. (1961). Orientation to the Vertical during Water Immersion. *Aerosp. Med.* 32:209.

Brubaker, R. S. and J. W. Wurst (1968). Spectrographic Analysis of Diver's Speech during Decompression. *J. Acoust. Soc. Amer.,* 43(4):798.

Buhlmann, A. (1961). Atemphysiologische Aspekte des Tauchens. *Der Weg in die Tiefe.* Documenta Geigy, Bull. Nr. 3. J. R. Geigy, Basel.

Buhlmann, A. (1963). Deep Diving. In *The Undersea Challenge,* B. Eaten, Ed., Proceedings of the Second World Congress of Undersea Activities, The British Sub-Aqua Club, London, pp. 52–60.

Buhlmann, A. (1963a). Respiratory Resistance with Hyperbaric Gas Mixtures. In *Proceedings of the Second Symposium on Underwater Physiology,* National Academy of Sciences–National Research Council, Publ. 1181, Washington, D.C.

Buhlmann, A. A. (1969). The Use of Multiple Inert Gas Mixtures in Decompression. In *The Physiology and Medicine of Diving,* P. B. Bennett, and D. H. Elliot, Eds., Williams & Wilkins, Baltimore.

Burnett, H. J. (1961). Suit for Divers and an Intercommunication Therefor. U.S. Patent 3,003,136.

Bunuel, R. G., A. Dziedzic, and S. Andersen (1965). Senils de perception du system sonar du marsouin *Phocoena phocoena* L., on fonction du ciametre d'un obstacle filiform. *C. R. Acad. Sci. Paris,* 260:295.

Butler, R. A. and R. F. Naunton (1967). The Effect of Stimulus Sensation Level on the Directional Hearing of Unilaterally Deafened Persons. *J. Aud. Res.,* 7:15.

Butson, A. R. C. (1949). Acclimatization to Cold in the Antarctic. *Nature,* 163:132.

Buxton, C. (1938). The Application of Multiple Factorial Methods to the Study of Motor Abilities, *Psychometrika,* 3(2).

Cannon, W. B. (1939). *The Wisdom of the Body,* 2nd ed., New York. Norton.

Carhart, R. (1951). Basic Principles of Speech Audiometry. *Acta Otolaryngol.* 40:62.

Carlsson, H. (1960). *Manuellt Arbete i Kyla.* Unpublished report to Forsvarets Forskningsanst., Stockholm, Rept. no. 1260–8508.

Carlsson, H. (1962). *Enkla Manuella Prestationer: Apparatur,* Forsvarets Forskningsanst., Avd 1, Stockholm, FOA 1 Rept. A1061–F150.

Carlsson, H. (1963). *Enkla Manuella Prestationer: Storande Inflytelser.* Forsvarets Forkskningsanst., Avd 1, Stockholm, FOA 1 Rept. A1061–F150.

Carpenter, F. G. (1953). Depressant Action of Inert Gases on the Central Nervous System in Mice. *Am. J. Physiol.* 178:505.

Carpenter, F. G. (1955). Inert Gas Narcosis. In *Proceedings of the First Symposium on Underwater Physiology, National Academy of Sciences—National Research Council,* Washington, D.C.

Carpenter, M. C. (1967). Man of Two Worlds. In *The World Book Encyclopedia Year Book,* Field Enterprises Educational Corporation, Chicago.

Case, E. M. and J. B. S. Haldane (1941). Human Physiology under High Pressure. Effects of Nitrogen, Carbon Dioxide, and Cold. *J. Hyg.* 41:225.

Case, E. M. and J. B. S. Haldane (1942). Tastes of Oxygen and Nitrogen at High Pressures. *Nature* 148:84.

Cattel, J. (1890). Mental Tests and Measurements. *Mind* 15:373.

Chambers, R. M., D. A. Morway, E. L. Beckman, R. DeForest, and K. R. Coburn (1961). *The Effects of Water Immersion on Performance Proficiency.* U.S. Naval Air Development Center, Philadelphia, Penn., Rept. no. MA–6133.

Chan, D. (1964). An Apparatus for the Measurement of Tactile Acuity. *Amer. J. Psych.* 73(3):489.

Chaplin, J. P. (1968). *Dictionary of Psychology.* Dell Publishing Company, New York.

Cherkin, A. (1968). Molecules, anesthesia, and memory. In A. Rich and N. Davidson (Eds.) *Structural chemistry and molecular biology.* San Francisco: Freeman and Company,

Cherry, C. (1966). *On Human Communication.* M.I.T. Press, Cambridge, Mass.

Christianson, R. A. (1968). *A Study of Visual Acuity Underwater Using an Automatic Landolt Ring Presentation Technique.* Ocean Systems Operations of North America, Rockwell Corporation, Los Angeles, Calif.

Clark, B. (1970). The Vestibular System. *An. Rev. Psychol.* 21:273.

Clark, R. E. (1961). The Limiting Hand Skin Temperature for Unaffected Manual Performance in the Cold. *J. Appl. Psychol.* 45:193.

Clark, R. E. and A. Cohen (1960). Manual Performance as a Function of Rate of Change in Hand Skin Temperature. *J. Appl. Physiol.,* 15(3):496.

Clarke, R. W., F. D. Humm and L. F. Nims (1944). *The Efficiency of Preoxygenation in the Prevention of Decompression Sickness.* U.S. National Research Council, Committee on Aviation Medicine, Washington, D.C., Rept. no. 31.

Coleman, R. F. and W. R. Krasik (1971). *Oral Muzzle Pressure Effects in Underwater Communication.* U.S. Office of Naval Research, Communication Sciences Laboratory, Gainesville, Fla., Rept. no. 19.

Coles, R. R. A. (1965). Ears and Their After Effects. *N. Diving Mag.* 10:3.

Coles, R. R. A. and J. J. Knight (1960). *Report on an Aural and Audiometric Survey of Qualified Divers and Submarine Escape Training Tank Instructors.* Royal Naval Personnel Research Council, Portsmouth, England, (RNPRC) Rept. 29.

Curnow, J. (1894). Auditory Vertigo Caused by Working in Compressed Air. *Lancet* 2:1088.

Damant, G. C. C. (1930). Physiological Effects of Work in Compressed Air. *Nature* 126:606.

D'Amato, H. E. and A. H. Hegnauer (1953), Blood Volume in a Hypothermic Dog. *Amer. J. Physiol.* **173**:100.

Daniels, F., Jr., D. C. Fainer, C. L. Bommarito, and D. E. Bass (1951). Acclimatization to Cold in Man. *Fed. Proc. Amer. Soc. Exp. Biol.*, **10**:32.

Day, R. H. (1969). *Human Perception.* John Wiley, New York.

Defant, A. (1961). *Physical Oceanography.* Vol. 1, Macmillan, New York.

Denton, E. J. (1956), Recherces sur l'absorption de la lumiere par le cristallin des Poissons. *Bull. Inst. Oceanogr., Monaco,* no. 1071:1.

Diachenko, J. A. (1971). *A Study of a Cutaneous Code Applied to the Communication Needs of the Working Diver.* Naval Medical Research Institute, Bethesda, Maryland. Research Rept. no. 2, August 1972, AD 750–268.

Diachenko, J. A. (1972). Personal communication.

Doherty, E. T., H. Hollien and C. L. Thompson (1967). *Preliminary Measurements of Pressure Response to Low Frequency Signals in Shallow Water.* Communication Sciences Laboratory, Gainesville, Fla., ONR Grant Nonr 580 (20), Rept. no. 9.

Duane, T. D., R. J. Emrich and H. G. Shepler (1958). *Lens System Designed for Water-to-Air Vision in the Submerged Human Eye,* U.S. Naval Air Development Center, Johnsville, Pa., Rept. no. 3.

DuBois, R. and P. Regnard (1884). Note sur l'Action des hautes pressions sur la fonetion photogenenique du lampyre. *C.R. Soc. Biol., Paris,* Ser. 8, **1**:675.

Dugal, L. P. and M. Therien (1947). Ascorbic Acid and Acclimatization to Cold Environment. *Canad. J. Res.,* **25**(Sec. E):111.

Duncan, B. K. (1934). A Comparative Study of Finger Maze Learning by Blind and Sighted Subjects. *J. Genet. Psychol.* **44**:69.

Duntley, S. Q. (1960). *Improved Monographs for Calculating Visibility by Swimmers (Natural Light),* U.S. Navy Bureau of Ships, Washington, D.C. Contract no. 65–72039, Rept. no. 5–3.

Duntley, S. Q. (1963). Light in the Sea. *J. Opt. Soc. Amer.* **53**:214.

Dureuil, M. and A. R. Ratsimamanza (1948). Action des Variations Brusques de Temperature sur la Capacite de Travail Force du Rat Normal. *C.R. Soc. Biol.* Paris **142**:720.

Edholm, O. G. and A. C. Burton (1955). *Man in Cold Environment.* Edward Arnold, London.

Edstrom, J. E. and H. Rockert (1962). The Effect of High Pressure on the Histology of the Central Nervous System and Sympathetic and Endocrine Cells. *Acta Physiol. Scand.* **55**:225.

Eldred, E. (1960). Posture and Locomotion. Chapter XLI, in *Handbook of Physiology: Neurophysiology,* Vol. 2, J. Field, H. W. Magoun, and V. E. Hall, Eds., American Physical Society, Washington, D.C.

Empleton, B. E., E. H. Lanphier, J. E. Young and L. G. Goff (1968). *The New Science of Skin and Scuba Diving,* Association Press, New York.

Engelmann, W. (1928). Untersuchungen über die Schall-localization bei Tieren. *Z Ps.,* **105**:317.

Fairbanks, G., W. L. Everett and R. D. Jaeger (1954). Method for Time or Frequency Compression of Speech. *Trans. Inst. Radio Engineers* **AU2**:7.

Fant, G. and J. Lindquist (1968). *Pressure and Gas Mixture Effects on Diver's Speech.* Speech Transmission Laboratory—QPRS No. 1, Department of Speech Communication, Royal Institute of Technology, Stockholm, Sweden.

Fant, G. and B. Sonesson (1964). Speech at High Atmospheric Pressures. *J. Acoust. Soc. Amer.* 36:2002.

Fant, G. and B. Sonesson (1967). Diver's Speech in Compressed—Air Atmosphere. *Mil. Med.* 132:434.

Farmer, J. C., W. G. Thomas, and M. J. Preslay. (1973) Human auditory responses during hyperbaric helium–oxygen exposures. In *Psychoacoustic and Electrophysiologic Studies of Hearing Under Hyperbaric Pressure,* W. G. Thomas and J. C. Farmers, Eds., University of North Carolina, Report NR 101–027, June 1973, p. 40.

Faucett, R. E. and P. R. Newman (1953). *Operation Hideout: Preliminary Report.* U.S. Naval Submarine Medical Research Laboratory, Naval Submarine Base, Groton, Conn., Rept. no. 228.

Faust, K. J. and E. L. Beckman (1966). Evaluation of a Swimmer's Contact Air-Water Lens System. *Mil. Med.* 131:779.

Feinstein, S. H. (1966). Human Hearing Underwater: Are Things As Bad As They Seem? *J. Acoust. Soc. Amer.* 40:1561.

Fenn, W. O. (1967). Possible Role of Hydrostatic Pressure in Diving. In *Proceedings of the Third Symposium on Underwater Physiology.* Williams & Wilkins, Baltimore.

Fenn, W. O. (1969). The Physiological Effects of Hydrostatic Pressures. In *The Physiology and Medicine of Diving,* P. B. Bennett, D. H. Elliot, Eds., Williams & Wilkins, Baltimore.

Ferris, S. H. (1972). Magnitude Estimation of Absolute Distance Underwater. *Percept. Moto. Skills* 35, 963.

Fife, W. P., P. O. Edel, J. M. Holland and I. Fischer (1971). *Preliminary Studies of Hydrogen-Oxygen Breathing Mixtures for Deep Sea Diving.* Lecture, Annual Scientific Meeting, Aerospace Medical Association, Houston, Texas.

Fluur, E. (1970). L'Audition en atmosphere comprimee. *Rev. Physiol. Subaquatique Med. Hyperbare* 2(1):31.

Fluur, E. and J. Adolfson (1966). Hearing in Hyperbaric Air. *Aerosp. Med.* 37:783.

Forlano, G. (1950). The Effect of Ambient and Body Temperature upon Reaction Time. *Tech. Data Dig.* 15:18.

Fowler, B. (1970). Personal communication.

Frank, N. J. (1950). *Introduction to Electricity and Optics,* 2nd ed., McGraw-Hill, New York.

Frankenhaeuser, M., V. Graff-Lonnevig and C. M. Hesser (1960). Psychomotor Performance in Man as Affected by High Oxygen Pressure (3 Atmospheres). *Acta Physiol. Scand.* 50:1.

Frankenhaeuser, M., V. Graff-Lonnevig and C. M. Hesser (1963). Effects on Psychomotor Functions of Different Nitrogen-Oxygen Gas Mixtures at Increased Ambient Pressures. *Acta Physiol. Scand.* 59:400.

Frazier, R. G. (1945). Acclimatization and the Effects of Cold on the Human Body as Observed at Little America III, on the United States Antarctic Service Expedition 1939–1941. *Proc. Amer. Phil. Soc.* 89:249.

Friberg, S., Jr., A. Muren, and N. Rogberg (1971). Rebreathing Studies at 10 Atmospheres. *Forsvarsmedicin* 7:3.

Fry, G. A., C. S. Bridgman and V. J. Ellenbrock (1949). The Effect of Atmospheric Scattering on Binocular Depth Perception. *Amer. J. Optom.* 26:9.

Galton, F. (1883). *Inquiries into Human Faculty and Its Development*, MacMillan, New York.

Gault, R. J. (1925). Progress in Experiments on Interpretation of Speech by Touch. *J. Abnormal Soc. Psychol.* 20:118.

Gaydos, H. F. (1958). The Effect on Complete Manual Performance of Cooling the Body While Maintaining the Hands at Normal Temperatures. *J. Appl. Physiol.* 12:373.

Gaydos, H. F. and E. R. Dusek (1958). Effects of Localized Hand Cooling versus Total Body Cooling on Manual Performance. *J. Appl. Physiol.* 12:377.

Geldard, F. A. (1960). Some Neglected Possibilities of Communications, *Science*, 131(3413), 1583.

Geldard, F. A. (1961). Cutaneous Channels of Communications. In *Sensory Communications*, W. A. Rosenblith, Ed., John Wiley, New York, Chapter 4.

Gentry, R. L. (1967). Underwater Auditory Localization in the California Sea Lion (*Zalophus Californianus*). *J. Aud. Res.* 7:187.

Gerstman, L. J. (1967). Breathing Mixture and Depth as Separate Effects on Helium Speech. In *Man-In-The-Sea: Symposium Proceedings*, Metropolitan Chapter, New York Human Factors Society.

Gerstman, L. J. G. R. Gamertsfelder and A. Goldberger (1967). Breathing Mixture and Depth as Separate Effects on Helium Speech. In *Man-In-The Sea: Symposium Proceedings*, Metropolitan Chapter, Human Factors Society.

Gibson, J. J. (1966). *The Senses Considered as Perceptual Systems*, Houghton Mifflin, Boston.

Gill, J. S. (1971). The Admiralty Research Laboratory Processor for Helium Speech. *In Proceedings of a Navy Sponsored Workshop*. R. L. Sergeant and T. Murry, Eds., Naval Submarine Medical Research Laboratory, Groton, Conn., Rept. no. 708.

Glaser, E. M. (1950). Immersion and Survival in Cold Water. *Nature* 166:1068.

Goldberg, L. (1943). Quantitative Studies on Alcohol Tolerance in Man. *Acta Physiol. Scand.*, 5, Suppl. XVI.

Goldberg, L., K. Bjerver, and H. Goldschmidt. Statometric Recording and Quantitative Evaluation of Standing Steadiness or Body Sway by a New Device-Statometer IV. Unpublished paper.

Golden, R. M. (1966). Improved Naturalness and Intelligibility of Helium—Oxygen Speech, Using Vocoder Techniques. *J. Acoust. Soc. Amer.* 40:621.

Goldman, R. F., B. S. Brechenridge and E. L. Beckman (1965). "Wet" versus "Dry" Suit Approaches to Water Immersion Protective Clothing. *Aerosp. Med.*, 37(5).

Gollan, F. and Clark, L. C. (1967). Prevention of Bends by Breathing an Organic Liquid. *Trans. Assn. Amer. Physicians* 80:102.

Grant, A. H. (1963). SCAL: Skindiver's Contact Air Lens. *Rev. Optom.*, 100(21):22.

Graybiel, A. (1951). Spatial Disorientation in Flight. *Mil. Surg.*, 108(4):287.

Green, J. B. (1861). Diving with and without Armour. Reported in *The Aetiology of Compressed Air Intoxication and Inert Gas Narcosis* (P. B. Bennett), London, Pergamon Press, 1966.

Greenbaum, L. J. and E. C. Hoff (1966). *A Bibliographical Sourcebook of Compressed Air Diving and Submarine Medicine,* Vol. III, Office of Naval Research and Bureau of Medicine and Surgery, U.S. Department of the Navy, Washington, D.C.

Greenfield, A. D. M. and J. T. Shepherd (1950). A Quantitative Study of the Response to Cold of the Circulation through the Fingers of Normal Subjects. *Clin. Sci.* 9:323.

Greenstone, L. (1970). Personal communication.

Guldberg, F. O. (1897). Die Circularbewegung als tierische Grundbewegung, ihre Ursache, Phänomenalität und Bedeutung. *Z. Biol.* 17:419.

Hamilton, P. M. (1957). Underwater Hearing Thresholds. *J. Acoust. Soc. Amer.* 29:792.

Hanna, T. D. (1964). *Effects of Total Body Water Immersion on Weight Discrimination.* Paper presented at the 35th annual meeting of the Aerospace Medical Association.

Hansen, R. G. (1952). *Effects of Jaw Restriction on Speech Intelligibility.* Wright Air Development Center, Wright-Patterson Air Force Base, Ohio, WADC Tech. Rept. no. 52-223.

Harashima, S. and I. Shigeno (1965). Occupational Disease of the Ama. In *Physiology of Breath-Hold Diving and the Ama of Japan,* H. Rahn and T. Yokoyama, Eds., National Academy of Sciences—National Research Council (Publ. 1341). Washington, D.C.

Harris, J. D. (1969). *Hearing Loss in Decompression.* U.S. Navy, Submarine Medical Center, Submarine Base, Groton, Conn., Rept. no. 591.

Harris, J. D. and R. L. Sergeant (1970). *Sensory Behavior of Naval Personnel: Monaural/Binaural Minimum Audible Angle of Auditory Response.* U. S. Navy, Submarine Medical Center, Submarine Base, Groton, Conn., Rept. no. 607.

Hegnauer, A. H., W. J. Schriber and H. O. Haterius (1950). Cardiovascular Response of Dogs to Immersion Hypothermia. *Amer. J. Physiol.* 161:455.

Hemmings, C. C. and J. H. Lythgoe (1965). The Visibility of Underwater Objects. In J. N. Lythgoe and J. D. Woods, Ed., *Symposium of the Underwater Association of Malta,* Rept. no. 23, published by the Association, pp. 23–30. Guildford, England.

Henriksson, N. G. and L. Gleisner (1966). Vestibular Activity at Experimental Variation of Labyrinthine Pressure. *Acta Otolaryng.* 61:380.

Henriksson, N. G., L. Gleisner and G. Johansson (1966). Experimental Pressure Variations in the Membranous Labyrinth of the Frog. *Acta Otolaryng.* 61:281.

Herderer, C. and L. Andre (1940), De l'intoxication par les lautes pressions d'oxygene. *Bull. Acad. Med., Paris* 3(123):294.

Hesser, C. M., J. Adolfson and L. Fagraeus (1971). Role of CO_2 in Compressed-Air Narcosis. *Aerosp. Med.* 42:163.

Hill, L. and M. Greenwood (1906). The Influence of Increased Barometric Pressure on Man. *Proc. Roy. Soc.* B77:442.

Hill, L., R. H. Davis, R. P. Selby, A. Pridham and A. E. Malone (1933). *Deep Diving and Ordinary Diving.* Report of a committee appointed by the British Admiralty.

Hill, L. and J. J. McLeod (1903). The Influence of Compressed Air on Respiratory Exchange. *J. Physiol.* **29**:492.

Hirsh, I. J. and C. E. Sherrick (1961), Perceived Order in Different Sense Modalities. *J. Exp. Psychol.* **62**:423.

Hoff, E. C. and L. J. Greenbaum (1954). *A Bibliographical Sourcebook of Compressed Air, Diving and Submarine Medicine,* Vol. II, Office of Naval Research and Bureau of Medicine and Surgery, U.S. Department of the Navy, Washington, D.C.

Hoke, B., D. L. Jackson, J. Alexander and E. Flynn (1971). *Respiratory Heat Loss from Breathing Cold Gas at High Pressures,* Summary of NMRI/EDU studies, unpublished report.

Hollien, H. (1971). *Underwater Sound Localization in Humans.* Communication Sciences Laboratory, Rept. 23, University of Florida, Gainesville, Fla.

Hollien, H. (1972). Personal communication.

Hollien, H. and J. F. Brandt (1969). Effects of Air Bubbles in the External Meatus on Underwater Hearing Thresholds. *J. Acoust. Soc. Amer.* **46**:384.

Hollien, H., J. F. Brandt and J. Malone (1968). *Underwater Speech Communication.* Abstracts of Four Studies in Underwater Communication. University of Florida Communication Science Laboratory, Gainesville, Fla., Rept. 20.

Hollien, H., R. F. Coleman and H. Rothman (1970). *Evaluation of Diver Communication Systems by a Diver-to-Diver Technique,* Communication Sciences Laboratory, University of Florida, Gainesville, Fla., ONR Contract N00014-68-A-0173-0008, Tech. Rept. no. 21.

Hollien, H., R. F. Coleman, C. L. Thompson and K. Hunter (1970), Evaluation of Diver Communication Systems under Controlled Conditions. In *Undersea Technology Handbook,* Compass Publications, Arlington, Va.

Hollien, H., R. F. Colemna, C. L. Thompson and K. Hunter (1968). *Intelligibility of Diver Communication Systems.* Office of U.S. Naval Research, Gainesville, Fla. CSL/ONR Progress Rept. no. 11.

Hollien, H. and C. L. Thompson (1967). *A Diver Communication Research System* (*DICORS*). Communication Sciences Laboratory, University of Florida, Gainesville, Fla., CSL/ONR Rept. no. 2.

Hollien, H., C. L. Thompson and B. Cannon (1971). *Speech Intelligibility as a Function of Ambient Pressure and HeO₂ Atmosphere,* Communication Sciences Laboratory, University of Florida, Gainesville, Fla., Rept. no. 18.

Hollien, H. and G. Tolhurst (1969). A Research Program in Diver Communication. *Naval Res. Rev.* Office of Naval Research, Arlington, Va., December, pp. 2201.

Holywell, K. and H. Harvey (1964). Helium Speech, *J. Acoust. Soc. Amer.* **36**:210(L).

Horvath, S. M. and A. Freedman (1947). The Influence of Cold Upon the Efficiency of Man. *J. Aviat. Med* **18**:158.

Howard, I. P. and W. B. Templeton (1966). *Human Spatial Orientation.* John Wiley, New York.

Howes, D. (1957). On the Relation between the Intelligibility and Frequency of Occurrence of English Words. *J. Acoust. Soc. Amer.* **29**(2):296.

Hutchinson, W. R. and W. R. Shiller (1968). *Taste Thresholds in a Submarine Environment*, U.S. Naval Submarine Medical Research Laboratory, Groton, Conn., Rept. no. 530.

Ide, J. M. (1944). *Signalling and Homing by Underwater Sound; for Small Craft and Commando Swimmers*, U.S. Naval Research Laboratory, Washington, D.C., Sound Rept. no. 19.

Ide, J. M. (1958). *Progress on Underwater Sound Gear for Small Craft and Swimmers.* U.S. Naval Research Laboratory, Washington, D.C. Rept. no. 37.

Imbert, G., J. Chouteau and J. Alinat (1968). *Sur l'utilisation des methodes psychometriques et ergonomiques en physiologie hyperbare*, Proceedings of the Physiology Studies no. 3/68, Centre d'Etudes Marines Avancées, Marseilles.

Ingvar, D. H. and J. Adolfson (1964). *Elektroencefalografistudier i hyperbar luft (Electroencephalography in Hyperbaric Air).* Internal unpublished report to the Chief of Naval Operations of the Royal Swedish Navy.

Isele, R. W., K. W. Berger, W. H. Lippy and A. L. Rotolo (1968). A Comparison of Bone Conduction Thresholds as Measured from Several Cranial Locations. *J. Aud. Res.* **8**:415.

Johnson, F. H. (1957). The Action of Pressure and Temperature. Proceedings of *7th Symposium of the Society of General Micro-biology, London*, R. E. Williams, and C. C. Spicer, Cambridge University Press, London.

Junod, T. (1835). Recherches sur les effect physiologiques et therapeutiques de la compression et de rarefaction de l'air, tant sur le corps que les membres isoles. *Ann. Gen. Med.* **9**:157.

Keatinge, W. R. (1969). *Survival in Cold Water.* Blackwell Scientific Publications, Oxford, England.

Keatinge, W. R. and M. Evans (1960). Effect of Food, Alcohol and Hyoscine on Body-Temperature and Reflex Responses of Men Immersed in Cold Water. *Lancet* **2**:176.

Keller, H. (1967). Use of Multiple Inert Gas Mixtures in Deep Diving. *Proceedings of the Third Symposium on Underwater Physiology*, C. S. Lambertsen, Ed., Williams & Wilkins, Baltimore.

Keller, H. and A. A. Buhlmann (1965). Deep Diving and Short Decompression by Breathing Mixed Gases. *J. Appl. Physiol.* **20**:1267.

Kelley, J. S. (1968). Visual Studies. In *Results of Psychological Studies Conducted during Chamber Saturation Dives from 200 Feet to 825 Feet*, M. Bradley, J. Vorosmati, and P. G. Linaweaver, Eds., U.S. Navy Deep Submergence Systems Project Technical Office, Rept. no. 1.

Kelley, J. S., P. G. Burch, M. E. Bradley and D. E. Campbell (1968). Visual Function in Divers at 15 to 26 Atmospheres. *Mil. Med.* **133**(10):827.

Kennedy, R. S. (1972). Personal communication.

Kenny, J. E. (1971). Diver Communications. *Ocean Ind.* **60**:36.

Kent, P. R. (1966). Vision Underwater. *Amer. J. Optom.* **43**:553.

Kiessling, R. J. and C. H. Maag (1960), Performance Impairment as a Function of Nitrogen Narcosis. *J. Appl. Psychol.*, **46**:91.

Kinney, J. A. S. (1972). Personal communication.

Kinney, J. A. S., S. M. Luria, and D. O. Weitzman (1968). Visibility of Colors Underwater. *J. Opt. Soc. Amer.* **57**:802.

Kinney, J. A. S., S. M. Luria, and D. O. Weitzman (1968a). *Responses to the Underwater Distortion of Visual Stimuli.* U.S. Navy, Submarine Medical Center, Submarine Base, Groton, Conn. Rept. no. 541.

Kinney, J. A. S., S. M. Luria, and D. O. Weitzman (1969). Visibility of Colors Underwater Using Artificial Illumination. *J. Opt. Soc. Amer.* **59**:624.

Kinney, J. A. S., S. M. Luria, and D. O. Weitzman (1969a). Effect of Turbidity on Judgments of Distance Underwater. *Percept. Mot. Skills* **28**:331.

Kinney, J. A. S., S. M. Luria, D. O. Weitzman, and H. Markowitz (1970). *Effects of Diving Experience on Visual Perception Underwater.* U.S. Navy, Submarine Medical Center, Submarine Base, Groton, Conn. Rept. no. 612.

Knotts, J. R. and W. R. Miles (1929). The Maze-Learning Ability of Blind Compared with Sighted Children. *J. Genet. Psychol.* **36**:21.

Koch, H. L. and J. Ufkess (1926). A Comparative Study of Stylus Maze Learning by Blind and Seeing Subjects. *J. Exp. Psychol.* **9**:118.

Kohl, O. A. and W. F. Searle (1957). *Subjective and Articulation Tests of Deep and Shallow Water Divers Communications,* U.S. Navy Experimental Diving Unit, Washington Navy Yard, Washington, D.C., Rept. no. 1–58.

Kos, C. M. (1944). Effects of Barometric Pressure Changes on Hearing. *Trans. Amer. Acad. Ophtalmol. Otolaryng.* **49**:75.

Kunnapas, T. M. (1967). *Distance Perception as a Function of Available Visual Cues,* Psychology Laboratory, University of Stockholm, Rept. no. 231.

Kylstra, J. A. (1965). Survival of Submerged Mammals. *New Eng. J. Med.* **272**:198.

Kylstra, J. A. (1965a). Breathing of Pressure Oxygenated Salt Solutions. *Dis. Chest* **47**:157.

Kylstra, J. A. (1967). Advantages and Limitations of Liquid Breathing. *Proceedings of the Third Symposium on Underwater Physiology,* C. J. Lambertsen, Ed., Williams & Wilkins, Baltimore.

Kylstra, J. A. (1968). Experiments in Water-Breathing. *Sci. Amer.* **219**(2):66.

Kylstra, J. A. (1968a). Dysbarism: Osmosis Caused by Dissolved Gas? *Science* **161**: 289.

Kylstra, J. A., I. S. Longmuir, and M. Grace (1968) Dysbarism: Osmosis Caused by Dissolved Gas? *Science* **161**:289.

Kylstra, J. A., R. Nantz, J. Crowe, W. Wagner, and H. A. Saltzman (1967), Hydraulic Compression of Mice to 166 Atmospheres. *Science* **158**(3802):793.

Kylstra, J. A., C. V. Paganelli, and E. H. Lanphier (1966). Pulmonary Gas Exchange in Dogs Ventilated With Hyperbarically Oxygenated Liquid. *J. Appl. Physiol.* **21**:177.

Kylstra, J. A., C. Paganelli, and H. Rahn (1967). Some Implications of Dynamics of Gas Transfer in Water-Breathing Dogs. *Ciba Foundation Symposium on Development of the Lung,* A. V. S. de Rench and R. Porter, Eds., Little, Brown, Boston.

Kylstra, J. A., M. O. Tissing, and A. van der Maen (1962). Of Mice as Fish. *Trans. Amer. Soc. Artif. Intern. Org.* **8**:378.

Lambertsen, C. J. (1955). Respiratory and Circulatory Actions of High Oxygen Pressure. In Proceedings of *Underwater Physiology Symposium*, National Academy of Sciences, Publ. 377. Washington, D.C.

Lanphier, E. H. (1966). *Decompression Procedures*, Committee on Hyperbaric Oxygenation, Fundamentals of Hyperbaric Medicine, National Academy of Sciences–National Research Council, Washington, D.C.

LeBlanc, J. A. (1956). Evidence and Meaning of Acclimatization to Cold in Man. *J. Appl. Physiol.* 9:395.

Lee, O. (1963). *The Complete Illustrated Guide to Snorkel and Deep Diving.* Doubleday, New York.

Leggiere, T., J. McAniff, H. Schenck, and J. Van Ryzin (1970). Sound Localization and Homing of Scuba Divers. *Mar. Technol. Soc. J.* 4(2):27.

Lester, C. J. and V. Gomez (1898). Observations Made in Caisson of the New East River Bridge as to the Effect of Compressed Air upon the Ear. *Arch. Otol. N.Y.* 27:1.

Levi, L. (1972). Stress and Distress in Response to Psychosocial Stimula. *Acta Med. Scand.*, Suppl. 528.

Licklider, J. C. R. and G. A. Miller (1951). The Perception of Speech. In *Handbook of Experimental Psychology*, S. S. Stevens, Ed., John Wiley, New York.

Liden, G. (1954). Speech Audiometry. *Acta oto-laryng*, Suppl. 114.

Liden, G. and G. Fant (1954). Swedish World Material for Speech Audiometry and Articulation Tests. *Acta oto-laryng.*, Suppl. 116.

Lockhart, J. M. (1966). Effects of Body and Hand Cooling on Complex Manual Performance. *J. Appl. Psychol.*, 5:533.

Lord, G. P., G. F. Bond, and K. E. Schaefer (1966), Breathing under High Ambient Pressure. *J. Appl. Physiol.* 21:1833.

Lundgren, C. E. G. (1965) Alternobaric Vertigo—A Diving Hazard. *Brit. Med. J.* 2:511.

Lundgren, C. E. G. and L. U. Malm (1966). Alternobaric Vertigo among Pilots. *Aerospace Med.* 37:178.

Luria, S. M. (1968). *Stereoscopic Acuity Underwater*, U.S. Navy, Submarine Medical Center, Submarine Base, Groton, Conn. Rept. no. 510.

Luria, S. M. (1970). *Duction, Field of View, and Improved Stereoacuity for Navy Divers*, U.S. Navy, Submarine Medical Center, Submarine Base, Groton, Conn., Rept. no. 623.

Luria, S. M. and J. A. S. Kinney (1969). *Visual Acuity Underwater without a Face Mask*, U.S. Navy, Submarine Medical Center, Submarine Base, Groton, Conn., Rept. no. 581.

Luria, S. M. and J. A. S. Kinney (1970). Underwater Vision. *Science*, 167:14.

Luria, S. M., J. A. S. Kinney, and S. Weissman (1967). Estimates of Size and Distance Underwater. *Amer. J. Psychol.* 80:282.

Luria, S. M., J. A. S. Kinney, and S. Weissman (1967a). Distance Estimates with "Filled" and "Unfilled" Space. *Percept. Mot. Skills* 24:1007.

Luria, S. M., H. Newmark, and H. T. Beatty (1970). *Effect of a Submarine Patrol on Visual Processes.* U.S. Navy, Submarine Medical Center, Submarine Base, Groton, Conn., Rept. no. 641.

Lythgoe, J. N. (1968), Visual Pigments and Visual Range Underwater. *Vision Res.* 8:997.

Lythgoe, J. N. and C. C. Hemmings (1967). Polarized Light and Underwater Vision. *Nature,* 213(5079):893.

MacLean, D. J. (1966), Analysis of Speech in a Helium-Oxygen Mixture under Pressure. *J. Acoust. Soc. Amer.* 40:625.

Mackworth, N. H. (1953). Finger Numbness in Very Cold Winds. *J. Appl. Physiol.* 5:533.

Marshall, J. M. and W. O. Fenn (1950). The Narcotic Effects of Nitrogen and Argon on the Central Nervous System of Frogs. *Am. J. Physiol.* 163:733.

Marsland, D. A. (1938). Effects of High Hydrostatic Pressure upon Cell Division in *Arbacia* Eggs. *J. Cell. Comp. Physiol.* 12:57.

Marsland, D. A. (1939). Mechanism of Protoplasmic Streaming. The Effect of High Hydrostatic Pressure upon Cyclosis in *Elodea canadensis. J. Cell. Comp. Physiol.* 13:23.

McCormick, E. J. (1964). *Human Factors Engineering,* McGraw-Hill, New York.

McCray, J. M. (1970). *Cutaneous Communications,* U.S. Army Electronics Command, Fort Monmouth, New Jersey, Tech. Rept. no. ECOM-3303.

McKee, D. L. (1972). *A Study of Underwater Diver Tactile Sensitivity.* U.S. Naval Postgraduate School, Monterey, Calif., Masters thesis, March.

McKenney, J. (1969). Mighty Mouth. *Skin Diver* 13:38–39, 76.

Meijne, N. G. and J. P. Straub (1966). Oxygen Tolerance and Biochemical Response of Anesthetized Dogs during Oxygen Ventilation at 3 ATA. In *Proceedings of the Third International Conference on Hyperbaric Medicine,* I. W. Brown, Jr. and B. G. Cox, Eds., National Academy of Sciences–National Research Council, Washington, D.C.

Meiselman, H. L. (1968). Adaptation and Cross-Adaption of the Four Gustatory Qualities. *Percept. Psychophys.* 4:368.

Miles, S. (1965). *Underwater Medicine,* Staples Press, London.

Miles, S. (1969). *Underwater Medicine,* 3rd ed., J. B. Lippincott, Philadelphia.

Miller, H. E. (1971). Cochlear Potentials at 11 Atmospheres. *Laryngoscope* 81:979.

Miller, J. W., R. Radloff, H. M. Bowen, and R. L. Helmreich (1967). The Sea Lab II Human Behavior Program. In *Project Sea Lab Report: An Experimental 45-Day Undersea Saturation Dive at 205 Feet.* D. C. Pauli and G. P. Clapper, Eds., U.S. Government Printing Office, Washington, D.C.

Mills, A. W. (1956). Finger Numbness and Skin Temperature. *J. Appl. Physiol.* 9:447.

Mohl, B. (1964). Preliminary Studies on Hearing in Seals. *Vidensk. Medd. Dansk Naturhist Foren.* 127:283.

Money, K. E. (1970), Motion Sickness. *Phys. Rev.* 50(1).

Montague, W. E. and J. F. Strickland (1961). Sensitivity of the Water Immersed Ear to High- and Low-Level Tones. *J. Acoust. Soc. Amer.* 33:1376.

Morgan, C. T., J. S. Cook, A. Chapanis, and M. W. Lund, Eds. (1963). *Human Engineering Guide to Equipment Design.* McGraw-Hill, New York.

Moritz, A. R. and J. R. Weisiger (1945). Effects of Cold on the Air Passages and Lungs. *Arch. Intern. Med.* 75:233.

Morrow, C. T. (1970). *Diver-to-Diver Communications: Speech in Diving Masks.* LTV Research Center, Anaheim, Calif., ONR Contract No. N00014-69-C-0189, Rept. no. 859.

Morrow, C. T. (1971). *Diver Communication Microphone Development and Installation.* Advanced Technology Center, Inc., Dallas, Texas, Rept. no. B-90000/1 CR-14.

Morway, D. A., R. G. Lathrop, R. M. Chambers, and L. Hitchcock (1963), *The Effects of Prolonged Water Immersion on the Ability of Human Subjects to Make Position and Force Estimations.* U.S. Naval Air Development Center, Johnsville, Penn.

Moskowitz, M. R. (1968). *Scales of Intensity for Single and Compound Tastes.* Harvard University, Ph.D. Thesis.

Moskowitz, H. R. (1970). Ratio Scales of Sugar Sweetness. *Percept. Psychophys.* 7(5):315.

Munz, F. W. (1958). Photosensitive Pigments from Retinas of Deep-Sea Fish. *J. Physiol.* 140:220.

Munz, F. W. (1958a). The Photosensitive Retinal Pigments of Fish from Relatively Turbid Coastal Waters. *J. Gen. Physiol.* 42:445.

Munz, F. W. (1964). The Visual Pigments of Epipelagic and Rocky Shore Fish. *Vision Res.* 4:441.

Murray, G. D. (1943). *Effect of Preoxygenation on Resistance to Decompression Illness,* U.S. Navy, NATC, Pensacola, Fla., School of Aviation Medicine, Project X-141 (Av-R6-4).

Murry, T. (1969). *A Method for Analyzing Phonemic Errors in Underwater Speech Intelligibility Testing.* University of Florida, Communication Science Laboratory, Gainesville, Fla., Rept. no. 24, September.

Murry, T. and R. L. Sergeant (1970). *Navy Diver/Swimmer Vocabularies: Phonemic Intelligibility in Hyperbaric Environments.* U.S. Naval Submarine Medical Center, Groton, Conn., Rept. 648, December.

Musoy, T. (1969). *A Method for Analyzing Phonesic Errors in Underwater Speech Intelligibility Testing,* Communication Sciences Laboratory, University of Florida, Gainesville, Fla., ONR Rept. no. Nonr 580 (20), Rept. no. 24.

Nagel, C. O. and J. B. Monical (1954). The Design and Development of a Contact Lens for Underwater Seeing. *Amer. J. Optom, Arch. Amer. Acad. Optom.,* 31(9): 468.

Nashimoto, I. (1967). The Use of Oxygen during Decompression of Caisson Workers. In *Decompression of Compressed Air Workers in Civil Engineering,* R. I. McCallum, Ed., Oriel Press, Newcastle-upon-Tyne, England.

Nashner, L. J. (1970). *Sensory Feedback in Human Postural Control.* Massachusetts Institute of Technology, MVT-70-3, Sc.D. Thesis.

Nelson, J. G. (1968). Effects of Water Immersion and Body Position upon Perception of the Gravitational Vertical. *Aerosp. Med.* 39:806.

Nesson, J. W. and W. R. Shiller (1968). *Taste Thresholds to Bitter Compounds during a Submarine Patrol.* U.S. Navy, Submarine Medical Research Laboratory, Groton, Conn., Rept. no. 538.

Newburg, L. H. and C. R. Spealman (1943). *Physiological Responses to Immersion in Cold Water.* U.S. National Research Council, Committee on Aviation Medicine, Washington, D.C., Rept. no. 164.

Newman, R. (1960). "The Feasibility of Speech Transmission Using the Skin as the Sensor," Paper presented at the USAF Air Research and Development Command 7th Annual Science and Engineering Symposium. November.

Nixon, C. W., W. E. Mabson, F. Trimboli, J. E. Endicott, and B. E. Welch (1968). Observations on Man in the Oxygen-Helium Environment at 380 mm Hg Total Pressure: IV Communications. *Aerosp. Med.* **39**:1.

Nixon, C. W., W. E. Mabson, F. Trimboli, and B. E. Welch (1969). Study of Man during a 56-Day Exposure to an Oxygen–Helium Atmosphere at 258 mm Hg Total Pressure: XIV. Communications. *Aerosp. Med.* **40**:(2):113–123.

Nixon, C. W. and M. C. Somner (1968). Subjective Analysis of Speech in Helium Environments. *Aerosp. Med.* **39**:139.

Nixon, C. W. and N. E. von Gierke (1959). Experiments on the Bone-Conduction Threshold in Free Sound Field. *J. Acoust. Soc. Amer.* **31**:1121.

Nourrit, P. (1970). Les barotraumatismes cochlearies, *Rev. Physiol. Subaquatique Med. Hyperbare* **2**(1):24.

Odend'Hal, S. and T. C. Poulter (1966). Pressure Regulation in the Middle Ear Cavity in Sea Lions: A Possible Mechanism. *Science* **153**:768.

Oliver, J. C. and F. Demard (1970). Effects sur l'audition d'un sejour en atmosphere comprimee d'helium. *Rev. Physiol. Subaquatique Med. Hyperbare* **2**(1):30.

Ono, H., J. P. O'Reilly, and L. M. Herman (1970). Underwater Distance Distortion within the Manual Work Space. *Hum. Factors* **12**(5):473.

Paganelli, C. V., N. Bateman, H. Rahn (1967). Artificial Gills for Gas Exchange in Water. Underwater Physiology. *Proceedings of the Third Symposium on Underwater Physiology,* C. J. Lambertsen, Ed., Williams & Wilkens, Baltimore.

Panck, D. W. and J. C. Stevens (1965). *Psychofit, a Computer Program for the Treatment of Psychophysical Data Laboratory of Psychophysics.* Harvard University, Cambridge, Mass., PPR 315.

Panel on Psychology and Physiology (1949). *A Survey Report on Human Factors in Undersea Warfare,* Committee on Undersea Warfare, National Research Council, Washington, D.C.

Penrod, K. E. (1949). Oxygen Consumption and Cooling Rates in Immersion Hypothermia in the Dog. *Amer. J. Physiol.* **157**:436.

Pesch, A. J. (1972), Personal communication.

Pesch, A. J., R. G. Hill, and W. F. Klepser, Jr. (1970). *Capabilities of Operators as Divers vs Submersible Manipulator Controllers in Undersea Tasks.* General Dynamic, Electric Boat Division, Rept. no. U417:70:043.

Pettersson, H. (1935), Eddy-Viscosity in Stratified Water. *Medd. Oceanogr. Inst. Goteborg,* no. 11.

Philp, R. B. (1964). The Ameliorative Effects of Heparin and Deploymerized Hyaluronate on Decompression Sickness in Rats. *Can. J. Physiol. Pharmacol.* **42**(6):819.

Pierce, A. H. (1901). *Studies in Auditory and Visual Space Perception,* Longmans Green, New York.

Piggins, D. (1970). Refraction of the Harp Seal, *Pagophilus groenlandicus.* (Erxleben, 1777). *Nature* 227:78.

Pinto, O. F. (1966). Temporomandibular Joint Problems in Underwater Activities. *J. Prosthet. Dent.* 16(4):772.

Poli, C. (1909). Ergebnisse der Untersuchung des Gehorapparates bei Caisson-arbeitern von der Aufnahme zur Arbeit. *Mschr. Ohrenheilk.* 43:313.

Pollack, I. (1965). Iterative Techniques for Unbiased Rating Scales. *Quart. J. Exp. Psychol.* 17, Pt. 2.

Poock, G. K. (1967). *Prediction of Elemented Motion Performance Using Personnel Selection Tests.* University of Michigan, PhD. Thesis.

Poulton, E. C., M. J. Catton, and A. Carpenter (1964). Efficiency at sorting cards in compressed air. *Brit. J. Ind. Med.* 21:242.

Propst, A. S. (1965). *A Preliminary Study of Man-In-the Sea Diver Personnel and Training Implications,* Personnel Research Laboratory, Washington, D.C., Rept. No. WRM–66–5. Naval Personnel Program Support Activity (AD 621 627).

Provins, K. A. and R. Morton (1960). Tactile Discrimination and Skin Temperature. *J. Appl. Physiol.* 15:155.

Rawlins, J. F. P. and R. Tauber (1971). Thermal balance at depth. In *Proceedings of the Fourth Symposium on Underwater Physiology* C. J. Lambertsen, Ed., Academic Press, New York.

Raymond, L. W. (1967). Physiologic Mechanism of Maintaining Thermal Balance in High-Pressure Environments. *J. Hydronautics* 1(2):102.

Reilly, R. E. and B. J. Cameron (1968). *An Integrated Measurement System for the Study of Human Performance in the Underwater Environment,* BioTechnology, Inc., Falls Church, Va., Office of Naval Research, Contract no. N00014-67-C-0410.

Reysenbach de Haan, F. W. (1957). De Gehoorzin van Cetacea. *Vakl. Biol.* 37:117.

Reysenbach de Haan, F. W. (1957a). Hearing in Whales. *Acta oto-laryng.,* Suppl. 134.

Reysenbach de Haan, F. W. (1966). Listening under Water: Thoughts of Sound and Cetacean Hearing. In *Whales, Dolphins and Porpoises,* K. S. Norris, Ed., University of California Press, Berkeley.

Rodbard, S., H. Saiki, and A. Malin (1950). Body Fluid Redistribution in Induced Hypothermia and Hyperthermia. *Fed. Proc. Amer. Soc. Exp. Biol.* 9:107.

Ross, H. E. (1965). The Size-Constancy of Underwater Swimmers. *Quart. J. Exp. Psyhcol.* 17(4)329.

Ross, H. E. (1967). Water, Fog and the Size-Distance Invariance Hypothesis. *Brit. J. Psychol.* 17:329.

Ross, H. E. (1967a). Stereoscopic Acuity Underwater. In J. N. Lythgoe and J. D. Woods, Eds., *Symposium of the Underwater Association of Malta, Report 1966–67,* published by the Association, p. 61. Guildford, England.

Ross, H. E. (1968). Judging Distance Underwater. *Triton* 13:64.

Ross, H. E. (1970). Adaptation of Divers to Curvature Distortion Underwater. *Ergonomics* 13(4):489.

Ross, H. E., S. D. Crickmar, N. V. Sills, and P. E. Owen (1969). Orientation to the Vertical in Free Divers. *Aerosp. Med.* 40:728.

Ross, H. E., D. J. Dickinson, and B. P. Jupp (1970). Geographical Orientation Underwater. *Hum. Factors* 12(1):13.

Ross, H. E., S. S. Franklin, and G. Weltman (1969). *Adaptation of Divers to Distortion of Size and Distance Underwater.* Biotechnology Laboratory, Tech. Rept. 45.

Ross, H. E., S. S. Franklin, G. Weltman, and P. Lennie (1970). Adaptation of Divers to Size Distortion Underwater. *Brit. J. Psyhcol.* 61(3):365.

Ross, H. E., S. R. King, and H. Snowden (1970). Vertical Distance Judgements Underwater. *Psychol. Forsch.* 33:155.

Ross, H. E. and P. Lennie (1968). Visual Stability during Body Movement Underwater. In J. N. Lythgoe and J. D. Woods, Eds., *Symposium of the Underwater Association of Malta,* Report published by the Association, Guildford, England, pp. 55–58.

Rubenstein, C. J. and J. K. Summitt (1971). Vestibular Derangement in Decompression. In *Proceedings of the Fourth Symposium on Underwater Physiology,* C. J. Lambertsen, Ed., Academic Press, New York.

Rubin, L. S. (1957). Manual Dexterity of the Gloved and Bare Hand as a Function of Ambient Temperature and Duration of Exposure. *J. Appl. Psychol.* 41:377.

Ruch, T. C. (1955). The Nervous System: Sensory Functions. Chapter 18 in *A Test Book of Physiology,* J. F. Fulton, Ed., W. B. Saunders, Philadelphia.

Russotti, J. S. and J. R. Duffy (1969). An *Investigation of Three Methods for Unscrambling Helium Speech Produced at Depths of 800 and 1000 Feet.* U.S. Navy, Submarine Medical Center, Groton, Conn. Rept. no. 602.

Schaeffer, A. A. (1928). Spiral Movements in Man. *J. Morphology* 45:293.

Schaefer, K. E., G. F. Bond, W. F. Mazzone, C. R. Carey, and J. Dougherty (1968). *Carbon Dioxide Retention during Prolonged Exposure to High Pressure Environment,* U.S. Navy, Submarine Medical Center, Submarine Base, Groton, Conn., Rept. no. 520.

Schaefer, K. E. and C. R. Carey (1954). *Influence of Exposure to Various Carbon Dioxide Concentrations on Flicker Frequency and Alpha Blocking.* U.S. Navy, Submarine Medical Research Laboratory, Submarine Base, Groton, Connecticut, Rept. no. 251.

Schilling, C. W. and I. A. Everley (1942). Auditory Acuity among Submarine Personnel III. *USN Med. Bull.* 40:665.

Schilling, C. W. and W. W. Willgrube (1937). Quantitative Study of Mental and Neuromuscular Reactions as Influenced by Increased Air Pressure. *U.S. Nav. Med. Bull.* 35:373.

Scholander, P. F., M. T. Hammel, K. Lange-Andersen, and Y. Loyning (1957). Metabolic Acclimation to Cold in Man. *Fed. Proc. Amer. Soc. Exp. Biol.* 16:114.

Schone, H. (1965). On the Role of Gravity in Human Spatial Orientation. *Aerosp. Med.* 35:764.

Schreiner, H. R. (1968). Safe Ascent after Deep Dives. *Rev. Physiol. Subaquatique Med. Hyperbare* 1:28.

Schreiner, H. R. (1969). Advances in Decompression Research. *J. Occup. Med.,* 11(5):229.

Schulkin, M. and A. W. Pryce (1965). The Ocean In *System Engineering: Handbook* Machol, R. E., Ed., MacGraw-Hill, New York.

Schusterman, R. J. and R. F. Balliet (1970). Visual Acuity of the Harbor Seal and the Steller Sea Lion Underwater. *Nature,* **226**:563.

Schusterman, R. J. and R. F. Balliet (1970a). Conditioned Vocalization as a Technique for Determining Visual Acuity Thresholds in the Sea Lion. *Science,* **169**: 498.

Schwartz, I. and N. E. Sandberg (1954). *The Effects of Time in Submarine Service on Vision.* Submarine Medical Research Laboratory, Naval Submarine Base, Groton, Conn., Rept. no. 255.

Sellers, E. A., S. Reichman, and N. Thomas (1951). Acclimatization to Cold: Natural and Artificial. *Amer. J. Physiol.* **167**:644.

Sellers, E. A., S. Reichman, N. Thomas, and S. You (1951). Acclimatization to Cold in Rats: Metabolic Rates. *Amer. J. Physiol.* **167**:651.

Selye, H. (1971). The Evolution of the Stress Concept—Stress and Cardiovascular Disease. In *Society, Stress and Disease. The Psychosocial Environment and Psychosomatic Diseases,* L. Levi, Ed., Oxford University Press, London.

Sergeant, R. L. (1963). Speech during Respiration of Mixture of Helium and Oxygen. *Aerosp. Med.* **34**:826.

Sergeant, R. L. (1963a). *Speech Intelligibility during Prolonged Exposure to Helium–Oxygen,* U.S. Navy, Medical Submarine Research Laboratory, Groton, Conn., Memo Rept. no. 63–8.

Sergeant, R. L. (1966). *The Effect of Frequency Passband upon the Intelligibility of Helium–Speech in Noise,* U.S. Navy, Submarine Medical Center, Groton, Conn., Rept. no. 480.

Sergeant, R. L. (1966a). *Voice Communication Problems in Spacecraft and Underwater Operations,* U.S. Navy, Submarine Medical Center, Groton, Conn., Rept. no. 485.

Sergeant, R. L. (1967). Phonemic Analysis of Consonants in Helium Speech. *J. Acoust. Soc. Amer.* **41**:66.

Sergeant, R. L. (1969). Distortion of Speech. Chapter 10 in *The Physiology and Medicine of Diving and Compressed Air Work,* P. B. Bennett and D. H. Elliott, Eds., Williams and Wilkins, Baltimore.

Sergeant, R. L. and C. L. McKay (1968). *The Intelligibility of Helium–Speech as a Function of Speech-to-Noise Ratio,* U.S. Navy, Submarine Medical Center, Groton, Conn., Rept. no. 555.

Seusing, J. and H. Drube (1960). The Significance of Hypercapnia in the Occurrence of Depth Narcosis. *Klin. Wochschr.* **38**:1088.

Shaeffer, A. A. (1928). Spiral Movements in Man. *J. Morpholog.* **45**:293.

Shambaugh, G. E., Jr. (1967). The Symptom of Vertigo. *Arch. Otolaryng.* **85**:515.

Sherrington, C. S. (1906). *The Integrative Action of the Nervous System.* Yale University Press, New Haven, Conn.

Sivian, L. J. (1943). *Exchange of Acoustic Pressures and Intensities in Air–Water Systems,* National Defence Research Committee, Div. 6, Sect. 6.1 Rept. no. 6.1–NDRC–727.

Sivian, L. J. (1943a). *On Hearing in Water vs Hearing in Air, with Some Experimental Evidence,* National Defence Research Committee, Div. 6, Sect. 6.1 Rept. no. 6.1–NDRC–838.

Sivian, L. J. (1947). On Hearing in Water vs Hearing in Air. *J. Acoust. Soc. Amer.,* 19:461.

Skreslet, S. and F. Aarefjord (1968). Acclimatization to Cold in Man Induced by Frequent SCUBA Diving in Cold Water. *J. Appl. Physiol.* 24:117.

Smith, J. L. (1899). The Pathological Effects due to Increases of Oxygen Tension in the Air Breathed. *J. Physiol.* 24:19.

Smith, P. F. (1965). *Bone Conduction, Air Conduction and Underwater Hearing.* U.S. Navy Submarine Medical Center, Groton, Conn., Report 65-12.

Smith, P. F. (1969). *Underwater Hearing in Man: I. Sensitivity.* U.S. Navy, Submarine Medical Center, Submarine Base, Groton, Conn. Rept. no. 569.

Smith, R. C. and J. E. Tyler (1967), Optical Properties of Clear Natural Water. *J. Opt. Soc. Amer.* 57(5):589.

Spealman, C. R. (1949). Laboratory and Field Studies, Wet Cold. In *Physiology of Heat Regulation and the Science of Clothing,* Ed. L. H. Newburg, W. B. Saunders, Philadelphia.

Stang, P. R. (1967). *The Effects of Water Temperature on Manual Performance and Choice Reaction Time of Free Divers.* University of Miami, M.S. Thesis.

Stang, P. R. and E. L. Wiener (1970). Diver Performance in Cold Water. *Human Factors,* 12(4):391.

Starch, D. (1908). Perimetry of the Localizations of Sounds. *Psychol. Monogr.,* no. 38.

Steinberg, H. and A. Summerfield (1957). Influence of a depressant drug on acquisition in rate learning. *Quart. J. Exp. Psychol.,* 9:138.

Stevens, S. S. (1960). The Psychophysics of Sensory Function. *Amer. Sci.* 48:226.

Stevens, S. S. (1969). Sensory Scales of Taste Intensity. *Percept Psycholphys.* 6:302.

Steward, J. L. (1971). *Speech in Helium: Theory and Measurements,* Santa Rita Technology Inc., Los Altos, California, Final Rept. on N00014-68-C-0405.

Stigler, R. (1912). Versuche über die Beteilingung der Schwereempfindung an der Orientierung des Menschen im Raume. *Archiv. Physiol.* 148:573.

Strauss, M. B. (1970). Physiological Aspects of Mammalian Breath-Hold Diving: A Review. *Aerosp. Med.* 41:1362.

Strom, G. (1960). Central Nervous Regulation of Body Temperature. In *Handbook of Physiology,* Section 1: *Neurophysiology,* Vol. II, Ed: J. Field, H. W. Magonn, and V. E. Hall, Eds. American Physiological Society, Washington, D.C.

Summit, J. K. and S. D. Reimers (1971). *Noise a Hazard to Divers and Hyperbaric Chamber Personnel.* U.S. Navy, Experimental Diving Unit, Washington, D.C., Res. Rept. 5–71.

Summitt, J. K. (1970). Personal communication.

Tauber, J. F., J. S. P. Rawlins, and K. R. Bondi (1969). *Theoretical Thermal Requirements for the Mark II Diving System,* U.S. Naval Medical Research Institute, Bethesda, Md., Rept. no. M4306.02-6010B-2.

Teichner, W. H. and D. E. Olson (1971). A Preliminary Theory of the Effects of Task and Environmental Factors on Human Performance. *Hum. Factors* 13(4): 295.

Teeter (1970). Unpublished paper, University of Pennsylvania.

Therien, M. (1949). Contribution a la physiologie de l'acclimatation au froid. *Laval. Med.* 14:1062.

Thomas, W. G., J. K. Summitt, and J. C. Farmer (1973). Human auditory thresholds during deep saturation helium-oxygen dives. *J. Acoust. Soc. Am.* 53(1):347.

Thompson, B. P. and I. R. Streimer (1971). *A Study of Diver Performance with Communication Aids—Part II*, Bio Marine Industries, Inc., Devon, Penn., ONR Contract N00014-70-C-0162.

Thompson, B. P. and C. L. Thompson (1970). *A Study of Diver Performance with Communication Aids*, Bio Marine Industries, Inc., Devon, Penn., ONR Contract N00014-70-C-0162, Phase 1 Report.

Tobias, J. V. and S. Zerlin (1959). Lateralization Threshold as a Function of Stimulus Duration. *J. Acoust. Soc. Amer.* 31:1591.

Tolhurst, G. C. (1971). Factors for More Efficient Communication. *Nav. Res. Rev.* Office of Naval Research, Arlington, Va., p. 24.

U.S. Navy Diving Manual (1970) NAVSHIPS 250-538, Washington, U.S. Government Printing Office.

Vanderwalker, J. G. (1971). Tektite II: Sciences' Window on the Sea. *Nat. Geogr.* 140:(2):257.

Vaughan, W. S., Jr. and A. S. Mavor (1972). Diver Performance in Controlling a Wet Submersible During Four Hour Exposures to Cold Water. *Hum. Factors* 14(2): 173.

Verplanck, W. S. (1949). Visual Communications. Chapter 12 in *Human Factors In Undersea Warfare*, Panel on Psychology and Physiology, National Research Council, Washington, D.C.

Vorosmarti, J. and M. E. Bradley (1970, March). Alternobaric Vertigo in Military Divers. *Mil. Med.* 1350:182.

Wainwright, W. N. (1958). Comparison of Hearing Thresholds in Air and in Water. *J. Acoust. Soc. Amer.* 30:1025.

Wald, G., P. V. Harper, H. C. Goodman, and H. P. Krieger (1942). Respiratory Effects upon the Visual Threshold. *J. Gen. Physiol.* 25:891.

Walsh, J. M. and A. J. Bachrach (1971). *Timing Behavior in the Assessment of Adaptation to Nitrogen Narcosis*, U.S. Naval Medical Research Institute, Rept. no. 2.

Waterman, D. and P. F. Smith (1970). *An Investigation of the Effects of a Helium–Oxygen Breathing Mixture on Hearing in Naval Personnel*, U.S. Naval Submarine Medical Center, Submarine Base, Groton, Conn. Memo Rept. 70-7.

Webb, P. (1951). Air Temperatures in Respiratory Tracts of Resting Subjects in Cold. *Amer. J. Physiol.* 167:835.

Webb, P. and J. F. Annis (1966). *Respiratory Heat Loss with High Density Gas Mixtures*, U.S. Office of Naval Research, Yellow Springs, Ohio, Report under Contract Nonr-4965(00), Webb Associates, Inc.

Webster, A. P. (1955). Some Theoretical Aspects of the Use of Multiple-Gas Mixtures for Deep-Sea Diving. In *Proceedings of the Underwater Physiology Symposium*, L. G. Graff, Ed. National Academy of Sciences—National Research Council, Washington, D.C.

Weitzman, D. O., J. A. S. Kinney, and S. M. Luria (1969). *Effects on Vision of*

Repeated Exposure to Carbon Dioxide, U.S. Navy, Submarine Medical Center, Submarine Base, Groton, Conn., Rept. no. 566.

Weitzman, D. O., J. A. S. Kinney, and A. P. Ryan (1966). *A Longitudinal Study of Acuity and Phoria among Submariners,* U.S. Navy, Submarine Medical Center, Submarine Base, Groton, Conn. Rept. no. 481.

Weltman, G., R. A. Christianson, and G. H. Egstrom (1965). Visual Fields of the SCUBA Diver. *Hum. Factors* 7:423.

Weltman, G., R. A. Christianson, and G. H. Egstrom (1965a). *A Diver Restraint Device for Underwater Experimentation,* Biotechnology Laboratory, University of California, Los Angles, Calif., Rept. no. 30.

Weltman, G., R. A. Christianson, and G. H. Egstrom (1970). Effects of Environment and Experience on Underwater Work Performance. *Hum. Factors* 12(6):587.

Weltman, G. and G. H. Egstrom (1966). Perceptual Narrowing in Novice Divers. *Hum. Factors* 8:499.

Weybrew, B. B. (1967). Patterns of Psychophysiological Response to Military Stress. In *Psychological Stress,* M. M. Appley and R. Trumbull, Eds. Appleton-Century-Crofts, New York.

White, C. E. (1955). *Effect of Increased Atmospheric Pressure upon Intelligibility of Spoken Words,* U.S. Navy, Medical Research Laboratory, U.S. Naval Submarine Base, Memo Rept. 55–8.

Whiteside, T. C. D. (1960). The Effect of Weightlessness on Some Postural Mechanisms. *Aerosp. Med.* 31:324.

Williams, T. (1970), *Optical Properties of the Sea.* U.S. Naval Institute, Annapolis, Maryland.

Willott, J. F. and R. L. Sergeant (1968). *Auditory Feedback and Helium–Speech,* U.S. Navy, Submarine Medical Center, Groton, Conn. Rept. no. 544.

Wolff, R. C. and K. E. Penrod (1950). Factors Affecting Rate of Cooling in Immersion Hypothermia in the Dog. *Amer. J. Physiol.* 163:580.

Wood, J. D. (1969). Oxygen Toxicity. In *The Physiology and Medicine of Diving,* P. B. Bennett and D. H. Elliott, Eds., Williams & Wilkins, Baltimore.

Woods, J. D. (1963). Demonstration of a New Device for Communication between Divers. In *The Undersea Challenge,* B. Eaton, Ed., Proceedings of the Second World Congress of Undersea Activity, London, England.

Woodworth, R. S. and H. Schosberg (1954). *Experimental Psychology,* Rev. Ed., Holt, Rinehart, and Winston, New York.

Woodworth, R. S. and H. Schlosberg (1960). *Experimental Psychology,* Holt, Rinehart and Winston, New York, Chapter 12–13.

Workman, R. D. (1964). *Oxygen Decompression Following Air Dives for Use in Hyperbaric Oxygen Therapy,* U.S. Navy Experimental Diving Unit, Rept. No. 2-64.

Workman, R. D. (1966). Current Research in Diving in the U.S. Navy. *The Faceplate,* Deep Sea Diving School, Experimental Diving Unit, Washington, D.C., March.

Workman, R. D. and C. M. Prickett (1957). *Visual Field Perimeter and Distortion in Diving Masks,* U.S. Navy Experimental Diving Unit, Washington, D.C., Rept. no. 4-57.

Worschel, P. (1951). Space Perception and Orientation in the Blind. *Psychol. Monogr.*, **65,**(332).

Wright, W. B. (1970). Personal communication.

Wulfeck, J. W., A. Weisz, and M. W. Raben (1958). *Vision in Military Aviation,* USAF Material Command, D.C., WADC Rept. no. 58-399. AD 207-780.

Wyszecki, G. and W. S. Stiles (1967). *Color Science,* John Wiley, New York.

Young, F. A. (1965). The Effect of Atropine on the Development of Myopia in Monkeys. *Amer. J. Optom., Arch. Amer. Acad. Optom.* 42:439.

Young, F. A. (1967). Animal Experimentation and Research on Refractive State. Synopsis of the Refractive State of the Eye: Symposium Proceedings, M. J. Hirsch, Ed., *American Academy Optometry* Series, 5:26.

Zetterstrom, A. (1948). Deep Sea Diving with Synthetic Gas Mixture. *Mil. Surg.* 103:104.

Zwislocki, J. (1957). In Search of the Bone Conduction Threshold in Free Field. *J. Acoust. Soc. Amer.* 29:795.

AUTHOR INDEX

SUBJECT INDEX

Absorption, 5, 7, 64
  coefficient, 53, 64
  of light, 4, 54
  of sound, 4
Acclimatization, cold, 25, 188-190
Accomodation, 47, 48, 50, 71
Acidosis, respiratory, 51
Acoustic energy, attenuated, 100, 101
Activity, diver, 278, 279
Acuity, auditory, 101, 104-122
  minimum, 54
  night, 52
  resolution, 77
  snellen, 49, 51
  stereoscopic, 75, 77, 80
  visual, 46-51, 56, 57, 59, 75, 96
Adaptation, dark, 48, 81
  perceptual, 89-93
  stress, 292
Aerial perspective, 73
Aerotitis media, 105
Air conduction, 107, 110, 111
Alcohol, 179
Alpha benzhydrol hydrochloride, 290
Alpha blocking, 51
Ama, 113
Angle, critical, 59
Argon, 292
Arm-hand steadiness, 299
Artificial gills, 29-31
Articulation index, 235-239, 249, 263
Ascorbic acid, 189
Aspirin, 22
Attenuation, 63, 246, 247, 267
Audiogram, 107-112

Audiometry, 108

Balance, 146-151
Bandwidth, 241, 242, 254, 272, 273
Barotrauma, 102, 104
Bennett Hand Tool Dexterity Test,
  295, 298, 304
Binaural hearing, 123
Binaural time difference, 124
Binocular convergence, 50
Binocular disparity, 74
Binocular vision, 75
Bishydroxycoumarin, 22
Blood, 178-181, 188
Bone conduction, 106, 107, 111, 116-
  118, 122, 130
Breathing apparatus, 27, 28, 31-37,
  242, 243, 248
Brightness, 67, 73

Caloric stimulation, 140, 141
Carbachol, 22
Carbon dioxide, 30, 51, 52, 141, 151,
  152, 286-289
Cavity, oral, 250, 252, 253, 256
Chamber, hyperbaric, 102-104, 294,
  300
Chemical Senses, 13, 167
Circulation, 177-181, 188, 189
Cochlea, 105, 107
Code alpha flag, 212, 213
Coding, 220, 226, 227
Coefficient, absorption, 53, 64
  scattering, 64
Cognition, 280, 298, 299, 303

ıe